£31.00

This book is to be returned on or before the last date stamped below.

Inman, V.T.

copy 2.

D1614641

Human Walking

HUMAN WALKING

VERNE T. INMAN, M.D., PH.D.

Late Professor Emeritus of Orthopaedic Surgery
University of California, San Francisco
School of Medicine
San Francisco, California

HENRY J. RALSTON, PH.D.

Biomechanics Laboratory
Department of Mechanical Engineering
University of California
Berkeley, California

FRANK TODD

Biomechanics Laboratory
Department of Mechanical Engineering
University of California
Berkeley, California

Edited and with a preface by Jean C. Lieberman, Ph.D.
Biomechanics Laboratory,
Department of Mechanical Engineering
University of California
Berkeley, California

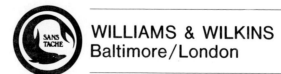

SANS TACHE

WILLIAMS & WILKINS
Baltimore/London

Copyright © 1981
Williams & Wilkins
428 E. Preston Street
Baltimore, MD 21202, U.S.A.

Made in the United States of America

Reprinted 1982

Library of Congress Cataloging in Publication Data

Inman, Verne Thompson, 1905–1980
   Human walking.

   Bibliography: p.
   Includes index.
   1. Walking. 2. Human locomotion. I. Ralston, Henry James, date, joint author. II. Todd, Frank, joint author. III. Title. [DNLM: 1. Gait. 2. Locomotion. WE103 I57h]
QP310.W3I55   612′.76   80-14669
ISBN-0-683-04348-X

Composed and printed at the Waverly Press, Inc.
Mt. Royal and Guilford Aves.
Baltimore, MD 21202, U.S.A.

IN MEMORIAM

Verne T. Inman, M.D., Ph.D., Professor Emeritus and former Chairman of the Department of Orthopaedic Surgery, University of California School of Medicine, San Francisco, died in San Francisco February 5, 1980.

Dr. Inman was a native Californian, born in San Jose November 6, 1905. He received both his medical education and formal training in human anatomy at the University of California.

Dr. Inman's primary research interest since his student days may be best described as functional anatomy. His studies on the actions of the shoulder joint, the clavicle, the abductor muscles of the hip, and the ankle are classics in the field. He was one of the pioneers in the use of electromyography in the analysis of muscle function.

Shortly after World War II, Dr. Inman, along with colleagues in engineering and physiology, became involved in lower limb prosthetics research. This led to the formation of the Biomechanics Laboratory at the University of California in San Francisco and Berkeley, of which he was director from 1957 to 1973, and consultant until the time of his death.

Dr. Inman had long expressed the wish to prepare a book summarizing the research studies on human walking in the Biomechanics Laboratory, and the present work is the culmination of that wish. Fortunately, Dr. Inman's own commitments to the book were completed before his death.

Verne T. Inman, M.D., Ph.D.
1905–1980

Preface

For the past 35 years, the investigators now working in the Biomechanics Laboratory have been gathering data on normal and abnormal human walking. A great amount of information has been accumulated with the use of many varied techniques.

The early studies (1944–1947) dealt with fundamental aspects of human walking, particularly in relation to problems faced by lower limb amputees. A number of techniques, either new or refined, were used in these studies, including motion pictures, force plates, interrupted lights, inserted pins, glass walkways, and electromyography. These early studies were described in the first finished work in a series of technical reports (Fundamental Studies, 1947). This two-volume report contains an extensive annotated bibliography of studies of human walking dating from the earliest times.

Later investigations included studies of the dynamics of human locomotion, of the energy expenditure of normal and disabled persons, and of the effects of immobilization of joints on energy expenditure, as well as a clinical evaluation of experimental orthotic devices. The understanding of the mechanics of human walking was greatly expanded by quantitative measurements of normal gait, which have also been used as a basis for describing, comparing, and evaluating how a handicapped person "typically" compensates for defects during walking. Other studies dealt with rotations of the spine, relative roles of gravitational and inertial work in the energy cost and character of human walking, dynamic relationships between various segments of the human body, and electromyographic recordings of activity of the muscles of the back and limbs during walking.

Unfortunately, for various reasons, much of the acquired information has till now not been published in readily accessible form. The major part appeared in the previously mentioned series of technical reports, which were not widely distributed and most of which are now out of print. It was, therefore, decided to write a comprehensive monograph on human walking, which would summarize the knowledge acquired by investigators at the Biomechanics Laboratory.

The book starts with a qualitative description of the displacements in the three planes of space of the various components of the skeletal system. The intent is to provide an overall view of human walking.

Chapter 2, on kinematics, begins with a definition of the basic requirements of walking: (1) continuous support against gravity and (2) alternating periodic motion of the lower limbs. Stride and step dimensions and phases of the walking cycle are defined. Typical walking speeds are given, followed by a detailed presentation of displacements and segment rotations in the side, front or rear, and top or bottom views.

Metabolic energy requirements are discussed in Chapter 3. After a statement of the units used, a short presentation of energy expenditures during lying, sitting, and standing is made for purposes of comparison. The relation between energy expenditures and speed during level walking is next discussed, followed by data on the energy expended per unit distance walked. The effects of slope-walking, stair-climbing, and variables of load, restraint, and terrain are considered. Finally, there is a discussion of work, power, and efficiency during walking.

Chapter 4, on kinetics, discusses the forces involved in human walking. Data are presented on joint moments, joint power, and mechanical energy levels of the different parts of the body.

Muscles supply the force to achieve the angular displacements involved in walking, and their characteristics and action are considered in Chapter 5. After a description of the functional characteristics of striated muscle, the skeletal mechanisms and changes in joint moments that permit the muscles to operate at their most effective lengths are presented. In conclusion, the phasic action of the individual muscle groups during walking is discussed, with emphasis on electromyographic data.

There follows (Chapter 6) a discussion of the implications of the previously presented findings, with special emphasis on orthopaedic conditions. A final chapter deals with the biomechanical principles underlying prosthetics.

Acknowledgments

In 1945, work started on projects that were later to be consolidated into the Biomechanics Laboratory of the University of California. The first projects were established through the action of the Committee on Prosthetic Devices, which later became the Advisory Committee on Artificial Limbs, under the National Academy of Sciences, National Research Council. The personnel of these projects consisted of specialists in engineering and medicine. The charge given was to acquire basic information on human walking and to utilize this information in the design and development of improved prosthetic and orthotic devices. Continuing financial support has since come from the Veterans Administration, with additional funding at various times from a variety of sources such as the National Institutes of Health; the Rehabilitation Services Administration and its predecessors, the Office of Vocational Rehabilitation, the Vocational Rehabilitation Administration, and the Social and Rehabilitation Service; and the National Aeronautics and Space Administration.

Charles W. Radcliffe, Professor of Mechanical Engineering, and Howard D. Eberhart, Professor Emeritus of Civil Engineering, University of California, Berkeley, who have long been active in the field of human walking, have kindly prepared Chapter 7 on lower limb prosthetics. Dr. Larry W. Lamoreux, Research Engineer, made important contributions to Chapter 2, Kinematics, and Chapter 4, Kinetics.

Mr. Mark Mikulich must be given major credit for the graphs, line drawings, and photographs. Mr. David Akers and Ms. Diane D. Ralston assisted in the preparation of several figures. Last, but not least, we are grateful to Mr. Stephen Feinstein, who took care of the numerous details relating to preparation of the manuscript.

The publishers have made every effort to trace the copyright holders for borrowed material. If they have inadvertently overlooked any, they will be pleased to make the necessary arrangements at the first opportunity.

Contents

CHAPTER 1

Introduction

Locomotion, a characteristic of animals, is the process by which the animal moves itself from one geographic position to another. The complete description of this process should include how starting, stopping, changes in speed, alterations in direction, and modifications for changes in slope are accomplished. These events, however, are transitory activities that are superimposed on a basic pattern. In walking and running animals, this pattern can be defined as a rhythmic displacement of bodily parts that maintains the animal in constant forward progression over a level surface. Nearly all studies of walking have considered only this basic operation, a restriction that is appropriate, because changes in speed, direction, etc., can be more readily interpreted as variations from the basic pattern.

The majority of mammals are quadripedal, and excellent studies have been published that reveal certain basic principles of quadripedal locomotion. Quadripeds, when walking slowly, tend to coordinate their four limbs so that three of their feet are on the ground. A crawling infant uses its limbs in a sequence that is essentially quadripedal, only advancing one while the other three support its body on the floor. This provides the stability of a tripod. This stability is lost the moment the animal becomes bipedal, and while bipedal locomotion seems simpler it requires greater neural control. The mastering of the erect bipedal type of locomotion is a relatively prolonged affair and appears to be a learned process, not the result of inborn reflexes. The congenitally blind child never spontaneously attempts to stand or walk but must be carefully taught (Scott, 1969). No one can watch the struggles of an infant as it first attempts to stand, holding onto the edge of a chair or tightly grasping in its hand the supporting fingers of a parent, without feeling that this is pure experimentation rather than the maturation of an inborn reflex. After the first few faltering steps, with many inevitable falls, greater stability and precision are rapidly acquired.

Popova (1935), working with Bernstein in Moscow, studied the mechanism of walking in the growing child. She identified three stages and pointed out that the characteristic patterns of walking seen in the adult are not achieved until the child reaches the age of 7–9 years. Apparently, before this age, the child is experimenting with its neuromusculoskeletal system, modifying the displacements that occur in various segments with changes in bodily proportions, and developing improved neural controls.

If walking is a learned activity, it is not surprising that each of us displays certain personal peculiarities superimposed on the basic pattern of bipedal locomotion. The literature is replete with reports on the physical variations in human beings. Physical anthropologists have studied the differences between races and measured the variations in skeletal parts. Anatomists are aware of the presence of individual variations, although when writing textbooks they customarily present only average relationships—often, however, with footnotes or reference to specific articles that describe the extent of individual differences. The manufacturers of clothing are acutely conscious of the dissimilarities in people. One need only go into a store that sells ready-made clothes to be impressed by the different sizes required to supply the population. Orthopedic surgeons are constantly confronted with variations from the so-called average, and they attempt to alter these differences to make them conform to their concept of normality. All of us are aware that individuals walk differently; one can often recognize an acquaintance by his manner of walking even when seen at a distance. Tall, slender people walk differently from short, stocky people. People alter their manner of walking when wearing shoes with different heel heights. A person walks differently when exhilarated than when mentally depressed. With these ideas in mind, one may legitimately question the usefulness of anthropometric data and averages in furthering our understanding of human walking.

Certainly everyone has his own idiosyncratic way of walking and there is no such thing as an average person. However, most of us do walk with reasonable facility and, as will be shown later, with surprising efficiency.

A conclusion that seems inescapable is that each of us learns to integrate the numerous variables that nature has bestowed on our individual neuromusculoskeletal systems into a smoothly functioning whole. Obviously, our bipedal plantigrade type of progression imposes gross similarities on our manner of walking. These are easily identified. We must oscillate our legs, and as we do our bodies rise and fall with each step. The movements parallel to the plane of progression are large and the individual variations in relation to the size of the total angular displacements are relatively small. When these aspects of human walking are considered, the use of average values helps to develop a general understanding of the basic relationships that exist between the major segments of the lower limb.

Upon these basic activities are superimposed numerous less obvious movements of individual parts of the body. These small movements occur in planes closer to the coronal and transverse planes of the body, and in these small movements, the individual variations are relatively large.

Furthermore, when the locations of axes of movement are determined and ranges of motion measured both in the cadaver and in the living, marked individual differences are disclosed. The differences in these small movements bestow on each of us a distinctive manner of walking. Here the use of average values can hinder the recognition of certain interrelationships that must exist between the participating joints. This is particularly true when one is trying to understand the functional behavior of the joints of the ankle and foot.

It is not necessary to belabor the point of individual dissimilarities in walking: the only reason for so doing is to emphasize that any serious description of human walking should attempt an explanation of the dissimilarities as well as the similarities. Finding such an explanation, of course, necessitates searching for a basic principle or fundamental concept, the application of which might reveal the reasons why we employ a basic pattern, modify it with growth, and superimpose individual variations upon it. Unfortunately, a fundamental concept does not emerge automatically or spontaneously through the accumulation of more and more data. At some point in the course of the investigations, a hypothesis must be formulated so that the deductions from the hypothesis can be compared with the measured observations. Agreement adds support to the hypothesis, and consideration of the hypothesis suggests new directions for future investigations.

A hypothesis is easily formulated that seems to explain most observations, including the peculiar behavior of the major segments of the body during walking. This hypothesis states that the human body will integrate the motions of the various segments and control the activity of the muscles so that the metabolic energy required for a given distance walked is minimized. In later sections, it will be shown that any interference with normal relationships between various segments of the body invariably increases the metabolic cost of walking.

The Process of Walking

The term *walking* is nonspecific. Its connotation is that of a cyclic pattern of bodily movements that is repeated over and over, step after step. Consequently, descriptions of walking customarily deal with what happens in the course of just one cycle, with the assumption that successive cycles are all about the same. Although this assumption is not strictly true, it is a reasonable approximation. Apart from the multiple variations that may occur between different individuals or within the same individual as a result of changes in the speed of walking or such factors as alterations in footwear, there are certain observable events that are shared by all.

Human walking is a process of locomotion in which the erect, moving body is supported by first one leg and then the other. As the moving body passes over the supporting leg, the other leg is swinging forward in preparation for its next support phase. One foot or the other is always on the ground, and during that period when the support of the body is transferred from the trailing to the leading leg there is a brief period when both feet are on the ground. As a person walks faster, these periods of double support become smaller and smaller fractions of the walking cycle until, eventually, as a person starts to run, they disappear altogether and are replaced by brief periods when neither foot is on the ground. The cyclic alternations of the support function of each leg and the existence of a transfer period when both feet are on the ground, are essential features of the locomotion process known as walking.

In the act of walking there are two basic requisites: (1) continuing ground reaction forces that support the body and (2) periodic movement of each foot from one position of support to the next in the direction of progression. These elements are necessary for any form of bipedal walking no matter how distorted by physical disability. They are equally necessary when prosthetic or orthotic devices are used.

These two basic requisites of walking give rise to specific body motions that are universally observable during walking. As the body passes over the weight-bearing limb, three different deviations from uniform progression in a straight line occur. With each step, the body speeds up and slows down slightly, it rises and falls a few centimeters, and it weaves slightly from side to side. These motions are related to one another in a systematic fashion.

The body must slow down and then speed up again during each step because the support provided by the legs does not remain directly under the body at all times. A supporting foot starts out ahead of the body where it tends to slow the body down, and then it passes under the body and to the rear, where it tends to speed the body up again. This motion is difficult to see, but easy to sense when a person carries a shallow pan of water. It is almost impossible to prevent the water from surging backward and forward as a result of the alternating accelerations and decelerations of the body.

As the body passes over the supporting leg it rises until the foot is directly underneath and then descends again as the foot passes behind. The highest point in elevation occurs when the speed is lowest, and the lowest point in elevation occurs when the speed is highest.

During the period of single support, the body also tends to shift laterally over the supporting limb. The pelvis achieves its maximal lateral displacement somewhat after midstance and then starts back toward the other side. The amount of lateral sway increases when the tread width is increased. Whereas individual variations in the measured magnitudes of these motions will always be observed in any group of people, the motions will be present to some degree in everyone. Normally there is symmetry in the movement, and the patterns repeat themselves with each successive cycle.

Although the displacements of the entire body through space may be described as translational, this translation is achieved by the angular displacements of various segments of the body about axes that lie in the proximity of joints. A principal task in describing human locomotion is to measure the angular displacements of the various segments during the translational movement of the body as a whole. Because the translational movements are the final product of the angular displacements of the individual segments and these are easily discernible and measurable, they may be used as one set of parameters for the description of the walking cycle. However, a description that deals solely with movement and ignores the forces that produce these motions constitutes only a small part of the entire story of human walking.

In truth, human walking is a complex phenomenon, and an adequate description of what occurs during a single cycle requires the consideration of such factors as floor reactions, total energy requirements, energy transfers within the body, and the phasic action of muscles.

Each of these factors has been investigated to varying degrees in separate research projects in the Biomechan-ics Laboratory. Although not bearing directly on a geometric description of walking, they were necessary to explain certain observations recorded during the overall studies. These are essentially asides, which do not fit nicely into the main description of walking. However, they do constitute basic information necessary for a full understanding of certain aspects of walking and they will be discussed under separate headings.

Walking is a complex integrated activity with multiple factors interacting simultaneously, but everyone has observed people walking and is acquainted with such obvious movements as oscillation of the legs and swinging of the arms. However, one tends to see only what one purposely looks for and attention must be directed to many important aspects of walking that will escape the casual observer. It seems reasonable, therefore, to introduce the reader into the complex description of walking by first presenting a general and qualitative description of important displacements of the various parts of the body. With such an overall view of human walking kept constantly in mind, it becomes possible at times to deviate from the main theme to explore in detail certain interesting phenomena. At first glance, some of these deviations may seem to be far removed from the principal thesis, but they are necessary to provide a basis for understanding why certain things occur as they do in the process of walking.

Major Displacements of the Body During Walking

Synchronous movements of nearly all the major parts of the body occur during walking at moderate speeds. The pelvis lists, rotates, and undulates as it moves forward. The segments of the lower limb show displacements in all three planes of space, while the shoulders rotate and the arms swing out of phase with the displacements of the pelvis and legs. It seems reasonable to begin the description of walking with a discussion of the translation of the body as a whole through space. To do this, the concept of the pathway of the center of mass of the body will be used. The center of mass of any body is a point such that if any plane is passed through it, the mass moments on one side of the plane are equal to the mass moments on the other. If the body is suspended at this center of mass, it will not tend to tip in any direction. During walking, the center of mass of the body, although not remaining in an absolutely fixed position, tends to remain within the pelvis. This is convenient for two reasons. Measurements of the movements of the pelvis in the three planes of space are readily made, and the pelvis becomes a suitable structure to separate the body into upper and lower parts, which behave phasically differently during walking.

In normal level walking, the center of mass describes a smooth sinusoidal curve when projected on the plane

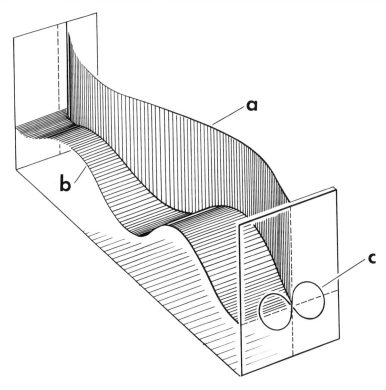

Figure 1.1. Displacements of center of mass in three planes of space during single stride (cycle). The actual displacements have been greatly exaggerated. The lateral displacement in a horizontal plane is shown in *a*, and the vertical displacement is shown in *b*. The combined displacements of *a* and *b* as projected onto a plane perpendicular to the plane of progression are shown in *c*.

of progression (Fig. 1.1). The total amount of vertical displacement in normal adult men is typically about 5 cm at the usually adopted speeds of walking. The summits of these oscillations appear at about the middle of the stance (foot on ground) phase of the supporting limb. The opposite limb is at this time in the middle of its swing (foot off ground) phase. The center of mass falls to its lowest level during the middle of double weight-bearing, when both feet are in contact with the ground. The curve is remarkably smooth and is found to fluctuate evenly between maxima and minima of displacements, with few irregularities. It is interesting to note that at their maximal vertical displacement, the head and the center of mass are slightly lower than when the subject is standing on both feet. In other words, in a smooth walk, a person is slightly shorter than when he is standing, so that if he were to walk through a tunnel the height of which corresponded exactly to his standing height he could do so without fear of bumping his head.

The center of mass of the body is also displaced laterally in the horizontal plane. In this plane too, it describes a sinusoidal curve, the maximal values of which alternately pass to the right and to the left in association with the support of the weight-bearing limb.

The curve is sinusoidal, at one-half the frequency of the vertical displacement.

When viewed from the back, the body is seen to undulate up and down and swing from side to side during each cycle. If the vertical and lateral displacements are pure sine waves, with the frequency of the vertical displacements being precisely twice that of the lateral displacements and the peaks being achieved at the same time, then the curve of displacement of the center of mass, as projected onto a plane at right angles to the line of progression, is in the form of a "U." At higher speeds of walking, this situation is approximated; at lower speeds, however, the peak of the curve for vertical displacement is reached slightly before the peak of lateral displacement. This causes the curve of movement of the center of mass as projected on a coronal plane (a vertical plane at a right angle to the line of progression) to resemble a slightly distorted lazy 8 (Fig. 1.2).

A general qualifying statement is appropriate at this point. In the remainder of this chapter, the motions of the major segments of the body will be qualitatively described. It should be emphasized that the angular displacements of the various parts of the body, as well as their phasic relationships, are altered with changes

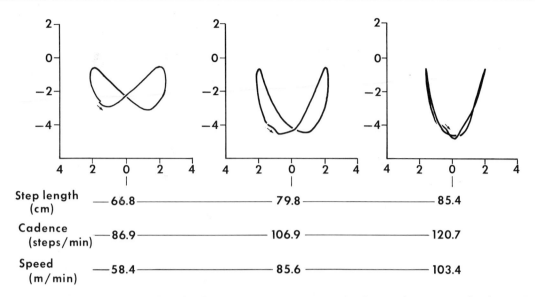

Figure 1.2. Effect of variations in speed on displacement of pelvis as projected onto plane perpendicular to plane of progression (see *c* in Fig. 1.1).

in the speed of walking. This will be discussed in detail in Chapter 2 but should be borne in mind in the immediately following discussion, for example, the discussion of the smooth sinusoidal displacements of the center of mass of the body. Achievement of these even sinusoidal displacements depends on smoothly coordinated angular displacements of the various segments of the lower limb.

For the sake of simplicity of presentation, a series of simple models will be employed to illustrate how the smooth sinusoidal displacement pathway is achieved in bipedal locomotion (Saunders et al., 1953). The first model will show the body as consisting solely of a bar representing the pelvis, with the center of mass depicted as a small block lying midway between the two hips (Fig. 1.3). The legs will be represented as rigid levers without foot, ankle, or knee mechanisms, articulated only at the hip joints, which will permit flexion and extension only. Such a system of quasilocomotion would produce something analogous to the process of stepping off distances with a pair of compasses or dividers, the pathway of the center of mass of such a system being a series of intersecting arcs. The radius of each arc would be equal to the length of the limbs, and with each step, the extent of flexion and extension of the hip joint would be the same. Locomotion of this type might be imitated, but imperfectly, by walking on one's heels with the knees fixed in extension. Such a type of locomotion would require that the center of masss be elevated to a height equal to the height of the center of mass in the standing person; it would also result in a severe jolt at the point of intersection of each two arcs, where there is an abrupt change in the direc-

tion of movement of the center of mass. Decreasing the total elevation, depressing the center of mass, and smoothing the series of interrupted arcs require coordinated movements involving all the joints of the lower limb. These individual movements can be considered as elements that contribute to the total process of walking. A qualitative description of the principal elements is presented in the following paragraphs to provide a basis for the quantitative descriptions in later chapters.

The First Element: Pelvic Rotation

In normal level walking, the pelvis rotates about a vertical axis alternately to the right and to the left, relative to the line of progression. At the customary cadence and stride of typical people, the magnitude of this rotation is approximately 4° on either side of the central axis, or a total of some 8°. This value usually increases markedly when speed is increased. Because the pelvis is a rigid structure, the rotations occur alternately at each hip joint and require a deviation from pure flexion and extension of the hips.

The significance of pelvic rotation can best be appreciated by a study of the theoretical model (Fig. 1.4). The effects of pelvic rotation are to flatten somewhat the arc of the passage of the center of mass in compass gait by elevating the ends of that arc. In consequence, the angles at the intersections of successive arcs are rendered less abrupt and, at the same time, are elevated in relation to the summits. In this way, the severity of the impact at floor contact is reduced. The force required to change the direction of the center of mass in the succeeding arc of translation is less, and the angular displacement at the hip in flexion and extension is reduced.

The Second Element: Pelvic List

In normal walking, the pelvis lists downward in the coronal plane on the side opposite to that of the weight-bearing limb (positive Trendelenburg). At moderate speeds, the alternate angular displacement is about 5°. The displacement occurs at the hip joint, producing an equivalent relative adduction of the supporting limb and relative abduction of the other limb, which is in the swing phase of the cycle. To permit pelvic list, the knee joint of the non-weight-bearing limb must flex to allow clearance for the swing-through of that member.

The effects of pelvic list on the pathway of the center of mass are evident in the experimental model (Fig. 1.5). As the lateral list occurs while the body is passing over the vertical supporting member in early stance phase, the center of mass is lowered. Thus, the summit of the arc is lowered, further flattening the pathway. In addition and perhaps more importantly, pelvic list contributes to the effectiveness of the abductor mechanism of

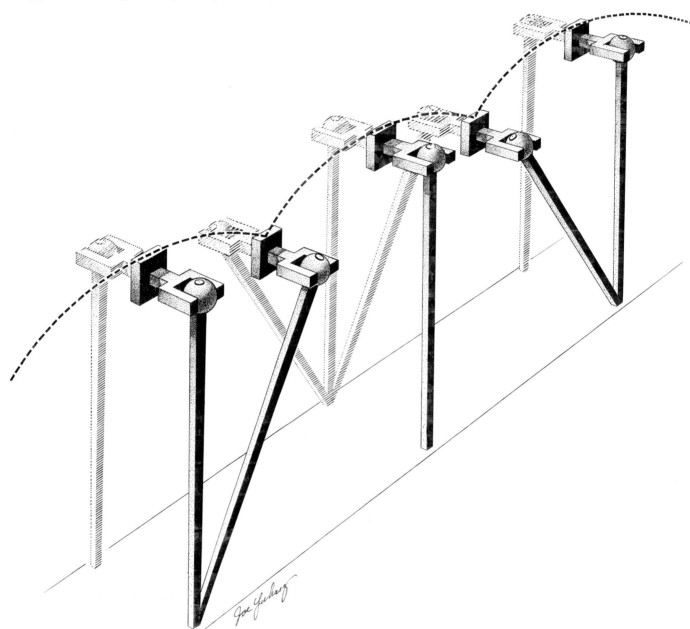

Figure 1.3. Simplified model depicting bipedal locomotion. The pelvis is a double-forked bar articulating with spheres depicting the hip joints and carrying a small block, that represents the center of mass of the body. The legs are straight members without knee, ankle, or foot components. Note that the pathway of the center of mass is through a series of intersecting arcs. (Reproduced, with permission, from Saunders, J. B. deC. M., Inman, V. T., and Eberhart, H. D. The major determinants in normal and pathological gait. *J. Bone Joint Surg.* 35-A:543, 1953.)

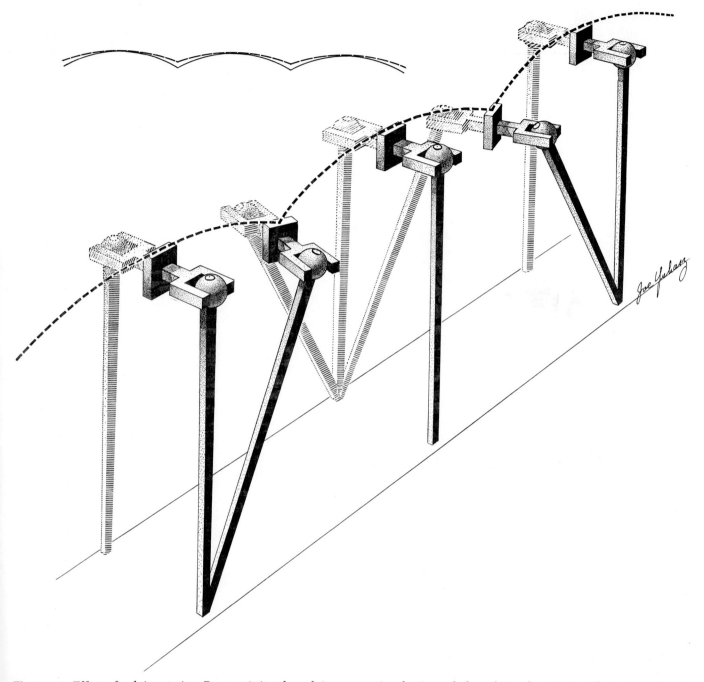

Figure 1.4. Effect of pelvic rotation. By permitting the pelvis to rotate in a horizontal plane during locomotion, the center of mass is prevented from falling as far during the phase of double weight-bearing as was shown in Figure 1.3. The *solid line* at the top represents the curve shown in Figure 1.3. (Adapted, with permission, from Saunders et al. *J. Bone Joint Surg. 35-A*:543, 1953.)

the hip (the abductor muscles and iliotibial tract). The latter effect will be discussed in greater detail in the section on the phasic action of muscles (Chapter 5).

The Third Element: Knee Flexion in Stance Phase

A characteristic of walking at moderate and fast speeds is knee flexion of the supporting limb as the body passes over it. This supporting member enters stance phase at heel strike with the knee joint in nearly full extension. Thereafter, the knee joint begins to flex and continues to do so until the foot is flat on the ground. A typical magnitude of this flexion is 15°. Just before the middle of the period of full weight-bearing, the knee joint once more passes into extension, which

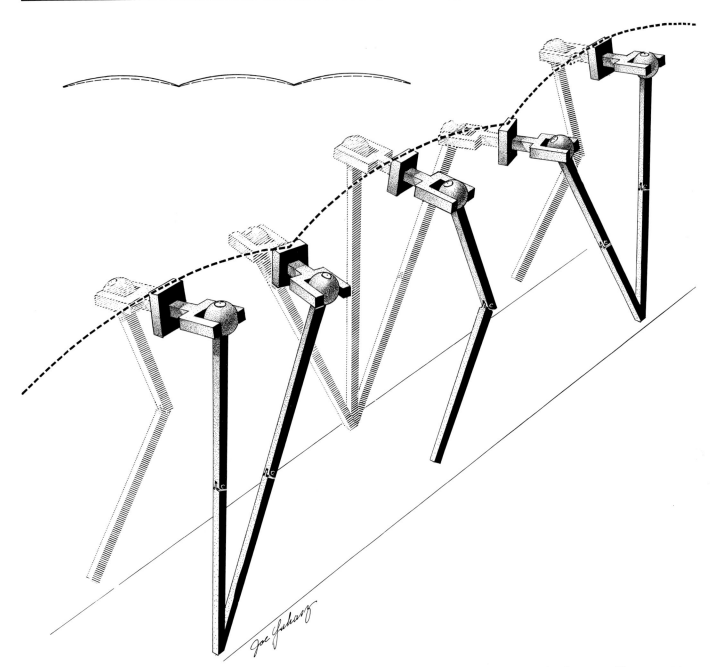

Figure 1.5. Effect of pelvic list. Normally the pelvis drops slightly on the non-weight-bearing side during walking (positive Trendelenburg). The result is that the center of mass need not be elevated as much when the body passes over the weight-bearing leg during midstance. Because of the pelvic list, the swinging leg becomes relatively too long to clear the floor during the midswing phase. Flexion of the knee allows for this clearance. The *solid line* at the top represents the curve shown in Figure 1.4. (Adapted, with permission, from Saunders et al. *J. Bone Joint Surg. 35-A*:543, 1953.)

is immediately followed by the terminal flexion of the knee. This begins simultaneously with heel rise, as the limb is carried into swing phase. During this period of stance phase, occupying about 40% of the cycle, the knee is first extended, next flexed, and again extended before its final flexion.

During the beginning and end of stance phase, knee flexion contributes to smoothing the abrupt changes at the intersections of the arcs of translation of the center of mass (Fig. 1.6).

These three elements of gait—pelvic rotation, pelvic list, and knee flexion during early stance phase—all act in the same direction by flattening the arc through which the center of mass of the body is translated. The

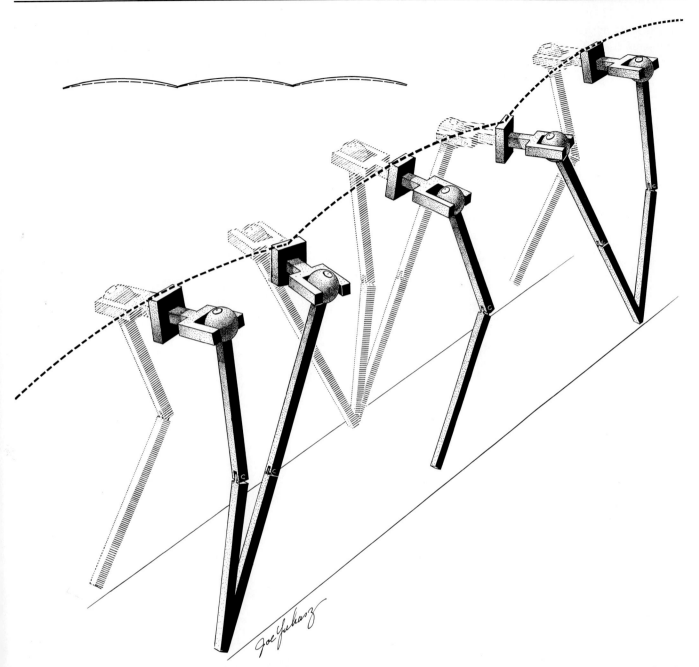

Figure 1.6. Knee flexion during stance. Except at very low speeds of walking, the knee undergoes approximately 15° of flexion immediately after heel strike and continues to remain flexed until the center of mass has passed over the weight-bearing leg. The effect of this knee flexion is twofold. Initially, it absorbs part of the impact of the body at heel strike and later it decreases the amount that the center of mass must be elevated as it passes over the weight-bearing leg. The *solid line* at the top represents the curve shown in Figure 1.5. (Adapted, with permission, from Saunders et al. *J. Bone Joint Surg. 35-A:543, 1953.*)

first—pelvic rotation—elevates the ends of the arc, and the second and third—pelvic list and knee flexion—depress its summit. The net effect is the passage of the center of mass through a segment of a circle, the radius of which is about 2.2 times longer than the length of the lower limb. The effective lengthening of the limbs reduces materially the range of flexion and extension at

the hip joint required to maintain the same length of stride.

The three elements so far discussed (pelvic rotation, pelvic list, and knee flexion) act to decrease the magnitude of the vertical displacement of the center of mass of the body. However, if no additional elements were active, the pathway of the center of mass would still consist of a series of arcs, and at their intersections the center of mass would be subject to a sudden change in vertical displacement. This would result in a jarring effect on the body. Thus, an additional mechanism must be active that smooths the pathway of the center of mass by a gradual change in the vertical displacement of the center of mass from a downward to an upward direction, converting what would be a series of intersecting arcs into a sinusoidal path. This is accomplished by certain movements in the knee, ankle, and foot.

The single most important factor in achieving the conversion of the pathway of the center of mass from a series of intersecting arcs to a smooth curve is the presence of a foot attached to the distal end of the limb. Through its action, the foot enables the pathway of displacement of the knee to remain relatively horizontal during the entire stance phase. This in turn allows the initial knee flexion to act more effectively in smoothing the pathway of the hip. To understand the mechanics involved, a series of simple drawings may be helpful. In

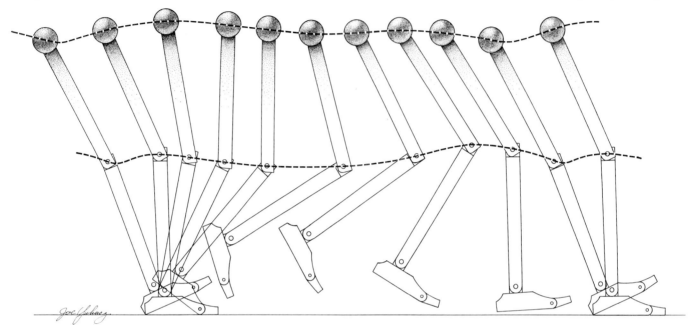

Figure 1.7. Pathway of knee in walking at moderate speed. Note that there is a slight elevation immediately after heel strike, but for the remainder of stance phase the pathway is relatively straight and shows only a slight declination from the horizontal. (Reproduced, with permission, from Saunders et al. *J. Bone Joint Surg.* 35-A:543, 1953.)

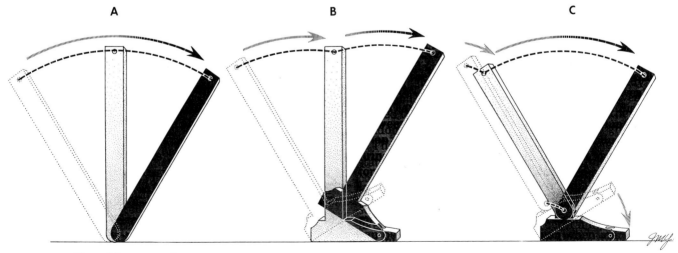

Figure 1.8. Effect of foot on pathway of knee. *A*, Arc described when there is no foot. *B*, Effect of foot without ankle. Note that the pathway now comprises two intersecting arcs. However, it does not fall abruptly at the end of stance and begins to resemble the normal pathway. *C*, Effect of foot with flail ankle. (Reproduced, with permission, from Saunders et al. *J. Bone Joint Surg.* 35-A:543, 1953.)

Figure 1.7, the actual pathway of the knee joint during stance phase is shown. Except for an initial rise, the pathway is relatively flat. In Figure 1.8, three other situations are shown. If no foot is attached to the shank, the pathway of the knee is an arc whose radius is the distance from the floor to the knee. By simply adding a foot rigidly fixed to the shank (no ankle), the pathway, although it is composed of two arcs, approaches more closely the normal course. Provision of a flail ankle results in a pattern resembling the pathway of the knee without any foot. Provision of a normal ankle, however (Fig. 1.9), with proper phasing of the extensor and flexor muscles and only a minor amount of motion occurring in the ankle joint, results in achievement of the normal pathway of the knee joint.

At the time of heel strike, the center of mass of the body is falling. This downward movement is decelerated by slight flexion of the knee against the resistance of the quadriceps. After heel strike, the foot is plantar flexed against the resisting tibialis anterior muscle. This plantar flexion of the foot occurs about a point where the heel contacts the floor. Rotation about this point causes the leg to undergo relative shortening and the ankle to be carried slightly forward in the direction of progression until the foot is flat. Contraction of the quadriceps acting on the knee and the tibialis anterior muscle on the foot causes these movements to be slowed, and the downward motion of the center of mass of the body is smoothly decelerated. In addition, as the foot receives the weight of the body during midstance, it pronates to a varying degree. Although this pronation contributes only a few millimeters to the further relative shortening of the leg, the elastic components in the plantar region of the foot assist in absorbing the shock of impact.

The center of mass begins its upward movement immediately after it has passed in front of the weight-bearing foot, as the forward momentum of the body carries the body up and over the weight-bearing leg. After the center of mass has passed over and in front of the foot, its immediate fall is delayed by relative elongation of the weight-bearing leg through extension of the knee, plantar flexion at the ankle, and supination of the foot. All these elements acting in proper relation-

Figure 1.9. Effect of ankle motion, controlled by muscle action, on pathway of knee. The smooth and flattened pathway of the knee during stance phase is achieved by forces acting from the leg on the foot. Foot slap is restrained during initial lowering of the foot; afterward, the plantar flexors raise the heel.

Figure 1.10. Interrupted light studies. The photograph was obtained by having a subject walk in front of the open lens of a camera while carrying small light bulbs located at the hip, knee, ankle, and foot. A slotted disc was rotated in front of the camera producing a series of white dots at equal time intervals. Note that the curve of displacement at the hip is a smooth curve but is not sinusoidal. This is due to the differences in phase of the two legs. (Reproduced, with permission, from Eberhart, H. D., and Inman, V. T. An evaluation of experimental procedures used in a fundamental study of human locomotion. *Ann. N. Y. Acad. Sci.* 51:1213, 1951.)

ships lead to the smoothing of the passage of the center of mass into an approximately sinusoidal pathway (Figs. 1.10–1.12).

The Sixth Element: Lateral Displacement of the Body

As mentioned previously, the body is shifted slightly over the weight-bearing leg with each step; there is a total lateral displacement of the body from side to side of approximately 4 to 5 cm with each complete stride. This lateral displacement can be increased by walking with the feet more widely separated (Fig. 1.13) and decreased by keeping the feet close to the plane of progression (Fig. 1.14). Normally, the presence of the tibiofemoral angle (slight genu valgum) permits the tibia to remain essentially vertical and the feet close together, while the femurs diverge to articulate with the pelvis.

Rotations in the Transverse Plane

Reference has already been made to the transverse rotations of the pelvis that occur during walking. These rotations are easily seen when attention is called to them. There are also other transverse rotations, involving the parts of the body above and below the pelvis, that merit attention.

Rotations of the Thorax and Shoulders

That the thorax and shoulders rotate during walking is easily seen. Interestingly, at moderate speeds of walking these rotations are approximately 180° out of phase with the pelvic rotation. The rotation of the shoulders produces arm swing, and even the casual observer recognizes that the forward swing of one leg is accompanied by a forward swing of the arm on the opposite side. This opposite rotation of the pelvis as compared with the shoulders appears to provide a balancing effect that smooths the forward progression of the body as a whole. Its suppression leads to inability to progress in a straight line at higher speeds of walking and, as will be shown, to increased energy expenditure through greater muscular effort.

Rotations of the Thigh and Leg (Shank)

Less obvious but still considerable are the transverse rotations of the thigh and shank (Levens et al., 1948). In contrast to the shoulders, the rotations of the thigh and shank are in phase with the pelvic rotation. The interesting fact is that their rotatory displacements increase progressively from pelvis to thigh to shank. Thus, the shank on the average rotates approximately 3 times as

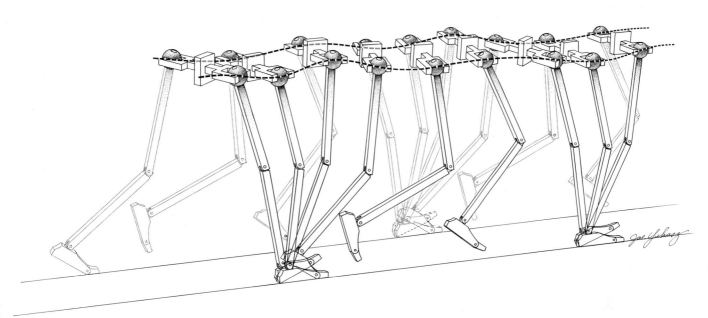

Figure 1.11. Vertical displacements of hip joints. Although the pathways of the hip joints are smooth curves they are not sinusoidal and they are 180° out of phase. (Reproduced, with permission, from Saunders et al. *J. Bone Joint Surg. 35-A*:543, 1953.)

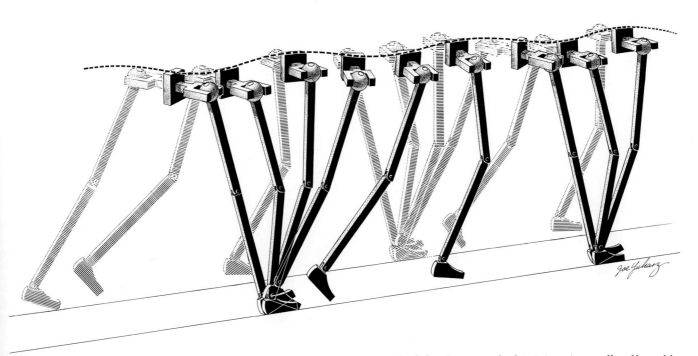

Figure 1.12. Sinusoidal pathway of center of mass. The center of mass, which lies between the hip joints, is equally affected by the displacements of each hip. The combined effect is a sinusoidal curve of low amplitude. (Reproduced, with permission, from Saunders et al. *J. Bone Joint Surg. 35-A*:543, 1953.)

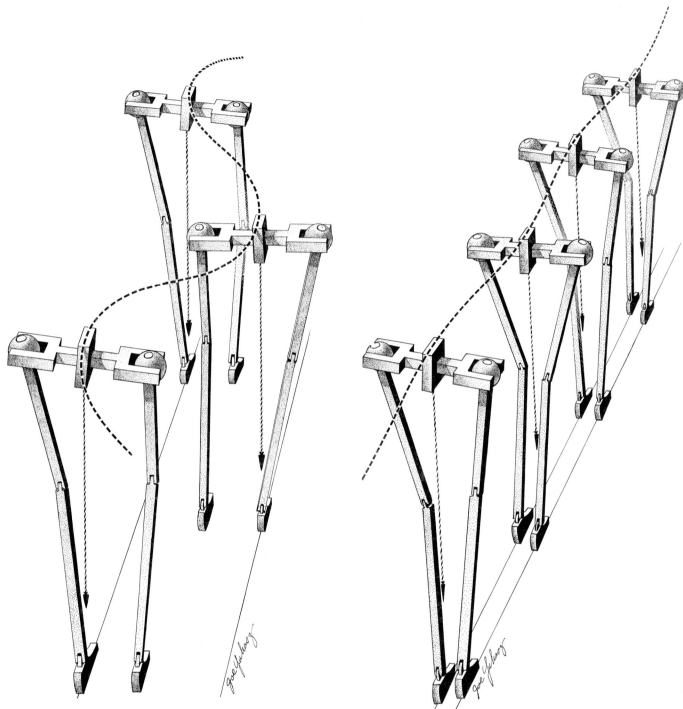

Figure 1.13. Lateral displacement of center of mass. During each step, the body is displaced over the weight-bearing leg. With a wide walking base (stride width) the amplitude is large. (Reproduced, with permission, from Saunders et al. *J. Bone Joint Surg. 35-A*:543, 1953.)

Figure 1.14. Effect of narrow walking base. By providing the model with a degree of genu valgum, the walking base is narrowed and the amplitude of lateral displacement is decreased while the shank remains vertical. (Reproduced, with permission, from Saunders et al. *J. Bone Joint Surg. 35-A*:543, 1953.)

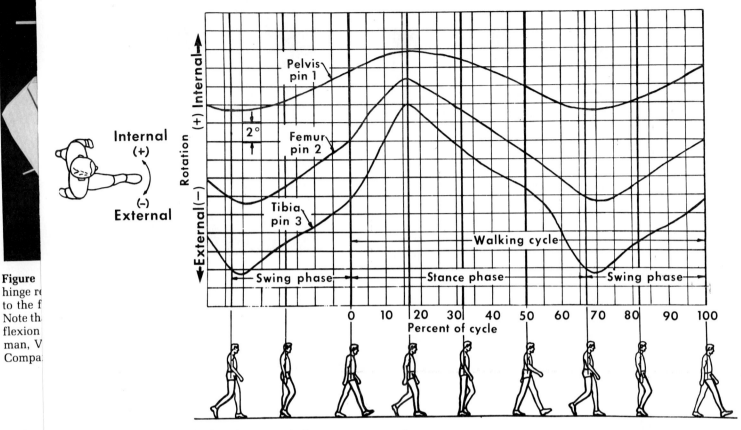

Figure 1.15. Rotations of pelvis, femur, and tibia in transverse plane: composite curves of 19 young male adults. (Adapted, with permission, from Levens, A. S., Inman, V. T., and Blosser, J. A. Transverse rotation of the segments of the lower extremity in locomotion. *J. Bone Joint Surg.* 30-A:859, 1948.)

much in a transverse plane as does the pelvis. These rotations, however, show marked differences and constitute one of the factors that provide distinctive characteristics to each individual's appearance when walking.

In general, the pelvis, thigh, and leg begin to rotate internally toward the weight-bearing leg at the beginning of its swing phase. This rotation is continued during the double-weight-bearing phase and into midstance. At midstance, there is an abrupt change and the leg begins to rotate externally and continues to do so until the beginning of its next swing phase (Fig. 1.15).

Rotations in the Ankle and Foot

During the swing phase of walking, the segments of the lower limb (including the foot) are free in space and can rotate internally without restriction (Fig. 1.16A). During stance phase, the foot is on the floor and external rotation of the leg occurs because mechanisms exist in the ankle and foot that permit the leg to rotate externally while the foot remains stationary. If such mechanisms did not exist, the foot would have to slip as shown in Figure 1.16B.

There is an interesting interrelationship between the ankle and the hindfoot that, to date, is not clearly understood. Both the ankle and subtalar joints are capable to varying degrees of absorbing the transverse rotations of the shank during the stance phase of walking.

The axis of the ankle joint has been found to vary in obliquity in the coronal plane from 2–23° (Inman, 1976). The ability of the ankle to participate in the absorption of the rotations of the shank depends on the obliquity of the ankle axis and the range of flexion and extension used. The effect of an oblique axis on the foot during swing phase and on the shank during stance phase is clearly shown in Figures 1.17 and 1.18. During swing, with the foot free, the foot toes outward on dorsiflexion and inward on plantar flexion (Fig. 1.17). During stance, with the foot fixed to the floor, relative dorsiflexion produces internal rotation of the shank and relative plantar flexion causes external rotation of the shank (Fig. 1.18). Therefore, the ankle joint, in proportion to the obliquity of its axis and the amount of dorsiflexion, may participate in the absorption of the transverse rotations of the shank during stance phase.

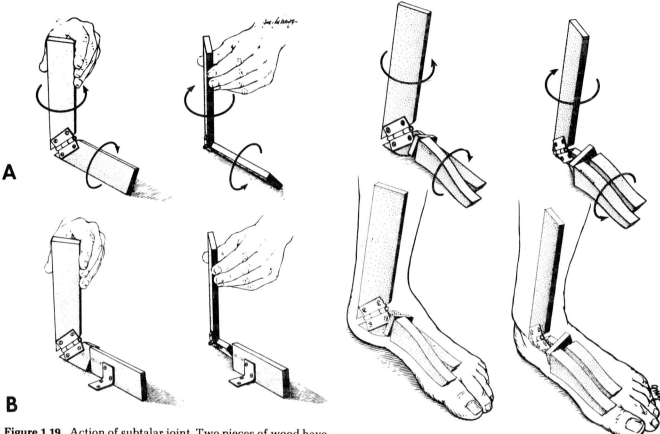

Figure 1.19. Action of subtalar joint. Two pieces of wood have been connected by a hinge whose axis is positioned between the vertical member (shank) and the horizontal member (foot) at 45°. Note that in *A* internal and external rotation of the shank around a vertical axis causes the foot to rotate around a horizontal axis. In *B*, a pivot joint has been inserted in the foot to represent the transverse tarsal joint, thus permitting the forefoot to remain in a fixed position. (Reproduced, with permission, from Inman, V. T., and Mann, R. A. Biomechanics of the foot and ankle. In Mann, R. A. (ed.) *DuVries' Surgery of the Foot.* Ed. 4. The C. V. Mosby Company, St. Louis, 1978.)

Figure 1.20. Action of subtalar joint, represented as hinge located at angle of 45° to shank and foot. The forefoot has been divided into two segments. The medial segment represents the three medial rays articulating with the hindfoot through the talonavicular joint. The lateral segment represents the two lateral rays articulating with the hindfoot through the calcaneocuboid joint. Note that rotation of the shank is accompanied by supination and pronation of the foot. (Reproduced, with permission, from Inman and Mann, *DuVries' Surgery of the Foot.* The C. V. Mosby Company, St. Louis, 1978.)

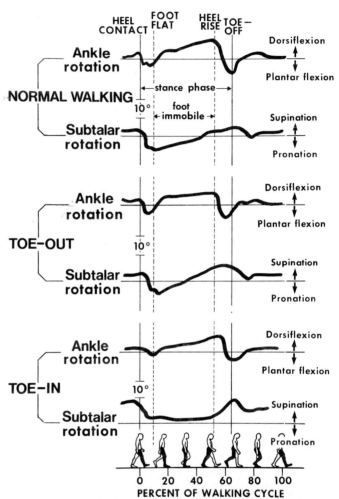

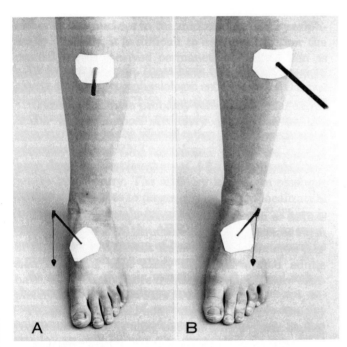

Figure 1.21. Rotation of leg accompanied by pronation and supination of foot. *A,* Internal rotation of leg causing foot to pronate. *B,* External rotation of leg causing foot to supinate. (Reproduced, with permission, from Inman, V. T. *The Joints of the Ankle.* The Williams & Wilkins Company, Baltimore, 1976.)

Figure 1.22. Synchronous motions in ankle and subtalar joints. Note that variations in the degree of toe-out and toe-in cause variations in the magnitude, phasic action, and angular movements of both ankle and subtalar joints. (Adapted, with permission, from Wright, D. B., Desai, S. M., and Henderson, W. H. Action of the subtalar and ankle-joint complex during the stance phase of walking. *J. Bone Joint Surg. 46-A:*361, 1964.)

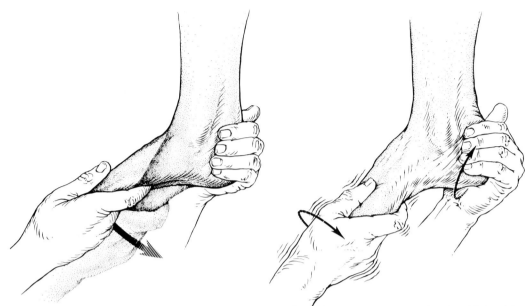

Figure 1.23. Change from mobile to rigid foot. With heel everted, maximal midfoot motion is permitted; with heel inverted and forefoot fixed, the foot becomes rigid.

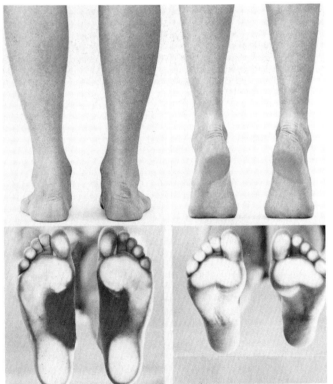

Figure 1.24. Rising on toes. Note that as the body weight is transferred to the forefoot, the heels invert, the legs rotate externally, and the longitudinal arches rise. The barograph records the distribution of weight (white areas) between all the metatarsal heads and the toes. (Reproduced, with permission, from Inman and Mann, *DuVries' Surgery of the Foot.* The C. V. Mosby Company, St. Louis, 1978.)

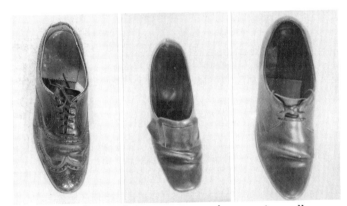

Figure 1.25. Crease between cap and vamp in well-worn shoes.

nation to occur and results in the lateral metatarsals and toes participating to a greater degree in bearing the body weight.

To distribute the weight between all metatarsal heads, the foot must deviate laterally at push-off. That this occurs normally in walking is confirmed by the inspection of any well-worn shoe. A crease in the leather is evident in the region of the juncture of the cap and vamp of the shoe. This crease is always oblique to the longitudinal axis of the shoe (Fig. 1.25) and marks the position of the metatarsophalangeal articulations. The crease shows individual variations in obliquity in accordance with the variations in the angle of the metatarsophalangeal break. Figure 1.26 shows the variation

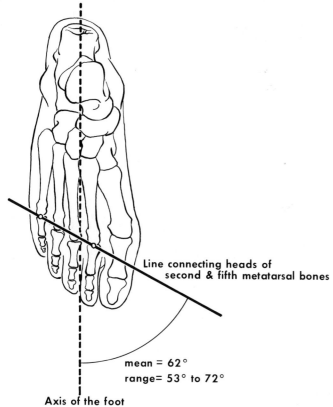

Line connecting heads of
second & fifth metatarsal bones

mean = 62°
range= 53° to 72°

Axis of the foot

Figure 1.26. Angle of metatarsal heads: the angle between the long axis of the foot and a line connecting the heads of the second and fifth metatarsals, measured in 100 randomly selected x-rays. (After Moskowitz, P. S. *Anthropometric Studies of the Human Metatarsus as Seen on X-Ray. I. Normal Feet. Student thesis (unpublished, 1967.)*

in the angle of the metatarsal heads and the long axis of the foot in 100 randomly selected x-rays.

Summary

The major angular displacements of the body during walking have been presented. Most of these movements can be easily seen by any careful observer. The fact that there is upward and downward motion of the body is irritatingly apparent when one views an individual out of step in a parade. The larger motions of the hip, knee, and ankle that occur in the plane of progression are familiar to everyone. That there is a lateral shift of the body over the weight-bearing leg is not so obvious. However, everyone at some time has walked side by side with a companion. If one gets out of step with the other, their bodies are likely to bump (with appropriate apologies ensuing).

The counterrotation of the shoulders with its accompanying arm swing is familiar to all. The transverse rotation of the pelvis (together with its tilt toward the non-weight-bearing side) is readily detected, particularly in a person with tight-fitting pants. The synchronous transverse rotations of the remaining segments of the lower limb are not so apparent. However, if attention is concentrated on the foot during the entire stance phase, the following can often be seen: after heel strike, the foot may rotate medially to a varying extent before being placed flat on the floor. As the foot is loaded, it can be seen to pronate. As the heel is raised, there is a rapid but slight inversion of the heel as the foot supinates. This movement occurs because of the subtalar linkage and is indicative of the horizontal rotations of the leg.

After this general and qualitative description of the movements of the segments of the body during the walking cycle, it now becomes necessary to report in greater detail certain aspects of walking. These will be dealt with in chapters that follow.

The first topic to be presented will be the kinematics of walking: measurements of translational motions of the body segments and rotations at joints. A chapter will be devoted to the metabolic energy requirements during walking, followed by a chapter on kinetics. Muscles will next be discussed: their physiology and function and their phasic action during walking. Finally, the clinical implications and applications of the foregoing material will be presented, as well as the application of this combined knowledge to the mechanical design of prosthetic and orthotic devices.

CHAPTER 2   Kinematics

Stride Dimensions

The usual sequence of animal locomotion consists of three distinct phases, or stages. A start from rest to some level of speed is followed by a relatively long period of rhythmic or cyclic movements at fairly uniform average speed, which in turn is followed, upon arrival at the desired destination, by a brief period of controlled stopping. Lettre and Contini (1967) pointed out that a record of trunk speed clearly displays these three periods, which they named the development phase, the rhythmic phase, and the decay phase, respectively (Fig. 2.1). The rhythmic phase is the dominant feature of animal locomotion, and has been almost exclusively the subject of study by investigators of locomotion. Surprisingly little has been published on the starting and stopping phases.

The basic pattern of the rhythmic phase in human locomotion is seen in level walking. Changes in direction or speed, accommodation to changes or obstacles of the walking surface, or going up or down inclines, are accomplished by deviations superimposed on the basic pattern. Consequently, most studies of human locomotion have been restricted to level walking, usually at whatever speed the subject adopts at the time of the study.

The fundamental unit of the rhythmic phase of any form of locomotion that makes use of legs is the stride, or basic walking cycle, which is defined as the sequence of motions that occurs between two consecutive repetitions of a body configuration. Because there are many body segments involved in locomotion, identical cycles are rare, but variations in the functionally most important motions are relatively small, and the moving animal appears to be doing the same thing over and over again. Although any one cycle can usually be taken as representative of the locomotion pattern, a more representative depiction can be obtained by averaging a number of cycles. The basic test for achievement of a representative cycle is that the value of any measured variable must be the same at the end of the cycle as it was at the beginning.

A cycle (stride) has two dimensions: the time period from beginning to end, and the distance the body moves during the cycle. The time duration may alternatively be expressed by its reciprocal, the stride frequency, which is usually preferred because faster locomotion is characterized by a larger value. Walking speed can be obtained by dividing the stride distance by the stride duration, or by multiplying the distance by the frequency.

Changes in walking speed can be made by changing either the distance per stride or the frequency and keeping the other unchanged, but within the range of usual walking speeds, the normal person changes both. Typically, the plot of distance versus frequency appears to be linear over the range of usual walking speeds, 70–130 steps/min, leveling off at fast speeds toward a constant stride length (Fig. 2.2).

The normal person will consistently return to the same pattern when tested repeatedly, unless changes in footwear or the walking surface alter the pattern (Fig. 2.3). Zarrugh (1975) confirmed the earlier studies of Atzler and Herbst (1927) and Molen et al. (1972), which showed that if a person takes either shorter or longer strides than his natural ones at any speed, the energy required per meter is increased. These studies explain the consistency that a person shows in his stride frequency–stride length relationship. There are, however, wide variations in this relationship between individuals, only part of which can be accounted for by differences in leg length or body height (Fig. 2.4).

The stride length defines the major displacements made by the body during a walking cycle, and the stride duration or frequency defines the amount of time in which these motions occur. Because time and distance are the fundamental parameters of motion, measurements of time and distance for each walking cycle (stride) represent the most basic description of walking. These two dimensions—time and distance for each

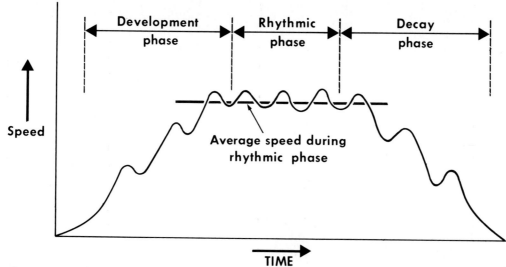

Figure 2.1. Trunk speed during complete act of human walking, from standing start to stop. (Adapted from Lettre, C., and Contini, R. *Accelerographic Analysis of Pathological Gait.* N.Y. University School of Engineering and Science, Technical Report No. 1368.01, 1967.)

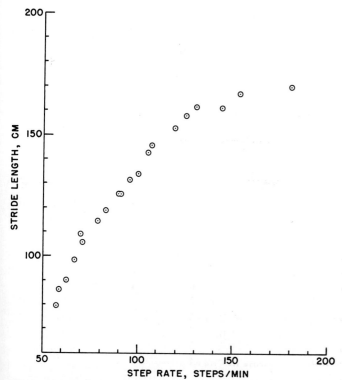

Figure 2.2. Relationship between stride length and step rate. Adult male walking over 43-m course. (Data from Table 19, page 260, Weber, W., and Weber, E. *Mechanik der menschlichen Gehwerkzeuge.* Dieter'schen Buchhandlung, Göttingen, 1836.)

walking cycle—are fundamental parameters that largely determine the patterns of motion of a particular gait.

Because a wide variety of stride length–stride frequency combinations can occur, these two dimensions should always be measured and specified whenever

data on gait are presented. Unfortunately, an awareness of the usefulness of this information has been developed only quite recently and existing data rarely include these dimensions. Speed by itself is insufficient because many combinations of stride frequency and stride length will produce any specified speed.

Leg length is presumed to be a significant determinant of stride length. It would be desirable to be able to normalize gait data for different people by using the ratio of stride length to leg length, where leg length is the distance from the center of the hip joint to the sole of the foot or shoe. Usually it is not practical, however, to locate the hip joint with precision, and one of several methods of estimating from body landmarks is used. A less specific normalization can be achieved by dividing stride length by total body height, which can be measured with greater uniformity and precision. Unfortunately, as shown in Figure 2.4, neither leg length nor total body height provides a satisfactory basis for normalization of body size. For the present, normalization of gait measurements with respect to body size must be regarded as a very significant but unresolved problem for the standardization of locomotion research.

Dean (1965) compiled step frequency and walking speed data from eleven assorted studies on 20 subjects. Normalizing the data for subject height, he fitted a straight line relating the step frequency to the square root of the velocity. The equation for such a line can be restated to describe a linear relationship between stride length and step frequency. The relationship takes the form:

$$\frac{\text{stride length/body height}}{\text{step frequency/min}} = 0.008$$

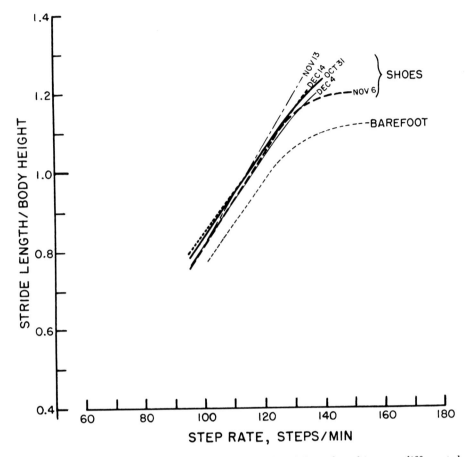

Figure 2.3. Stride length–step rate relationship. Single adult male subject on different days.

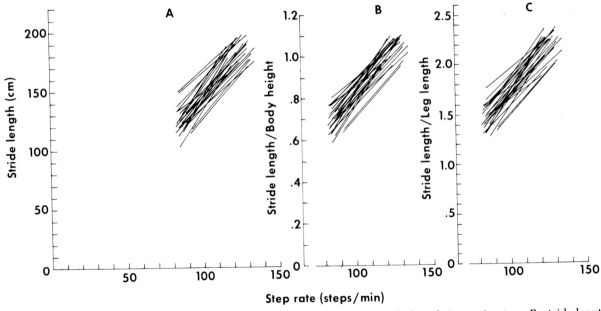

Figure 2.4. Stride length–step rate relationships. Twenty-five normal men. *A*, stride length in centimeters. *B*, stride length/body height. *C*, stride length/leg length (leg length = body height minus sitting height).

This easily remembered relationship provides a simple way to quickly relate experimental data to a consistent "normal" reference. Because only two of the 20 subjects of the Dean compilation are women, this equation is useful as a reference only for men. Large deviations from this value indicate an unusual walking pattern. Women will typically have a shorter stride length, the slope of the line will be less steep, and the line will intercept the vertical axis somewhat above the origin (Fig. 2.5). Existence of such a nonzero intercept means that the ratio of stride length to stride frequency will not be constant at all speeds.

While the relationship between stride length and frequency is a straight line over the range of usual walking speeds, below and above this range (approximately 60–132 steps/min), the stride length tends to become constant. Those investigators who have found a nonlinear relationship between stride frequency and length were fitting a line to data that include either the unusually slow or the unusually fast gaits.

Step Dimensions

During each cycle, or stride, there are two steps, one right and one left. Each of these steps has a dimension system, similar to that for a stride, for distance and time covered by the advancing foot (Fig. 2.6). If the gait is symmetrical, the two dimensions will be the same for both legs, but if there is asymmetry they will be different. Differences in these two basic gait variables would

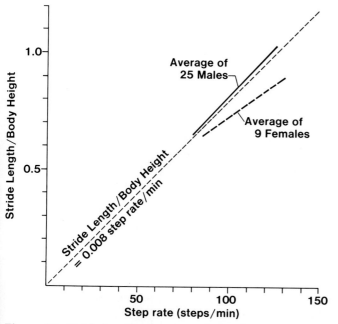

Figure 2.5. Stride length–step rate relationships. Average of the 25 males shown in Figure 2.4, average of 9 females, and line defined by equation on p. 23, as indicated.

appear to be the most satisfactory numerical indicators of asymmetrical, or "limping," gait. The step dimension refers to the leg that is moved forward. Thus, the right step length is the distance from the back of the left heel (at contact) to the back of the right heel (at contact), and the right step time is the time from left heel contact to right heel contact.

Note that, unlike the step dimensions, the *stride* dimensions for the two legs do not provide any indication of gait asymmetry because right and left strides are always equal, regardless of asymmetry, unless the subject is not walking in a straight line.

Phases

Each foot spends part of the walking cycle in contact with the walking surface and the remainder of the cycle in the air, moving to a new position. During the period of contact with the walking surface, the foot is relatively stationary and is providing support to the body, which means that there are forces acting between the foot and the walking surface. Various names have been given to this period of support, such as contact period, support phase, and the one used here, stance phase. In normal walking, the heel of the foot or shoe is the first to contact the surface and the toe is the last point of contact, so that the events of heel contact and toe-off define the beginning and end, respectively, of the stance phase. The stance phase of either foot, in a normal walk, always occupies more than half of the walking cycle, and the remainder of the cycle, during which the foot is in the air, is called the swing phase.

Each stance phase begins and ends with a time period during which both feet are in contact with the ground and body support is being transferred from one foot to the other. The usual term for this period is the double-support phase. If the gait is symmetrical, the two double-support periods will be equal in duration.

The system of cycle subdivisions used in a particular discussion depends on whether the subject of discussion is the whole body or just a lower limb. When the whole body is referred to, the cycle is divided into the two double-support phases and two single-support phases. When the action of a lower limb is described, the principal subdivisions are stance phase and swing phase.

The cycle is sometimes further divided into phases determined by events such as foot flat (early in stance phase) or heel rise (later in stance phase) or determined by whether the ground reaction forces are acting in a rearward, restraining direction, or in a forward, propelling direction. The usefulness of these divisions has not been demonstrated to the extent that they have come into general use.

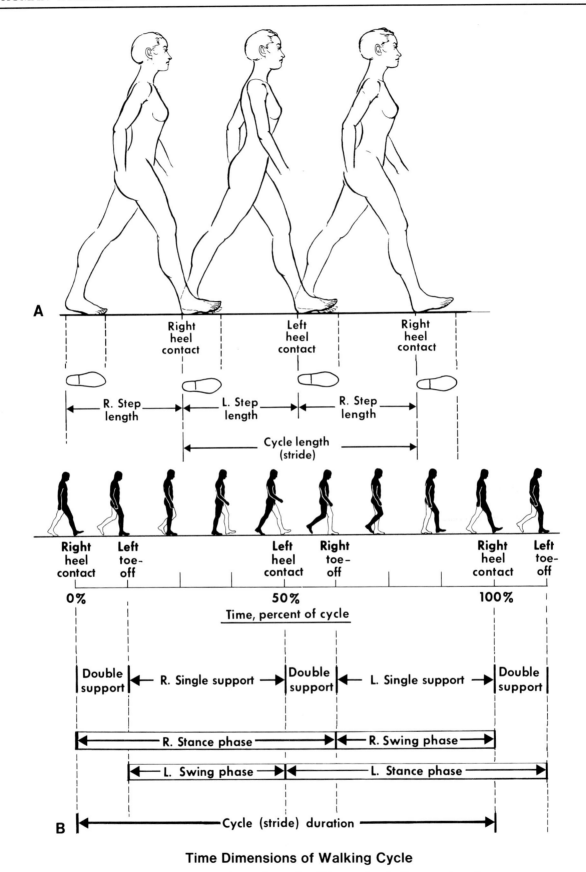

A

Right heel contact

Left heel contact

Right heel contact

R. Step length

L. Step length

R. Step length

Cycle length (stride)

Right heel contact

Left toe-off

Left heel contact

Right toe-off

Right heel contact

Left toe-off

0%   50%   100%

Time, percent of cycle

Double support

R. Single support

Double support

L. Single support

Double support

R. Stance phase

R. Swing phase

L. Swing phase

L. Stance phase

B

Cycle (stride) duration

Time Dimensions of Walking Cycle

Figure 2.6. Distance and time dimensions of walking cycle. *A,* distance (length). *B,* time.

If gait symmetry is assumed, stance phase time = ½ cycle time + double-support time, and swing phase time = ½ cycle time − double-support time, so that the duration of the double-support time specifies the duration of the other phases.

The various studies of the relationship of phase durations to walking speed have not shown good agreement. One source of difficulty seems to be that time intervals have not been measured with sufficient precision. In addition, the phase durations may not be properly measured by the techniques used. For example, different procedures for detecting foot contact may yield different times for the occurrence of the same event. The conditions of walking, such as footwear and the nature of the walking surface, will probably influence the relative phase durations, although this has not been clearly demonstrated. Figure 2.7 shows some representative relationships formulated by several investigators and indicates the need for further study.

Typical Walking Speeds

Each person is capable of walking at a variety of speeds, and will adopt at any one time a speed, from low to high, that meets his needs at that time. Because every feature of walking changes when walking speed changes, the measurement of any feature should be made over the whole range of useful speeds and the description should include the form of the changes that occur as the speed changes.

The concept of speed implies distance per unit time unit. However, as has been shown, in normal walking each person adopts at any speed a step rate that seems natural to him and that he will change only when he changes speed. When his walking speed increases or decreases, his step frequency increases or decreases correspondingly. This relationship permits using step (or stride) frequency as a measure of speed, and has the advantage of offsetting the factor of body size to some

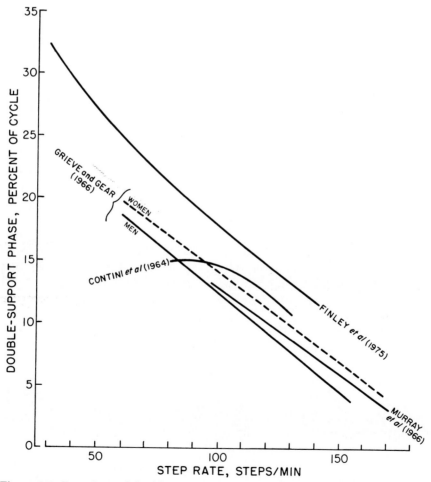

Figure 2.7. Durations of double-support phase determined in various studies.

degree when measurements on two or more subjects are compared or combined.

Although a wide range of walking speeds is used, most walking occurs at some intermediate level. Information on the frequency of various walking speeds has been published by Drillis (1958, 1961) in New York, Finley and Cody (1970) in Philadelphia, and Molen and Rozendal (1966) in Amsterdam. These studies of pedestrians on city streets are in fairly close agreement that the mean step rate for men is about 112 steps/min and for women, about 118 steps/min, and that the standard deviation for both is about 9% of the mean.

Although Murray et al. (1966, 1970) prepared her subjects by practice walking with a metronome set at 112/min, during the subsequent data-collecting her subjects (30 men, 30 women) displayed means and variations close to the values found on street pedestrians. When Murray's female subjects changed to high-heeled shoes, they took shorter steps and increased their step rate.

Rozendal (1973) recorded the step rate of people (including strollers) crossing an Amsterdam park and obtained mean values of 102 steps/min for men and 107 steps/min for women, thus indicating an effect of surroundings on walking speed.

Another influence on walking speed is the metabolic requirement. It has been shown that at any walking speed a person adopts the step rate that requires the least oxygen consumption per meter walked. There is also a speed at which the oxygen consumption per meter is a minimum; at the Biomechanics Laboratory, it has been determined that a person walking at this optimal speed will subjectively regard it as the "most comfortable" (Ralston, 1958). There is the expected individual variation, but the step rate at this speed is approximately 100 steps/min. The minimal energy walk appears to be somewhat below the speeds adopted by most urban pedestrians, but close to the average speed of walkers in the Amsterdam park (Rozendal, 1973).

The studies on urban pedestrians indicate that rarely will an adult man walk with a step rate outside the range of 75–140 steps/min. The equivalent range for the adult woman is 80–150 steps/min. The central part of this range, from 100–120 steps/min, corresponds to a medium speed gait for adult men. When gait patterns at various speeds are compared, a step frequency of about 110 steps/min can be considered as typical, while step rates below 100 or above 120 steps/min represent slow and fast gaits respectively. Comparable gait patterns for women are about 5 steps/min above these levels.

Principles of Motion

If a flat object is given a push that sets it in motion across a table whose surface provides negligible frictional resistance, it will glide across the table in the direction of the push. In addition, it may also rotate, or turn, about a point, called the center of rotation, centrally located on the object (Fig. 2.8). It can be experimentally demonstrated that no matter how the object is pushed, any rotation that occurs will always be about the same point. This point is the center of mass, sometimes called the center of gravity, of the object. Some additional observations can be demonstrated:

1. If the line of the push force passes through the center of mass, there will be no rotation.

2. The greater the distance between the line of force and the center of mass, the greater will be the rate of rotation for the same amount of force.

3. Two simultaneous forces of equal magnitude but applied in opposite directions and at equal distances from the center of mass will produce only the turning motion. The center of mass will remain at a fixed point (Fig. 2.9).

The two types of motion thus demonstrated are the components of any motion that a body can have. Translation is the component defined by motion of the center of mass, and rotation is the circular motion about the center of mass. In many situations, the description of motion is more easily understood by reference to points other than the center of mass, but it is always possible to describe any motion of a body as a combination of translation of the center of mass and rotation of the body about its center of mass.

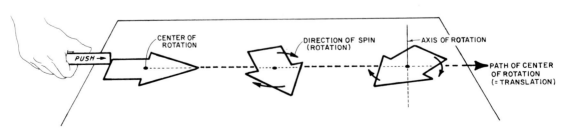

Figure 2.8. Translation and rotation, caused by force not passing through center of mass.

The center of rotation (which in this example coincided with the center of mass) indicates the location of an imaginary line called the axis of rotation. The axis of rotation is perpendicular to the table top, which is serving as the plane of motion (a plane can be imagined as a flat surface, like a table or wall without boundaries).

A quick push on an object will produce translational motion in a straight line, but a continuous force acting at an angle to the original path will produce a curved path of motion. For example, a ball thrown in the air would continue to travel in the direction in which it was moving when it left the hand if it were not for the force of gravity continuously pulling it toward the earth and producing a curved path.

Although it may be evident to an observer that an object is moving and rotating, measuring these motions requires specifying a system of targets on the moving

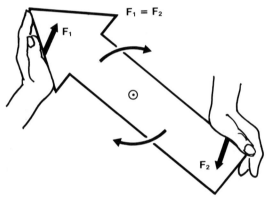

Figure 2.9. Force couple producing rotation only.

object and a system of reference targets that are not part of the object and assumed to be stationary. The motions are then described as the changes in position between the targets on the object and the reference targets.

The description of translation is in terms of the relationship between two points, while the description of rotation is in terms of the relationship between two lines. Measuring translation of a moving point requires specifying another point, called a reference point, which can be assumed to be stationary. The positions of the moving point relative to the reference point are then measured at appropriate time intervals. There are two components of the measurement: the *length* and the *direction* of the line connecting the two points. To determine direction, a reference line is required, usually one through the reference point (Fig. 2.10A).

The angle between the reference line and the line connecting the reference point and the moving point then indicates direction. An alternative method of indicating direction is to separate it into two length components (as in Fig. 2.10B), which provide the same information without using angles. A second reference line, at right angles to the first, is specified through the reference point, and the distance of the moving point from these lines is measured.

These reference lines are called axes; the horizontal one is conventionally called the x-axis and the vertical one, the y-axis. The location of a point is specified by distances, called coordinates, from the axes. The x-coordinate is the horizontal distance from the y-axis, and the y-coordinate is the vertical distance from the x-axis.

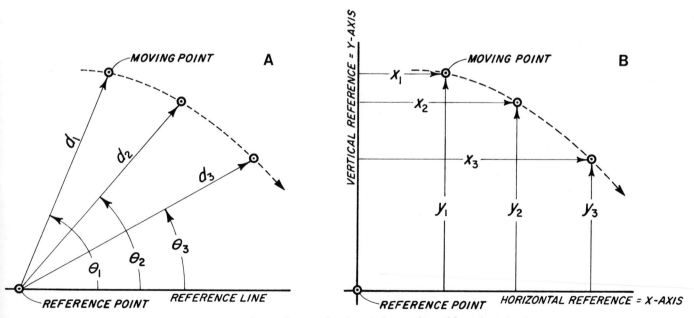

Figure 2.10. Measurement of translation of point. *A*, by angle and length. *B*, by coordinates.

In the description of human walking, translation as a function of time is of primary interest. Coordinates of target points are measured at time intervals with a duration short enough to provide a desired level of precision. The graphical presentation of the measurement is in the form of a plot of the coordinate values against time. The vertical and horizontal coordinates are plotted separately, so that the translation measured of the point in Figure 2.10 is presented by one plot describing the horizontal component and a second plot describing the vertical component of the motion (Fig. 2.11).

If a body is rotating, the translation path of a target point that is not at the center of rotation will oscillate about the translation path of the center of rotation. The greater the distance of the target from the center of rotation, the greater will be the oscillation, and the less true will be the indication of the path of the object as a whole (Fig. 2.12). On the other hand, any line on the object will serve equally as an indicator of the body rotation.

The measurement of rotation is accomplished by measuring the changes in the angle between a line specified on the moving object and a reference line assumed to be stationary (Fig. 2.13). The reference line is usually one of the reference lines specified for determining the direction of the moving point.

This discussion has described the measurement method when a flat two-dimensional object is moving across a flat two-dimensional surface, that is, all measurements are confined to a single plane.

Furthermore, the object in motion retains a fixed configuration; that is, its shape does not change. In kinematics, such a body is called a rigid body. Any point or line on the body used as a target for measurement maintains a fixed relationship with all other parts of the body.

This simple model, however, is not seen in locomotion. The process of locomotion always requires some change in configuration, so that the body cannot be called rigid. Further, the body is not flat (two-dimensional) but has thickness, which makes it three-dimensional. Finally, even in straight, level walking, body motions, both translational and rotational, can be seen in front, rear, and top views of the body, making it

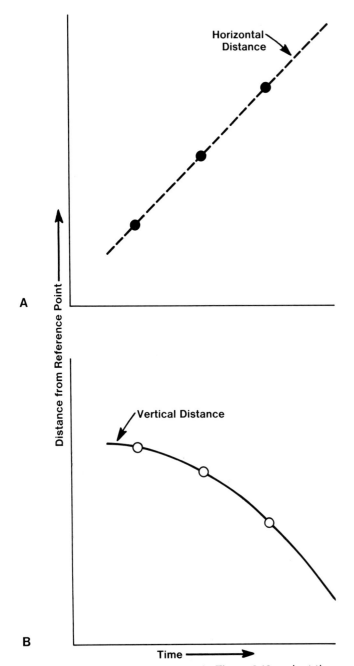

Figure 2.11. Plot of measurements in Figure 2.10 against time. A, horizontal displacement. B, vertical displacement.

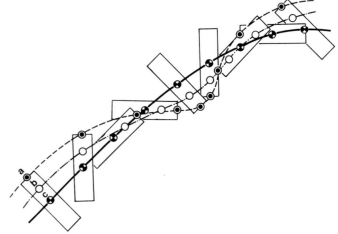

Figure 2.12. Paths of various target points on body in translation and rotation; C, target at center of mass; a, b, paths of target points at varying distances from center of mass.

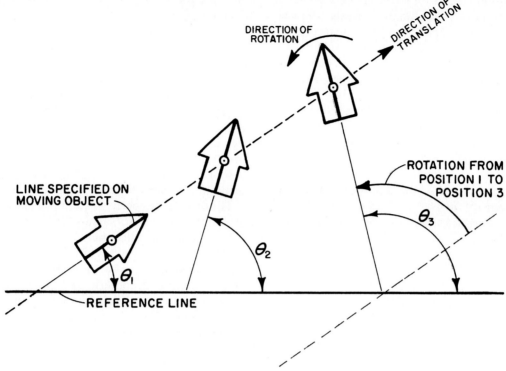

Figure 2.13. Measurement of rotation of object.

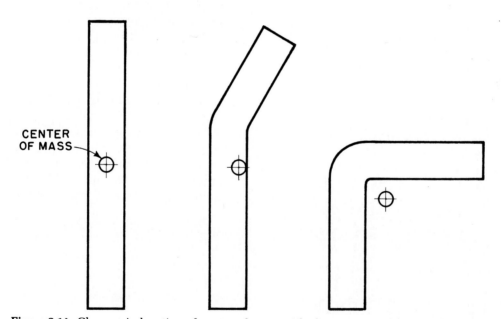

Figure 2.14. Changes in location of center of mass with changes in configuration of object.

evident that motions are not confined to the single plane corresponding to the side view.

Each of these variations from the simple rigid body single plane system makes the measurement and description of motion more complex.

A change in the configuration of a body results in a change in the location of the center of mass in relation to other points on the body (Fig. 2.14). Thus, a target cannot be placed on a nonrigid body and used to denote the center of mass. However, many bodies, including the human, are composed of relatively few segments, each of which can be regarded as a rigid body. Because the segments are linked and thus lack independence of movement, the points of attachment between the segments, the joints (rather than the centers of mass), are of principal kinematic significance. The targets for translational measurements are, therefore, placed as closely as can be estimated to the joint centers. The line between the joint centers at each end of the segment serves as the target for measuring and describing segment rotation. The joint nearest the center of the body is the proximal target and the joint at the other end of the segment is the distal target. The last segment of each limb does not have a distal joint, and it is the usual practice to use an indicator of the center of mass of the segment as the distal target.

The degree of segmentation in a particular study depends on the type of activity being studied and the degree of precision required. For human walking studies, the segments of particular interest are the thigh, shank, and foot for each leg. Although the foot is commonly described as a single segment, various studies have established a basis for a functional division into at least five segments (Inman, 1969; Bojsen-Møller and Lamoreux, 1979). However, when the feet are encased with shoes, as is usual for human walking studies, only two divisions can be discerned. There are no generally accepted terms for the foot subdivisions, but here they will be called a hindfoot–midfoot (heel and instep) segment, and a forefoot (toes) segment.

The rest of the body (head, both arms, and trunk) is often treated as a unit labeled HAT. Significant, though relatively minor, movements occur between the upper part of the trunk (thorax and shoulders) and the lower part (pelvis) and also between the upper part of the arm and the combined forearm and hand, and some studies have investigated these additional segmentations.

Even when the bodies are three-dimensional, the measurement and description of translation and rotation are in the two-dimensional form, which has been described. The three-dimensional target system is converted into a two-dimensional image by projecting images of the targets onto a flat surface or reference plane as diagramed in Figure 2.15. The measurements are then made on the projected image. Usually this is done by some variation of an optical system, of which photography is an example.

There are two effects that distort the measurements, and if uncorrected may lead to erroneous descriptions. One of these effects, analogous to parallax, is the result of the object being seen at different angles in different parts of the field of view (Fig. 2.16). The second is the result of the perspective effect making objects appear smaller as they become farther from the plane of projection (Fig. 2.17). Errors in both translational and rota-

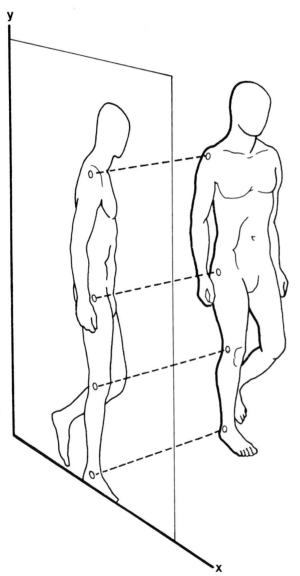

Figure 2.15. Conversion of three-dimensional target system to two-dimensional image.

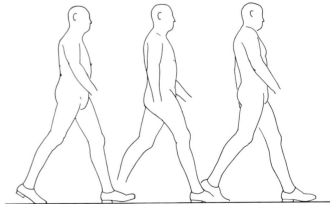

Figure 2.16. Effect, analogous to parallax, of object being viewed at different angles.

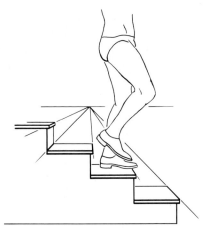

Figure 2.17. (Traced from photograph.) Perspective effect makes right foot look longer than left foot.

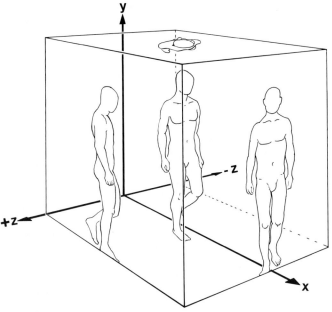

Figure 2.18. Axes and three planes of projection for measurement of three-dimensional motion.

tional measurements can occur from these effects. These errors can be corrected if measurements are taken from another view and used for appropriate computations.

As the term implies, three-dimensional motion requires a third coordinate measurement to specify the positions of a point in motion. A third axis, called the z-axis, is added, perpendicular to the x- and y-axes. Thus, two additional planes are created, one corresponding to a rear or front view and the other to a top or bottom view. The front or rear view is specified by the y- and z-axes and the top or bottom view is specified by the x- and z-axes (Fig. 2.18).

The location of a point can now be described by three coordinate measurements, x, y, and z. Translational motion is described by three components: changes in the values of the x-coordinate, of the y-coordinate, and of the z-coordinate. Because the projection on any one plane provides two of the three coordinate values, measurements need be made on only two projection planes to obtain the complete set of three coordinates.

On three-dimensional bodies, the points of interest such as centers of mass and joint centers are usually not at the surface but within the body and not accessible as targets for measurement. Though targets placed on the surface to indicate interior points may be reliable when the segment is in one position, the fidelity will be lost when the segment is moved to another position. Errors will occur from the parallax effect previously mentioned, and, in addition, as a result of rotations about axes not perpendicular to the plane of projection (Fig. 2.19). Such rotations take place when motion is not confined to a single plane, and the resulting errors can be corrected only with a three-dimensional analysis.

In order to measure accurately the rotations of a body moving in three dimensions, that body must be specified by three points or targets not lying on a straight line. All of the kinematic information on a body in motion is contained in the measurements of the x-, y-, and z-coordinate values of the three points specified for the object.

These individual elements of motion are not themselves usually of interest, because they may have no apparent relation to observable motions of the body. However, the elements can be combined in various ways to obtain descriptions of the translational and rotational motions desired.

Obtaining the three coordinate measurements on the three targets requires attaching the targets so that they are visible to two planes of projection, which are perpendicular to each other. This is physically difficult to accomplish, particularly on body segments with large ranges of motion. If the desired information is limited to a certain few of the possible motions, it is more economical to specify targets that provide that information directly, though there will usually be a loss in accuracy and precision.

Thus, if rotations as they appear in only one view are wanted, any line which remains approximately parallel to the plane of that view is sufficient. The measurements must be interpreted cautiously, however. Though the description implies that any observed rotation is about an axis perpendicular to the plane of measurement, apparent rotations may also be produced as a result of rotations about axes parallel to the measurement plane.

The rotation of a segment as it appears from each of the standard views is of some descriptive interest, but

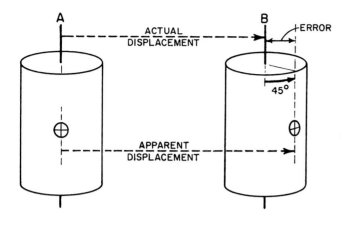

mined and are not in a fixed relationship to the external reference system used for describing segment rotations and translational motion. However, comparisons between measurements on projected images and those obtained with goniometers aligned to the anatomic axes have usually shown a similarity in pattern and amplitude, indicating that during walking most anatomic axes remain in fairly close alignment with the standard projection planes. In fact, the human body is constructed so that its movements tend to occur in the conventional viewing planes. As a consequence, it is customary to label body motions in relation to the standardized anatomic position (Fig. 2.20), in which the body is standing naturally except that the palms of the hands are facing forward.

A plane corresponding to a side view is called a sagittal section; the midsagittal plane divides the body into right and left halves. A plane corresponding to the front or rear view is called a coronal section, and one which corresponds to a top or bottom view is called a transverse section.

The system of naming angular motions is also based

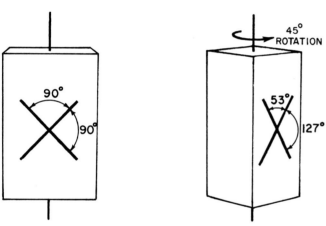

Figure 2.19. Errors arising from measurement on surface targets of rotating three-dimensional bodies. *A*, displacement. *B*, angle.

is of minor significance to the mechanics of walking. Because walking is accomplished by the action of muscles developing tension and producing rotation at the joints of the body, the angular changes between adjacent segments are the principal subject of rotation measurements during walking. The angular changes, called joint rotations, are described in the same form as segment rotations, that is, as changes in the angular relationship between two lines, one on each segment, as though the rotation were occurring about an axis perpendicular to both lines. There are also the same departures of the physical relationship of the segments from the one implied by the mathematical description.

Rotation axes at the joints are anatomically deter-

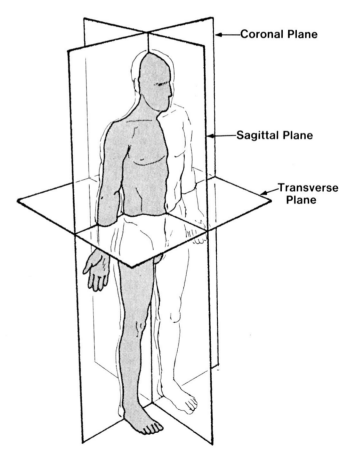

Figure 2.20. Reference planes of body in standard anatomic position.

on the standard viewing planes, with a separate term for each of the two directions in the plane. Figure 2.21 illustrates the generally accepted naming system for the joint rotations in the lower limb which will be described in the remainder of this chapter.

Movements of the Body Segments During Walking

Side View (Sagittal Plane)

Of the three standard views of the body, the side view is of the greatest interest, because it is in this view that both the direction of walking and the interaction be-

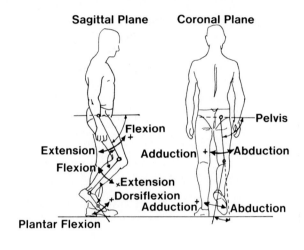

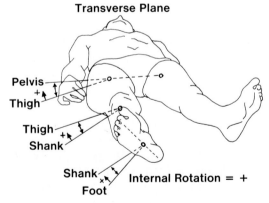

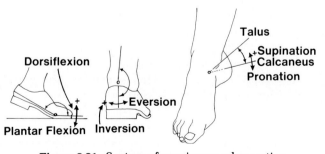

Figure 2.21. System of naming angular motion.

tween the body and the walking surface are seen. Most studies of walking have, in fact, been confined to measurements in this plane.

In this view, four types of measurement are made. Two of these are translational motions of points on the body, which are separated into vertical motion and progressional (horizontal, in the direction of walking) motion. The other two measurements, which are rotational, are concerned with the angle that each segment makes with the walking surface, and the joint angles, the angles between adjacent body segments.

A presentation of this type of study is shown in Figure 2.22, which was made by attaching lights to the subject, who then walked across a darkened room in front of a still camera with a rotating shutter that exposed the film 30 times/sec. The single flash exposure permits correlating the lights with anatomic points.

Certain observations of interest can be made on this typical walk. A walking cycle can be indicated by connecting the points of light on the subject at two consecutive right heel contacts. The cycle is further divided by connecting the points at the time the toe leaves the walking surface.

The path of each point on the body to which a light was attached is shown by the series of dots across the photograph. The path is predominantly horizontal, showing the progress of that point on the body in the direction of walking. There is also a vertical component of the motion, and these two components will be described separately. Figure 2.22 provides a visual image of the motions of the various parts of the body, but other procedures have proved to be more practical or more precise for obtaining measurements. The quantitative descriptions that follow are from other studies using various techniques that will not be described here but can be obtained by referring to the original publication.

Progressional Motion

The horizontal distance covered by any point during a walking cycle tends to be the same for all parts of the body. It can be seen, however, that successsive dots are sometimes closer together than at other times. This is most clearly seen at the knee. The time between successive dots is 1/30 sec, so the horizontal distance between them is a measure of the progressional velocity of the point at that time. The least variation in velocity is at the ear and the greatest is at the toe, where the target is stationary for over half the walking cycle.

If there were no variations in velocity, a plot of the horizontal displacement against time would be a straight line, depicted by the average displacement line in Figure 2.23. If there are variations, the displacement plot will oscillate about the straight line. Figure 2.23A

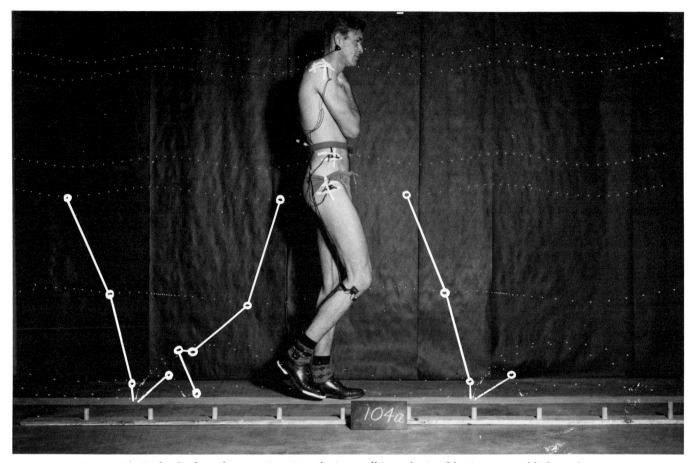

Figure 2.22. Path of selected anatomic points during walking, obtained by interrupted light technique.

shows a typical example of the horizontal displacement of targets at the hip, knee, and ankle. When the displacement curve of a point is steeper than the average displacement line, that point is moving ahead faster than the average velocity. Conversely, as the velocity of the point becomes less than the average velocity, the slope of the displacement curve becomes less than that of the constant velocity line.

The cyclic pattern of horizontal motion can be more easily visualized by subtracting the displacement due to the average velocity from the total displacement so that the value at the end of the cycle will be the same as at the beginning (Fig. 2.23B).

Head and trunk. Although the general shapes of the displacement curves are similar for the trunk and the head, the amplitudes of the motions decrease progressively from the pelvis toward the head (Fig. 2.24).

The trunk reaches a maximum (ahead of the average position) shortly after toe-off and a minimum (behind the average position) at about 5% of the walking cycle before each heel contact.

Thus, the trunk exceeds the average velocity during the 20% of the walking cycle centered around the dou-

ble-support period, and moves at less than the average velocity during the remainder of the cycle.

Although there is a tendency for the pattern during the second half of the cycle to duplicate that of the first half, the difference between the two halves is a sensitive indicator of right–left gait asymmetry.

The pelvic displacement pattern is of particular interest because the pelvis is where the legs, which are the principal organs of locomotion, are joined to the rest of the body. There is also a resemblance between the patterns of linear motion of the pelvis and the motion of the center of mass of the body, which, during walking, remains near the center of the pelvis.

Figure 2.25 shows the characteristic pattern of progressional motion of the pelvis and the changes that occur over a wide range of walking speeds. Note that as the walking speed increases, the progressional oscillation decreases in amplitude. This is true for other parts of the trunk and the head as well.

Joints of the lower limb. The progressional displacement of the joints of the leg has not received the amount of attention devoted to the study of progressional displacement of the pelvis. The data of Figure 2.23 are

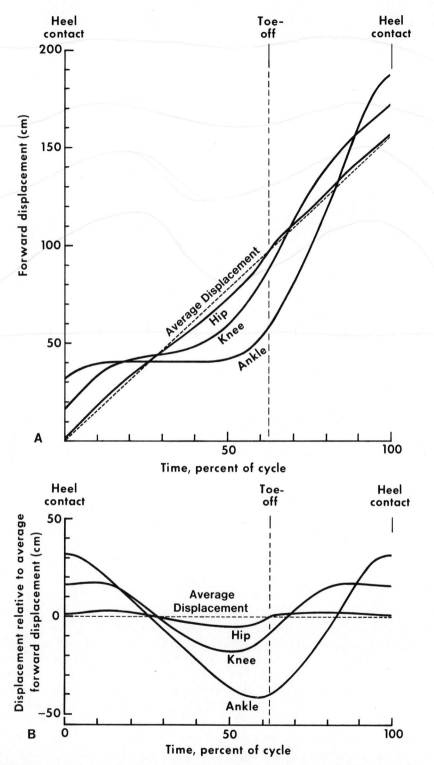

Figure 2.23. Forward displacement of targets at hip, knee, and ankle, and average displacement line, as indicated. *A,* actual displacements. *B,* displacements relative to average.

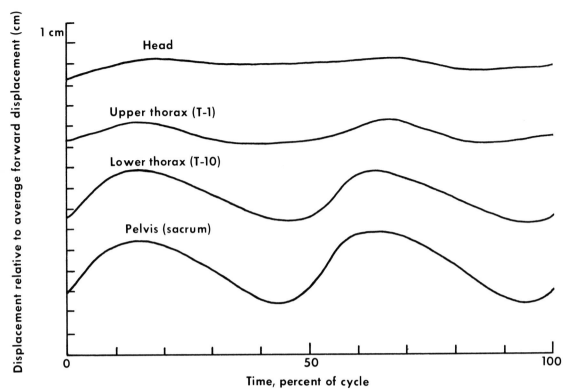

Figure 2.24. Deviations of head, upper thorax (T-1), lower thorax (T-10), and pelvis (sacrum), relative to average forward displacement.

typical. The amplitude of the oscillation increases as one moves progressively from the hip to the toe. The points about the foot, which remain stationary during much of stance phase, increase in amplitude of progressional motion as the speed, and consequently the step length, increases—in contrast to the trunk, which shows a decrease in amplitude.

Vertical Displacement

Trunk. As the path of the light at the ear (Fig. 2.22) indicates, one of the most evident characteristics of walking is the up-and-down motion of the head with each step. The head is at its lowest elevation during the middle of the double-support period, and at its highest during the middle of the single-support period. Measurements (Lamoreux, 1971; Waters et al., 1973) have established that the amount of vertical motion at the head is the same as that at any point along the entire spine and pelvis.

There is a close correlation between the stride length and the amount of vertical excursion (Fig. 2.26). Because stride length increases with walking speed, the amount of vertical motion per step becomes greater as the person walks faster. There is considerable individual variation in the relationship, as indicated by Figure 2.27, of the measurements on seven different subjects.

The maximal elevation of the pelvis tends to remain close to the value during standing, but because the trunk inclines increasingly as walking speed increases, the maximal elevation of the head decreases as the walking speed increases.

The various rotations of the pelvis will produce distortions in the measurement of vertical oscillation of the pelvis if the measurement is taken at a point on the surface of the body. The measurements of Figure 2.26 were obtained by using a frame which in effect measured the position of the center of the pelvis.

Joints of the lower limb. The pathways of the joints of the leg are illustrated in Figure 2.28. The figure was obtained by attaching lights to the locations of the joints as well as the heel and toe of the right leg. The subject walked in front of a camera with an open shutter so that the paths of the lights were recorded. The paths of Figure 2.28 are typical of normal walking, but the changes in elevation vary considerably between individuals and with walking speed (Murray and Clarkson, 1966). The change in heel elevation during the cycle is typically about double that of the toe and ankle which, in turn, are about two or three times those of the hip and knee.

Figure 2.29 plots the vertical displacements of the hip, knee, ankle, and toe against time for a typical walking cycle.

Hip. Figure 2.29 shows a typical vertical displacement

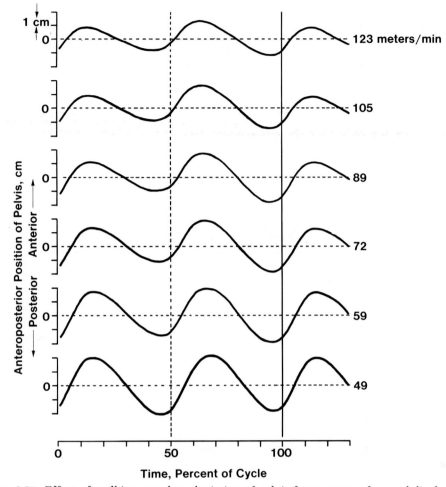

Figure 2.25. Effect of walking speed on deviation of pelvis from average forward displacement.

pattern of a target placed over the greater trochanter (commonly used as the external indicator of the hip joint location in the side view). As with the pelvis, there are two maximal and two minimal points during the cycle, but unlike those of the pelvis, the two halves of the cycle are not symmetrical. Instead, the curve separates into a stance phase section and a swing phase section, each of which has a minimal point shortly after the start of the phase. The maximum of the swing phase section coincides with maximal pelvic elevation, but the stance phase maximum precedes maximal pelvic elevation (see Fig. 2.23). In addition, toward the end of stance phase, instead of following the pelvis in its drop to a minimal height, the trochanter is lifted slightly, producing the slight irregularity of the curve at that time.

Knee. The prominence of the lateral femoral epicondyle is a suitable approximation of a side view location of the knee joint. A target at this location is at its lowest

elevation at the time of toe-off and rises to its highest elevation when the hip reaches its maximal swing phase flexion (about 85–90% of the cycle). The knee then drops to a secondary minimum at heel contact, rises slightly during the first fifth of stance phase, then drops gradually as toe-off is approached (Fig. 2.29). Although this is a typical pattern, some normal walkers vault over the forefoot, so that the highest stance phase elevation is reached at the same time as maximal body elevation at midstance. This pattern is also seen in above-knee amputees if extra elevation is required for the prosthetic foot to clear the floor during its swing phase.

Ankle. It is customary to use the prominence of the lateral (fibular) malleolus as the lateral indicator of the ankle axis, although anthropometric studies (Isman and Inman, 1969) place the lateral position of the ankle axis about a centimeter ahead of and a centimeter below this landmark. At heel contact, a target placed here is near its minimal elevation (see Fig. 2.29) and will be lowered

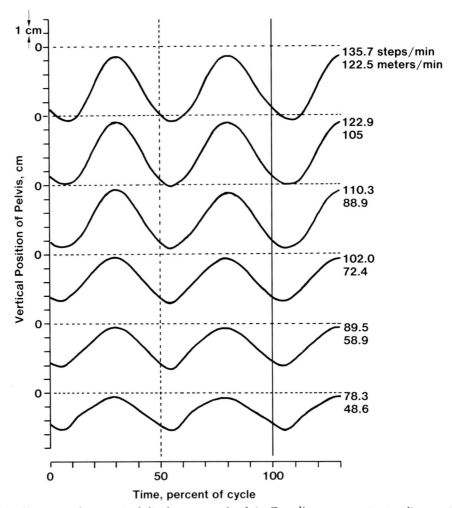

Figure 2.26. Effect of walking speed on vertical displacement of pelvis. Zero line represents standing position.

only another 2 or 3 cm as the foot is brought into full contact with the walking surface. Shortly after the midpoint of stance phase, the heel rises slightly, raising the ankle joint. The ankle joint continues to rise through the early part of swing phase, reaching a maximal elevation at the time the knee is maximally flexed (about 70% of cycle), then slowly descending until the foot is flat on the walking surface in the early part of stance phase.

Heel. Although the heel displacement is not included in Figure 2.29, Figure 2.28 indicates that the pattern of heel translation is essentially the same as that of the ankle but much greater in amplitude. Because stance phase begins when the heel makes contact with the walking surface, the heel is at its minimal elevation through the entire first half of stance phase. At the middle of stance phase the heel begins to rise from the floor and continues to rise until the maximum is reached

at about 5% of cycle after toe-off. The heel then drops toward the walking surface in a smooth path, with an abrupt drop just before heel contact.

Toe. Except for the latter half of the double-support period, the motion of targets at the toe and the toe break are identical. Both are at a maximal height just before heel contact, and are brought into contact with the walking surface at about 7½% of cycle. The conventional shoe tends to keep the toe slightly elevated until the heel rises during the latter part of stance phase (Fig. 2.29). The entire toe remains in contact until the middle of the double-support phase, when the foot straightens as the body weight is taken off that foot. As the toe leaves the walking surface, it is lifted, reaching usually, but not necessarily, a secondary maximal elevation at about 10% of cycle past toe-off. This maximum is followed by a slight decline at about 10% of cycle later, then rises to a maximum at 2 or 3% before the end of the cycle. This maximal toe elevation just before heel contact is about half the heel height just after toe-off (Murray and Clarkson, 1966).

Segment Rotations

In order to avoid confusion, the description of rotations of the body segments in the lateral view will be described as seen from the right side and will refer to the right limbs only. In some cases, the original measurements were made from and on the left side of the body; however, though there is usually some asymmetry in body motion, no consistent differences between the two sides are evident and symmetry will be assumed. The direction of rotation will be described as being clockwise or counterclockwise. The standard sign convention is that counterclockwise rotation is positive and clockwise rotation is negative.

Pelvis. Although there is considerable individual variation, the characteristic pattern of pelvic rotation seen from the right side is a counterclockwise rotation of a few degrees during the double-support period, when body support is being transferred from one foot to the other. During the single-support period, the pelvis must then rotate in a clockwise direction, but the timing of direction reversals and the amplitude and shape of the curve may vary with changes in the walking speed. Figure 2.30 shows such changes in one typical subject.

In this case, the amplitude of rotation increased from about 2° at a low walking speed (79 steps/min) to about 4° at a high walking speed (136 steps/min). Rotations of

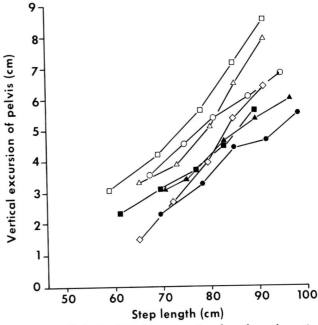

Figure 2.27. Relationship between step length and vertical excursion of pelvis in seven male subjects.

Figure 2.28. Path of targets on leg and foot during walking, obtained by continuous light technique.

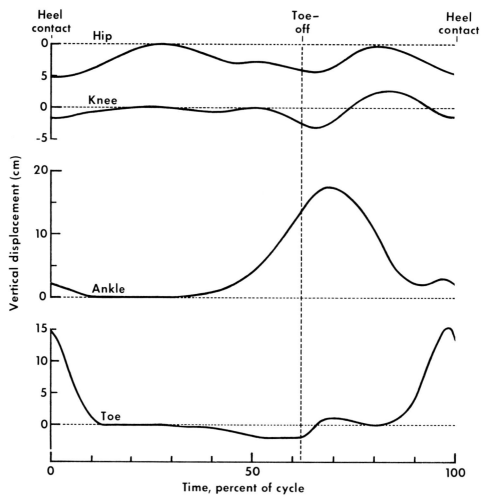

Figure 2.29. Typical vertical displacements of hip, knee, ankle, and toe in adult male subject. Walking speed, 86.5 m/min. Step rate, 111 steps/min.

as much as 7° have been measured on other subjects (Ryker, 1952).

Thigh. At heel contact, the thigh is at nearly its maximal counterclockwise inclination and typically rotates clockwise throughout most of stance phase. At about the time of heel contact of the other leg, the thigh reaches its maximal clockwise inclination and starts the counterclockwise rotation characteristic of swing phase. By the time of toe-off, the thigh is approximately vertical and continues to rotate counterclockwise until it reaches the maximal inclination at about 85–90% of the walking cycle. There is a slight amount of rebounding clockwise rotation during the final part of swing phase (Fig. 2.31).

At low walking speeds, if there is no knee flexion during stance phase, the thigh will rotate clockwise until the heel contact of the other leg (50% of cycle). Ordinarily, however, knee flexion during the first 15% of cycle has a counterclockwise effect on thigh rotation, producing the modifications pictured in Figure 2.31.

Thigh rotation is a principal element of the stride length, and consequently there is a close relationship between the amount of thigh rotation and the stride length. This will be discussed more fully when hip rotation is described.

Shank. The shank pattern is basically one of clockwise rotation during stance phase and counterclockwise rotation during swing phase (Fig. 2.31). The shank reaches its maximal counterclockwise inclination just before heel contact and has rebounded slightly (typically 3–5°) by the time heel contact occurs. There is a similar continuation of a few degrees at toe-off before the counterclockwise motion of swing phase begins.

The rotation during stance phase is modified from a simple curve to a sinuous one by the characteristic knee flexion–extension–flexion pattern of this period. When the knee is flexing, the curve is steeper (shank rotation is faster), and when the knee is extending, the curve is less steep (shank rotation is slower) (Fig. 2.31). As the

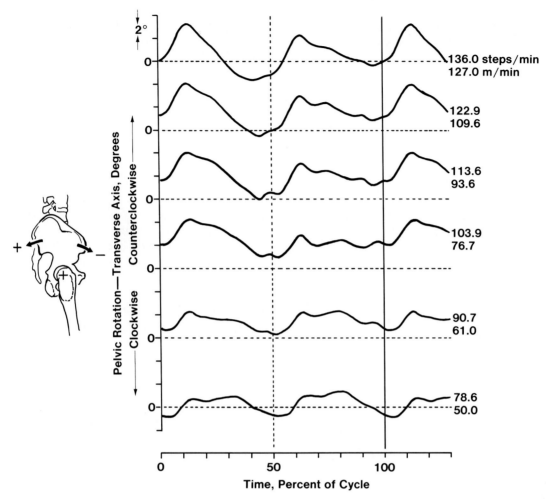

Figure 2.30. Rotation of pelvis as seen from right side of adult male subject during walking at six different step rates.

stride length increases, the maximal clockwise rotation (stance phase) increases, but the maximal counterclockwise rotation (swing phase) tends to remain constant regardless of the walking speed (about 55–60°, depending on the individual).

Hindfoot–midfoot. The part of the foot from the heel to the base of the toes is flat on the walking surface, unless the footwear has an elevated heel. During most of the studies reported on here, conventional shoes were worn, which typically incline the sole about 6 or 7°. As heel contact is approached, the foot is held at a maximally counterclockwise position of about 20° and is then lowered by the impact of heel contact to the flat position (Fig. 2.31).

The foot remains flat on the floor until the middle of stance phase, when at individually various times the heel lifts off the walking surface and a clockwise rotation begins and continues through the remainder of stance phase. Throughout swing phase, the hindfoot–midfoot rotates counterclockwise in preparation for heel contact.

Forefoot (toes). The curve of Figure 2.32 is a composite of eight male subjects which displays a representative pattern of forefoot rotation. At heel contact, the toe is inclined about 35° from the 7½° typical of the standing position. As the foot descends to the floor after heel contact, the toe comes to the 7½° angular position of the standing position, shortly after the ball of the foot contacts the floor. This position is maintained until the heel starts to rise (after 30% of cycle) when the tip of the toe is brought toward floor contact by clockwise rotation of the toe segment. The tip of the toe does not contact the floor until the middle of the double-support period. At this time, the ball of the foot rises from the floor, and the rate of clockwise rotation sharply increases, continuing until after toe-off. Along with the shank and the hindfoot–midfoot, the toe rotates counterclockwise until knee impact near the end of swing phase, after which there is a counterclockwise rotation of several degrees before heel contact. During swing phase in this group, there was an average 95° angular change from about 60° clockwise inclination reached

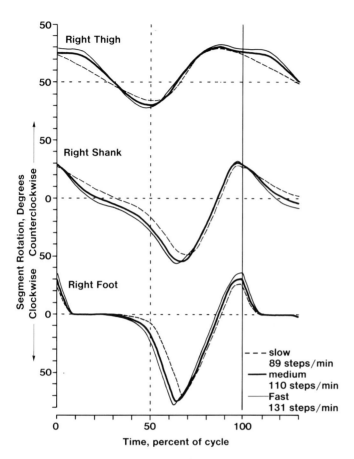

Figure 2.31. Rotations of thigh, shank, and foot as seen from right side of adult male subject during walking at three different step rates.

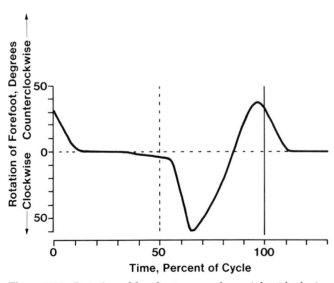

Figure 2.32. Rotation of forefoot as seen from right side during walking (average of eight adult male subjects). Average walking speed, 86 m/min. Average step rate, 108 steps/min.

just after toe-off to nearly 40° counterclockwise inclination just before heel contact.

Rotations Between Segments

Hip (angle between pelvis and thigh). Because the sagittal pelvic rotation is usually small, the pattern of hip rotation is nearly the same as that of thigh rotation already described (see Fig. 2.31).

The hip joint basically extends throughout most of stance phase, starts to flex at about the time that the foot of the other leg contacts the walking surface, and continues to flex through most of swing phase, reaching a maximum at about 85% of cycle, rebounding a few degrees, if at all, before heel contact (Fig. 2.33). If the knee does not flex during early stance phase, the hip joint extends from the beginning of stance phase, but usually the knee flexion after heel contact (see Fig. 2.34) maintains the hip in a nearly maximally flexed position during the first 10% of the walking cycle. The extension of the thigh characteristic of stance phase then begins and continues throughout the swing phase of the other leg.

As would be expected, the range of hip flexion–extension correlates with the stride length. Usually both flexion and extension are increased to contribute to increased stride length, but the increases tend to be greater for flexion than for extension. Some subjects have maintained a nearly constant level of maximal extension, increasing the stride length by increasing hip flexion at heel contact. These observations are not unexpected because the range of possible hip motion from the standing position is much greater in the direction of flexion than in the direction of extension.

Superimposing the hip angle curves for different speeds on a percent of cycle time base (Fig. 2.33) illustrates the above observations and also displays some additional significant characteristics.

First, there is the tendency for the time between maximal extension and maximal flexion to be constant in terms of the percent of cycle although, because the cycle time decreases with speed, the actual time in seconds between these events varies.

Second, the slopes of swing phase flexion and frequently of stance phase extension tend to be constant, indicating that as the cycle time decreases, the velocity of angular motion increases proportionately. This relationship is characteristic of the flexion–extension rotations at the other joints.

Knee (angle between thigh and shank). Like the hip, the knee characteristically reaches heel contact in a position slightly more flexed than the maximum reached during swing phase (Fig. 2.34). Additional flexion occurs, reaching a maximum at 15% of the walking

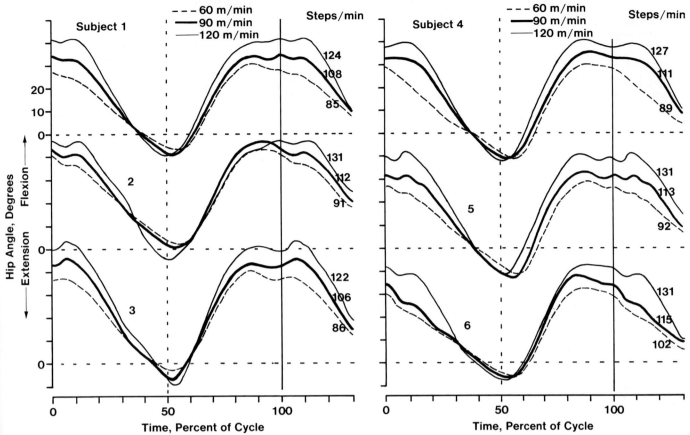

Figure 2.33. Effect of speed of walking on hip angle. Six adult male subjects. Speed varied uniformly from 60–120 m/min. Angle at standing position is zero.

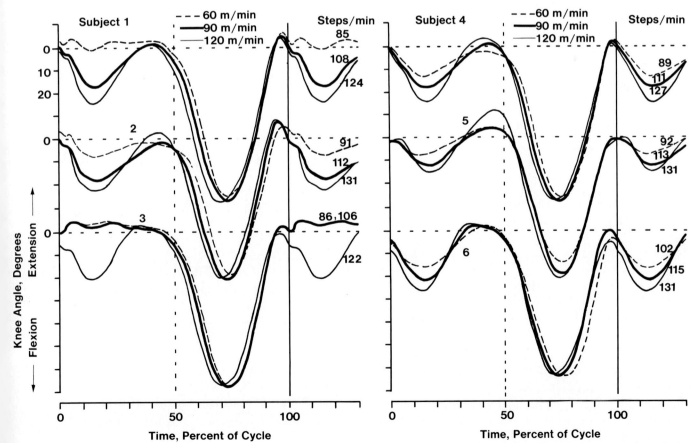

Figure 2.34. Effect of speed of walking on knee angle. Six adult male subjects. Speed varied uniformly from 60–120 m/min. Angle at standing position is zero.

cycle. The amount of this flexion closely correlates with the walking speed, increasing as the speed increases. The knee then starts to straighten, reaching maximal extension at about 40% of cycle. There is considerable individual variation in the time of maximal extension and there is a slight tendency for it to be earlier and less extended as the walking speed increases.

The knee then flexes until about 10% of the cycle time after toe-off. For most people, the amount of flexion increases with speed only a few degrees over the range of walking speeds. The average knee flexion for this group of seven was 63°, which is approximately the same as that of other studies (Murray, 1967; Murray et al., 1970; Lamoreux, 1971).

The knee then straightens, reaching maximal extension shortly before heel contact, with a rebound that puts the knee in slight flexion at the time of heel contact. At lower speeds, some individuals make heel contact before the knee fully extends, so that maximal extension occurs during the initial part of stance phase rather than near the end of swing phase. Though differing from the more common pattern, the gait appears normal and the pattern of rotations at the other joints shows no unusual features.

Ankle (angle between shank and foot). There tends to be more variation between people in the configuration of ankle plantar flexion–dorsiflexion curves than in the flexion–extension curves at the hip and knee (Fig. 2.35). At heel contact, the ankle angle is usually near the value in the standing position, but the ankle may be slightly dorsiflexed or somewhat plantar flexed, depending on the person. As the stride length increases, the ankle is increasingly dorsiflexed. Coincident with heel contact, the foot rapidly comes down to the floor with plantar flexion at the ankle, which for most people seems to be completed at 7½% of the walking cycle, regardless of the walking speed.

Once the forefoot is down, the ankle joint immediately changes to dorsiflexion, which generally continues until near the heel contact of the other leg (50% of cycle), although there are wide variations in the pattern during this period.

As toe-off is approached, there is a rapid plantar flexion that continues until shortly after toe-off, then a rapid dorsiflexion to provide toe clearance during swing phase. Dorsiflexion reaches a maximum at 80–85% of cycle. There follows a slight plantar flexion till about 95% of cycle, when there is a slight dorsiflexion in preparation for heel contact.

Metatarsophalangeal joint (angle between hindfoot-midfoot and forefoot). Each of the five toes (phalanges) articulates with a slender bone (metatarsal) that links it to the bones making up the arches of the foot. The row of five metatarsophalangeal joints is commonly referred

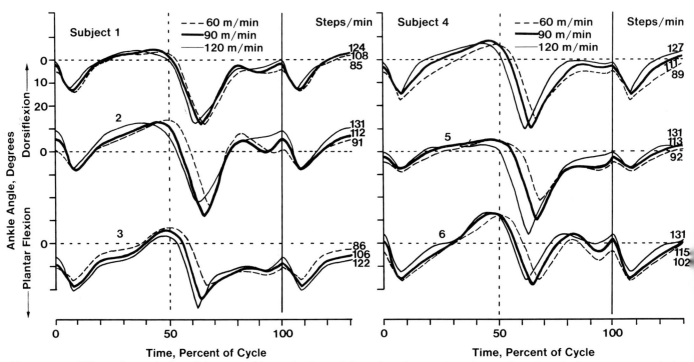

Figure 2.35. Effect of speed of walking on ankle angle. Six adult male subjects. Speed varied uniformly from 60–120 m/min. Angle at standing position is zero.

to as the toe break, the flexion of which is evident in and can be measured on the shoe.

Conventional shoe lasts are designed with a curve at the ball of the foot so that the instep is tilted downward and the toes upward. The apparent angle produced by this construction varies, but in the group of seven males whose data are presented in Figure 2.36, the range was from 164.5–170° (average 167.3°).

The curves of Figure 2.36 show that this angle was maintained during the central half of stance phase and never became greater (more straight) during the walking cycle. As the subject rose on his toes during late stance phase, the shoe became more bent (range of bending 28–48°) to an average maximal value of 134° at mid-double-support, then straightened as the load on the toes was taken off. The curves of Figure 2.36 show some small changes in the angle during swing phase, but it is probable that these are not true changes and are the effect on the projected image of inward and outward rotation of the foot during swing phase and early stance phase.

Front (or Rear) View (Coronal Plane)

Lateral Motion

As shown in Figure 2.18, specifying the location of a point in three-dimensional space requires determining the distance of that point from each of three reference axes. Because the side view can provide two of these, the third can be obtained with either a front (or rear) or a top (or bottom) view. Because most of the significant landmarks of the body are not visible in a top or bottom view, the front or rear view (coronal plane) is the appropriate one for measuring and describing lateral motion. As the subject walks toward or away from the camera, there is a large change in the distance between the subject and the camera which requires mathematical calculation to correct for the perspective effect. As a consequence, few displacement measurements in the coronal plane have been made and only the pelvis and the foot have been studied sufficiently to warrant discussion. The studies on the foot, however, have been confined to observations on the footprint (position of the foot during the midstance period) and will be discussed later with transverse plane measurements.

Pelvis. Although the path of progression of the body in walking is assumed to be a straight line, it is usual for a person to wander from side to side and thus obscure the cyclical side-to-side displacements of points on the body. Figure 2.37 shows the random lateral motion of the pelvis for two consecutive strides. By averaging a number of walking cycles, the random wanderings tend to cancel each other and the cyclic pattern emerges (Fig. 2.38).

At about the time of toe-off, the pelvis is centrally positioned over the line of progression and is moving toward the side of the weight-bearing foot. The maximal deviation (typically, 2 cm) is reached shortly after midstance, after which the pelvis starts toward the opposite side to follow an equivalent path while the other leg is weight-bearing.

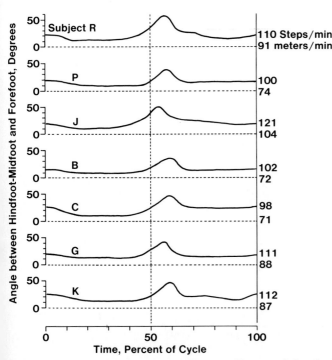

Figure 2.36. Angle between hindfoot–midfoot and forefoot during walking. Seven adult male subjects.

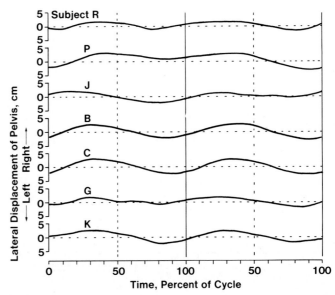

Figure 2.37. Lateral displacement of pelvis. Seven adult male subjects.

To the extent that pelvic motion is equivalent to the displacement of the center of mass, two factors are presumed to determine the amplitude of the side-to-side oscillations. One is the stride width (the side-to-side

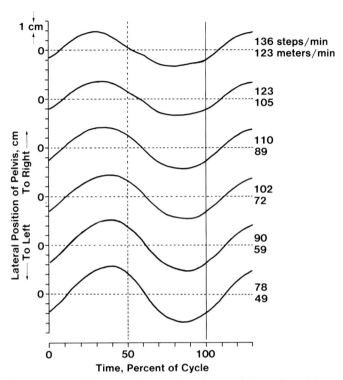

Figure 2.38. Lateral position of pelvis. Adult male subject. Zero line represents standing position.

distance between the positions of the feet), which correlates with the lateral shear forces acting on the body. The other is the length of time these forces act, which is a function of walking speed. Murray et al. (1966) and Chodera and Levell (1973), as well as some unpublished studies at this laboratory, have consistently observed that there is a slight increase in stride width as walking speed increases. It seems, however, that the effect of increased stride width on lateral pelvic motion is more than offset by the decreased step duration accompanying increased walking speed. Figure 2.39, which gives data on six subjects, shows each subject decreasing lateral motion as his walking speed increases. The figure also shows the variations to be found between individuals.

The effect of stride width is demonstrated by the data of Figure 2.40, an experiment during which the subject varied his stride width without changing the step rate. The "negative" values represent reversals in the timing of maximal positions, so that the maximal rightward displacement occurs during the left instead of the right stance phase.

Segment Rotations

Rotations in the coronal plane will be described as viewed from the rear and refer to the segments and joints of the right leg. The rotation axis, perpendicular to the coronal plane, is specified as pointing forward, so that clockwise rotations are positive and counterclockwise rotations are negative.

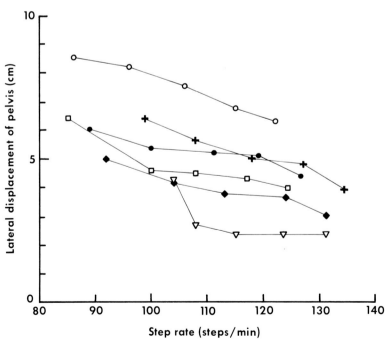

Figure 2.39. Lateral displacement of pelvis. Six adult male subjects.

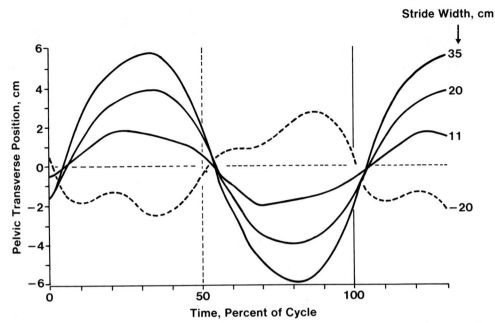

Figure 2.40. Lateral displacement of pelvis, as function of lateral distance between footprints, during walking at 78 m/min. One adult male subject.

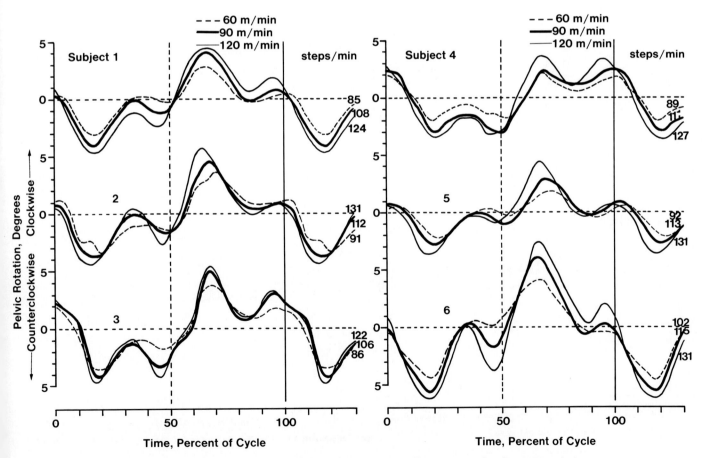

Figure 2.41. Pelvic rotations. Six adult male subjects walking at speeds of 60–120 m/min.

Pelvis. Figure 2.41 shows the pelvic rotation of six adult males each walking at three different speeds. Although there are pronounced variations between the individual subjects, there is general agreement in the basic pattern. At a moderate walking speed, the pelvis is level at heel contact, then during double-support period, it drops to the side of the leg approaching toe-off. Shortly after toe-off, the pelvis rotates to a level position which tends to be maintained until heel contact. Because the pelvis drops counterclockwise (rear view) when the left foot approaches toe-off and drops clockwise when the right foot approaches toe-off, the curve for the second half of the walking cycle is a mirror image of the curve for the first half.

As the walking speed increases, there is a progressive increase in the amount of drop of the pelvis to the side of the leg in swing phase. At the higher speeds, the pelvis is not lifted all the way to a level position during the latter part of swing phase.

Thigh. During stance phase, the foot is stationary on the floor while the pelvis moves from side to side (see Fig. 2.38). The leg segments between the foot and the

pelvis must accommodate to this motion by rotating in the coronal plane, clockwise (in the rear view) during the first part of stance phase and counterclockwise during the latter part. There is more lateral motion of the pelvis during the latter part of stance phase than during the first. Consequently, the amount of counterclockwise rotation typically exceeds the amount of clockwise rotation during stance phase. During swing phase, the thigh reverses direction and rotates clockwise until about 85% of cycle and then tends to remain unchanged until heel contact.

In a rear view projection, the effects of hip rotations in the side and top views are superimposed on this basic pattern. As a consequence, the measurements from motion picture film show various irregularities (Fig. 2.42).

By adding the pelvic rotation angle to the goniometrically measured hip abduction angle, the thigh rotation can be obtained with the effects of rotations in the other planes eliminated, producing a somewhat more regular curve than those in Figure 2.42. These measurements, over a range of speeds (50–127 m/min) are shown for a male subject and display the same general pattern (Fig. 2.43). Changes in speed produced only slight and inconsistent changes in the amount of rotation, but the times of maximal and minimal angles tended to occur earlier in the walking cycle at the faster speeds.

Shank. Figure 2.44 shows the angle between the walking surface and a line on the back of the shank measured in a rear view of eight male subjects. During the initial

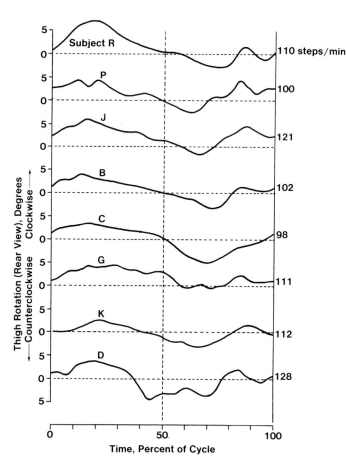

Figure 2.42. Thigh rotations. Eight adult male subjects, measured from motion picture film.

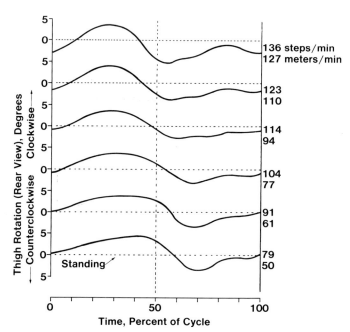

Figure 2.43. Thigh rotation. One adult male subject walking at speeds of 50–127 m/min, calculated from pelvic and hip angles.

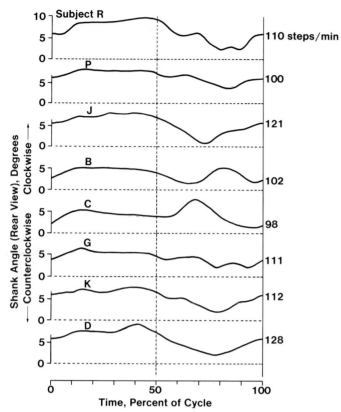

Figure 2.44. Shank angle from vertical, rear view. Eight adult male subjects.

rotations of the shank. This permits the inference that the foot is in a slightly clockwise position at the time of heel contact and rotates counterclockwise as the foot becomes flat on the floor. As the heel rises during the last half of stance phase, the heel portion of the foot rotates clockwise, but because the ball of the foot remains flat on the floor there must be some coronal rotation between the heel and the forefoot. This action is related to the transverse rotation of the shank and will be described more fully when the transverse rotations are described.

Joint Rotations (Abduction–Adduction)

Hip. The two principal factors influencing hip joint rotation in the coronal plane are the side-to-side motion of the trunk and the rotation of the pelvis in the rear view. The pattern of each of these movements is very consistent. The variations between subjects or those resulting from changes in walking speed are principally in amplitude (Fig. 2.38), so it is not surprising that the same consistency occurs in hip rotation.

Figure 2.45 presents the hip angular changes in one subject walking at six different speeds. The principal change is from a tendency at low speeds to keep the angle unchanged during midstance to a continuous adduction during this period at higher speeds. The amount

part of stance phase, as the foot settles to the walking surface, the shank usually rotates outward (clockwise for the right shank) several degrees. The shank maintains this inclination (average, 6½°) throughout the center half of stance phase. As the heel rises and moves outward, the shank then rotates inward (counterclockwise for the right shank) continuing into the early part of swing phase. This group displayed considerable variation in the rotation seen in the rear view during swing phase, but the net effect is to reverse the counterclockwise rotation and bring the shank near the outwardly inclined position characteristic of stance phase. In one case, subject C, the usual swing phase pattern of counterclockwise followed by clockwise rotation was reversed, although his gait did not differ from that of the other subjects in other characteristics. During the time the foot is flat on the floor, the shank, viewed from the rear, remains at a constant inclination.

Foot. The rotation of the foot in the coronal plane can be thought of as changes in the angle between the sole of the foot and the walking surface as seen from the rear. Such measurements have not been made, but the measurements between the shank and the foot in the coronal plane (to be discussed later) are typically opposite in direction and exceed in magnitude the coronal

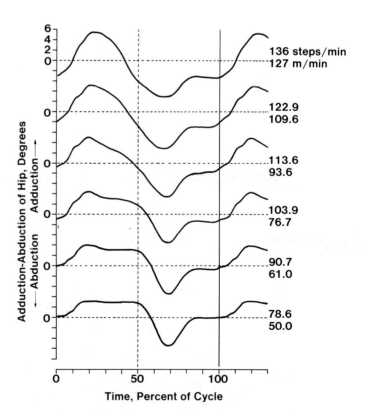

Figure 2.45. Abduction–adduction of hip. Adult male subject. Zero line represents standing position.

of rotation increased from 8 to 12½° (at 79 and 136 steps/min, respectively).

Knee. The descriptions of the coronal rotations of the thigh and shank show that they differ during midstance phase in that the thigh is continuously rotating counterclockwise while the shank remains nearly stationary. During swing phase, the thigh reverses to rotate clockwise at or shortly after toe-off, while the shank typically does not begin its clockwise rotation until midswing. These differences require an apparent knee abduction during the center half of stance phase and an apparent knee adduction during the first half of swing phase. The term "apparent" is used because the methods of measurement may involve the effects of flexion and extension in addition to true abduction and adduction.

Individual curves (Fig. 2.46) tend to show considerable variation, caused by the relatively large rotations in the other planes. Averaging the values of the seven individual curves produces the curve at the bottom of Figure 2.46.

Ankle. Except during the part of stance phase when the foot is flat on the walking surface, the heel is inclined to the rear view plane, typically as much as 70° during the toe-off period. Although not ordinarily reaching the same degree of inclination as the heel, the shank is continuously changing inclination, which typically varies from 20° counterclockwise to 60° clockwise. An-

gles determined from the projected images of such sharply inclined segments are unlikely to be valid indicators of the changes in the angular relationship between these segments, and consequently such measurements have not been reported. The simplest alternative procedure is to mount a potentiometer with one arm attached to the shank and the other to the foot or shoe. The axis of the potentiometer is aligned perpendicularly to either the shank (Karpovich and Wilklow, 1959) or the heel (Lamoreux, 1971).

In the standard anatomic position, the long axis of the foot is perpendicular to the long axis of the shank. This unusual relationship has led to the practice of using the terms abduction and adduction to refer to what would appear to be transverse rotations at the ankle. The terms inversion and eversion are applied to rear view rotations between the shank and heel that correspond to adduction and abduction at the other joints.

The characteristic pattern is for the foot to be slightly inverted (compared with the standing position) at the time of heel contact. As the toe comes down to the walking surface, there is a moderate amount of eversion and then little change until the heel rises late in stance phase. As the heel rises the foot is inverted, reaching a maximal value at about the time of toe-off. During swing phase, there is some eversion, followed by inversion in

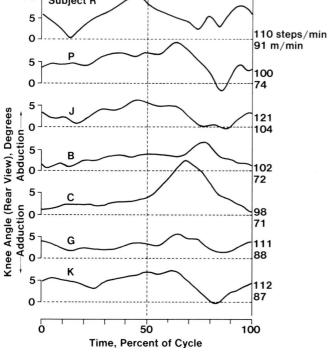

Figure 2.46. Knee angle, rear view. Seven adult male subjects during normal walking.

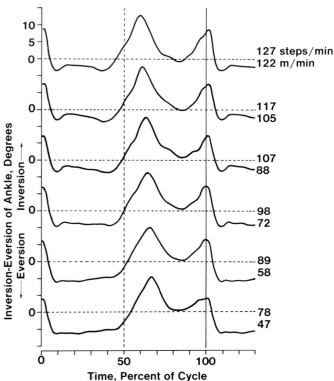

Figure 2.47. Inversion–eversion of ankle. Zero represents standing position.

preparation for heel contact. The pattern of Figure 2.47 is typical, although this subject displayed a greater amount of rotation than the average. There is no pronounced change in either the pattern or the amount of rotation as walking speed is changed.

Changes in the angle between a line on the back of the shank and a line on the back of the heel are principally the result of rotations about the talocalcaneal axis, commonly called the subtalar axis. This axis passes through the center of the joint between the heel bone (calcaneus) and the ankle bone (talus), emerging at the heel on the outside lower corner and from the top of the foot just ahead of the inner part of the junction between the shank and the foot.

Measurements taken about three axes perpendicular to the sole of the shoe can be mathematically transformed to equivalent rotations at estimated anatomic axes. Lamoreux (1976) applied this process to one subject with the results shown in Figure 2.48. The pattern of subtalar rotation indicated by these curves is very similar to those of Wright et al. (1964) measured with a goniometer aligned to the estimated subtalar axis.

Measurements (Isman and Inman, 1969) have demonstrated that the axis is usually inclined about 40° to the sole of the foot (average 42°, S.D. 9°, range 20–68°, n = 46). The projection of the axis onto the plane of the sole forms an angle internally inclined to the center line of the foot (average 23°, S.D. 11°, range 4–47°). The subtalar axis is thus oblique to the lines conventionally used for describing rotations of the shank and foot.

As a consequence, any rotation about this axis will appear to be producing rotations about axes perpendicular to all of the three standard viewing planes. The relative effects on these three apparent rotations will vary according to the location of the subtalar axis in relation to the anatomic reference lines.

The measurements by Inman (1976) on 102 cadaver specimens showed that the amount of possible rotation at the subtalar joint shows an exceptionally wide individual variation. There was a standard deviation of 11° about the mean of 24°. In this group, the smallest range of rotation was 4° and the greatest, 55°.

Although the patterns in the few examples described here show no marked differences, a wider sample can be expected to display the level of variation suggested by the anatomic studies.

There is a general impression among observers that the degree of flatfootedness, or pronation, correlates with a decreased inclination of the subtalar axis to the sole, a greater range of motion in the subtalar joint, an increased tendency to turn the foot outward during walking, and a greater amount of subtalar rotation during walking. Close and Inman (1953) and Wright et al. (1964) corroborated some of these observations but with very small samples. Wright and associates also demonstrated that turning the foot in or out from its natural position during walking altered the pattern in conformity with the above observation.

Toeing in reduces the inversion characteristic of the middle of stance period and may even cause eversion during this time. Toeing out, conversely, increases the rate of inversion during the middle of stance and also increases the amount of inversion during stance phase.

Top–Bottom View (Transverse Plane)

Because the three coordinate values (vertical, forward horizontal, side-to-side horizontal) for translational motion can be obtained in any two views, they have already been described in the preceding sections.

Segment Rotations

Rotations have been observed in the top view of all the body segments in which they have been measured. The top view of the body is called a transverse plane and rotations seen in this view are commonly called transverse rotations. In the conventional reference axis system (see Fig. 2.18), the vertical axis points upward, so that when rotations are viewed from above, counterclockwise rotations are positive and clockwise rotations are negative. As in the previous sections, rotations of the leg segments refer to the right leg. It is customary to consider transverse rotations of the leg segments as being inward (positive for the right leg) or outward (negative for the right leg).

Shoulder girdle. The shoulder girdle is capable of

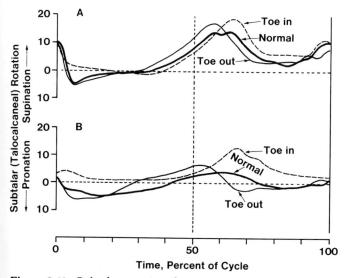

Figure 2.48. Subtalar rotation showing effects of toeing in and out. *A,* calculated from triaxial measurement of rotations between shoe and shank. *B,* measurements made with goniometer. One adult male subject.

considerable motion independent of the thorax, but during walking, the motion of a bar attached to the skin of the shoulders had about the same rotational motion as a pin in the spinous process of T-1 (Gregersen and Lucas, 1967).

The typical pattern of shoulder rotation is illustrated in Figure 2.49, which shows the tendency for the shoulder to rotate counterclockwise (in the top view) during left foot swing, and clockwise during right foot swing. A study on 10 males and 10 females demonstrated a tendency for the amount of shoulder rotation to decrease as walking speed increased, though this tendency was not true for all individuals (Fig. 2.50). The average values for the group of 20 subjects decreased from 8–6° at 49 and 98 m/min, respectively. The range in the amount of rotation in this study was from 2–16°.

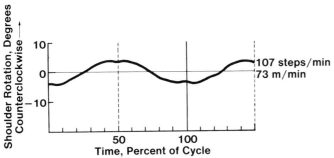

Figure 2.49. Transverse rotation of shoulder girdle. One adult male subject.

Pelvis. Viewed from above, the characteristic pattern of pelvic rotation is to bring the hip joint of the swinging leg forward, thus contributing to stride length. As the walking speed increases, with a corresponding increase in stride length, the amount of pelvic rotation increases (Fig. 2.51). The relationship between the amount of pelvic rotation and stride length for seven males is presented in Figure 2.52 to demonstrate the degree of individual variation.

The curve for transverse rotation of the pelvis appears to have two components. One component predominates at low walking speeds, reverses during the single-support phase, and is presumably related to the torque forces between the supporting foot and the walking surface. The other component reverses at or just after heel contact, increases with stride length, and is presumably related to leg swing. As the latter component increases, the former one becomes a relatively minor irregularity in the curve (see Fig. 2.51).

Vertebrae. Because the pelvic and shoulder rotations are out of phase with each other, there must be a point on the trunk between the two where the transverse rotation is at a minimum. Figure 2.53 shows the results of a study where rotations of metal pins inserted into the vertebral spines were measured. The experimental procedure precluded measuring the rotation of more than two vertebrae at a time, but the composite results on seven subjects demonstrated a well-defined trend. The first few thoracic vertebrae rotated about the same

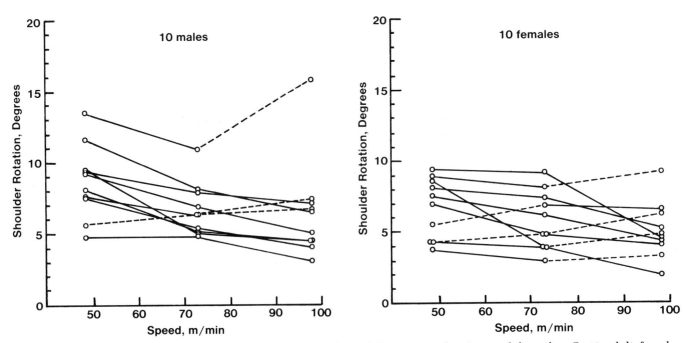

Figure 2.50. Amplitude of transverse shoulder rotation at three different speeds. *A*, 10 adult males. *B*, 10 adult females. *Connecting dashed lines* refer to subjects whose shoulder rotations increased with speed.

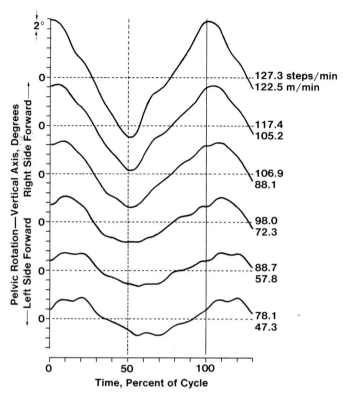

Figure 2.51. Transverse pelvic rotation. Single adult male subject walking at six different speeds.

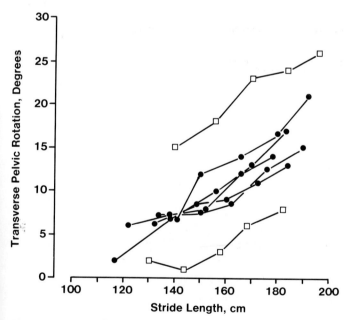

Figure 2.52. Amplitudes of transverse pelvic rotation. Seven adult male subjects walking at five different speeds.

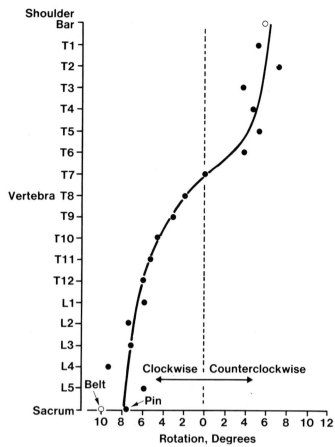

Figure 2.53. Transverse rotation of thoracolumbar spine. Left heel strike to right heel strike at 73 m/min.

brae rotated about the same as the pelvis. The data points of Figure 2.53 are average values of several experimental runs on each vertebra, and the individual measurements showed some variation between the subjects for the location of the point of minimal rotation. Other factors also affect the location; for example, the effect of carrying 10-kg weights in the hands was studied on two subjects, with the result of shifting the point toward the shoulders (Gregersen and Lucas, 1967).

Thigh. A study of the thigh rotation seen from above the body was conducted by Levens et al. (1948) using as a target a metal pin inserted into the femur and photographed with a motion picture camera mounted overhead. In all subjects, the thigh was rotating internally at heel contact and continued this rotation during the first quarter of stance phase. During the remainder of stance phase, the thigh rotated externally until some time during swing phase, when the thigh rotation changed direction and began the internal rotation observed at heel contact.

The curves for the 10 subjects were published in Fundamental Studies (1947). Among the subjects from whom a complete set of measurements was obtained

as the shoulder girdle, but at the level of the seventh thoracic vertebra there was an abrupt shift to minimal rotation and then a gradual increase in rotation of the remaining thoracic vertebrae so that the lumbar verte-

the range of rotation was from 9–23°, with a mean of 14°. The most common pattern is shown in Figure 2.54. The principal variations from this pattern were for the external rotation to be halted for a time during the middle of stance phase or for the change from external to internal rotation to occur later in swing phase than just after toe-off.

An equivalent measurement of thigh rotation can be calculated from the pelvic and hip rotations observed by Lamoreux (1971) (Fig. 2.55). The pattern was essentially the same as described previously, with minor changes occurring as walking speed was changed. The amount of rotation remained about the same throughout the range of speeds observed (79–136 steps/min).

The difficulty of measuring transverse rotation of the thigh has had the effect of severely limiting the amount of data collected. It is evident, however, from the measurements obtained, that a significant amount of rotation persistently occurs, but that more study is needed to determine the significance of the rotation and the variations that have been observed.

Shank. Levens et al. (1948) measured transverse rotation of the shank with the same procedure used for thigh rotation. The general pattern of rotation was about the same: internal rotation during early stance phase, then external rotation through the remainder of stance phase, and internal rotation during swing phase. The individual curves for each subject (Fundamental Studies, 1947) displayed the same types of variation seen in thigh rotation, but in this group of 10 subjects, there was no single pattern that could be considered typical or most common. Figure 2.56 presents examples of the three types of stance phase and the three types of swing phase patterns that were observed. It should be emphasized that the inclination of the shank during much of the walking cycle makes the measurements subject to

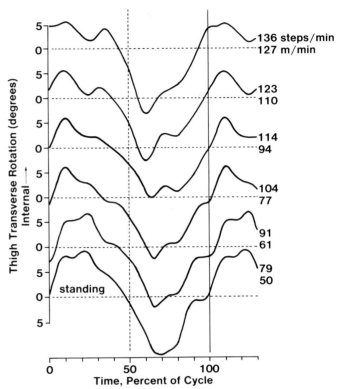

Figure 2.55. Transverse thigh rotation, calculated from transverse pelvic and hip angles. One adult male subject walking at six different speeds.

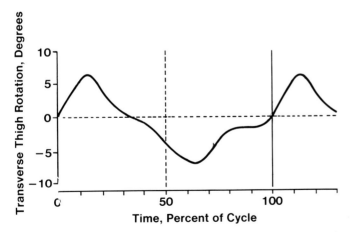

Figure 2.54. Typical transverse thigh rotations. Average of five adult male subjects.

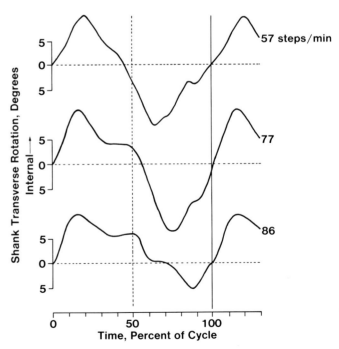

Figure 2.56. Typical transverse shank rotations. Three adult male subjects.

considerable distortion, especially during the double-support period.

Foot. The angular motion of the foot corresponding to the transverse rotation of the other body segments is measured on a line lengthwise on the sole of the foot as seen looking up through a transparent walking surface. This, in fact, is the way that it has usually been measured (Ryker, 1952). During most of stance phase, the foot is either flat on the floor or inclined only a few degrees. However, as toe-off is approached, the foot usually rises sharply and during early swing phase becomes inclined 60–70° to the walking surface. At such an inclination, measurements on the projected image may include considerable distortion. If the inclination angle is known, it is possible to calculate the foot angle that would be observed if the camera plane were kept perpendicular to the sole of the foot. Figure 2.57 shows the corrected curves of the foot angles for eight males. In part *A* of the figure, each curve (the average of two cycles) shows the angle between the center line of the right foot and the edge of the transparent walkway. The straight portion of the curve through most of stance phase indicates the amount of toe-out. In part *B* of the figure, the curves are superimposed with the value at midstance = 0, and the characteristic pattern becomes more evident.

At heel contact, the foot is in a position of slight outward rotation, but as the foot comes down into full

contact with the floor there is an internal rotation to bring the foot into the angular position to be maintained throughout most of stance phase. As the heel rises, internal rotation is resumed for several degrees until toe-off, at which time external rotation begins and continues, usually until the middle of swing phase. The curves display a variety of patterns during the latter part of swing phase, but all culminate in the slightly turned-out position characteristic of heel contact. No correlation between the amount of toe-out during stance phase and the pattern of swing phase behavior is apparent.

Although this small sample included a fairly wide range of toe-out during stance phase, none of the subjects displayed the toed-in foot which is occasionally observed but considered as within the normal range of variation from the average.

The series of footprints left by a wet foot or shoe demonstrates that the part of the foot in contact with the walking surface remains in a fixed position during that period of contact. The positions of the feet during stance phase influence the motions of the rest of the body and have been the subject of a number of studies. Unfortunately, a uniform system of reference lines has not been established, prohibiting a precise comparison between the various studies. However, certain observations can be considered to have become established.

The foot angle is the angle between a line from heel to toe, bisecting the foot, and a line which represents the principal direction of body motion. This angle is usually about 6 or 7° less than that taken naturally by the foot when standing still. The measurements have indicated that one foot is habitually turned out slightly more than the other. Most studies show the right foot turned outward more than the left foot, but some studies have shown the reverse.

As walking speed increases there is usually a slight decrease in the amount of toeing-out. Individual measurements on large groups of normal people (Morton, 1935; Asbelle and Canty, 1957; Murray et al., 1964) range from over 10° toeing in to about 25° toeing out. The lack of agreement between the various investigators on specifying the center line of the foot has led to a corresponding lack of agreement on average values for toe-out.

The stride width has been given various definitions, all of which are meant to indicate the distance between the track of the right foot and the track of the left foot. Because the feet are usually turned outward, the part of the foot used as a target will influence the actual measurement. It appears, however, that the inner borders of the heels tend to fall close to the line of progression, though with considerable step-to-step variation. The normal stride width varies from a wide-based 20 cm (placing the feet under the hip joints) to the other

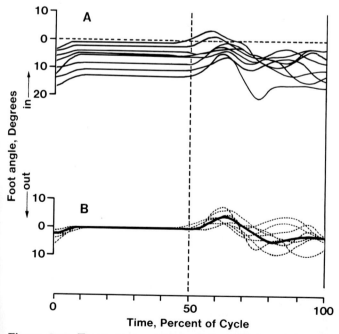

Figure 2.57. Transverse rotation of foot. Eight adult male subjects. *A,* angle relative to line of progression. *B,* above curves superimposed on value at midstance; heavy line, average.

extreme of the track of one foot crossing over the track of the other. It is characteristic for people to increase the stride width as they increase walking speed (Chodera and Levell, 1973; Murray et al., 1966).

Rotations Between Segments

Trunk (thorax–pelvis). As was pointed out, the rotation of the thorax is out of phase with that of the pelvis, so that a characteristic curve can represent the transverse rotation between the two segments (Fig. 2.58), although there is a wide variation between subjects. The rotation does not occur at one point on the spine although it is concentrated at the disc between T-6 and T-7 and is very low in the lumbar region (curve derived from Fig. 2.53).

Spine (vertebra–vertebra). Transverse rotation between the upper and lower parts of the trunk requires transverse rotation between at least some of the vertebrae in the spinal column. A study of the rotations, during walking, of all 17 vertebrae between the neck and the pelvis was made using metal pins inserted into the spinous processes (Gregersen and Lucas, 1967). The studies were conducted on seven adult males walking on a treadmill at 73 m/min. Though none of the subjects had more than eight vertebrae tested, a consistent pattern was evident when the data were assembled.

At this speed, vertebrae below T-7 rotated with a

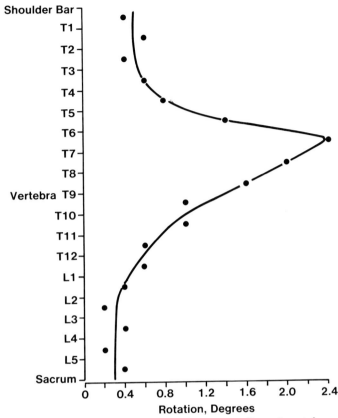

Figure 2.59. Transverse rotation between adjacent vertebrae. Seven adult males walking at 73 m/min.

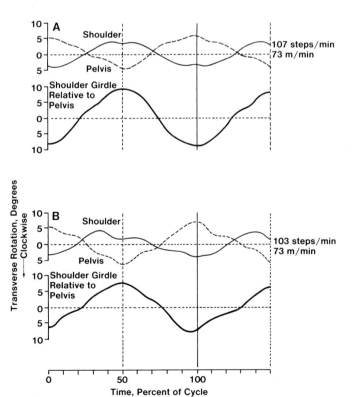

Figure 2.58. Transverse rotation of shoulder girdle relative to pelvis. *A*, adult male. *B*, adult female. Speeds as indicated.

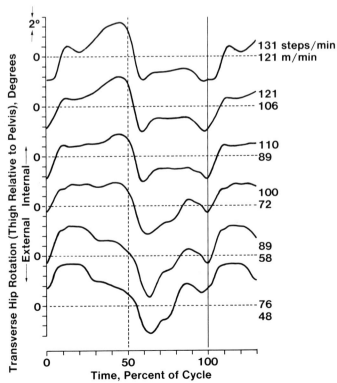

Figure 2.60. Transverse hip rotation. One adult male subject at six different speeds. Zero line represents standing position.

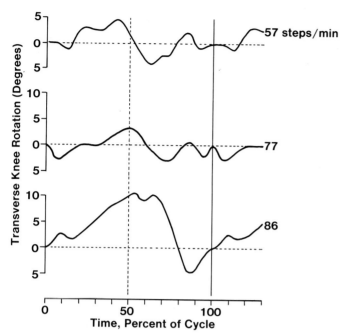

Figure 2.61. Transverse knee rotation. Same subjects as in Figure 2.56.

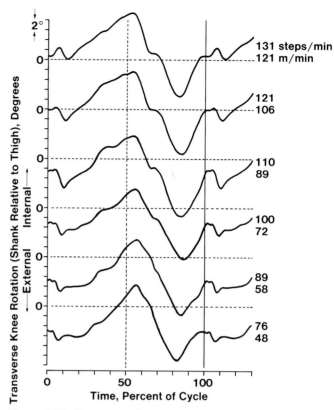

Figure 2.62. Transverse knee rotation. Single adult male subject at six different speeds.

pelvic pattern (forward on the side of the swinging leg) whereas those above T-7 rotated with a shoulder pattern (forward on the side opposite to the swinging leg). The amount of rotation was least at the T-7 level and increased progressively as the levels increased above and below T-7.

The rotation between vertebrae was a maximum (average 2.3°) between T-6 and T-7 and became very low between the upper thoracic vertebrae (average 0.5°) and between the lower lumbar vertebrae (average 0.3°) (Fig. 2.59). Just as there is a wide variety of patterns of transverse pelvic rotation, it is probable that a larger study would display a variety of patterns of spinal rotation. Walking with 10-kg weights in the hands resulted in the shifting upward of the level of change from pelvic to thoracic pattern. Changes in walking speed probably have a similar effect, although this was not studied.

Hip (pelvis–thigh). In the study of transverse rotations of the lower limb by Levens et al. (1948), the transverse rotation of the hip joint was calculated by subtracting the pelvic from the femoral rotation. The results indicated that typically the femur rotated internally (5°) relative to the pelvis during the first quarter of stance phase, then rotated externally about 7° during the remainder of stance and early swing phase. Swing phase is characterized by internal rotation of the thigh relative to the hip, which continues into the first quarter of stance phase.

More recently, an electrogoniometric device was developed and used by Lamoreux (1971), which measured

hip rotation directly. This was used on one male subject at a wide range of walking speeds. At low walking speeds, corresponding to those of the study by Levens et al., the pattern described above appeared although with greater amplitude of motion (Fig. 2.60).

As the walking speed increased, however, the pattern progressively changed to one significantly different from that at the low speed. More study is needed to determine how typical the pattern of this one subject is over the range of walking speeds.

Knee (thigh–shank). During the time the foot is flat on the walking surface (between approximately 7½ and 45% of the walking cycle), the thigh is rotating externally, typically about 10° (see Fig. 2.61). Because the foot is not rotating (Fig. 2.57), the thigh rotation must be absorbed at the knee and ankle joints. The measurement of transverse rotation of the shank provides an indication of the rotation at the knee and ankle joints. When the shank rotates with the thigh, there must be rotation at the ankle joint, or if the shank is stationary, like the foot, there must be transverse rotation at the knee. The variety of patterns illustrated in Figure 2.56 implies a variety of patterns in the use of the knee and ankle joints.

Where the transverse rotations of the thigh and shank are known, the transverse rotation of the knee can be calculated. Figure 2.61 is the result of such calculations

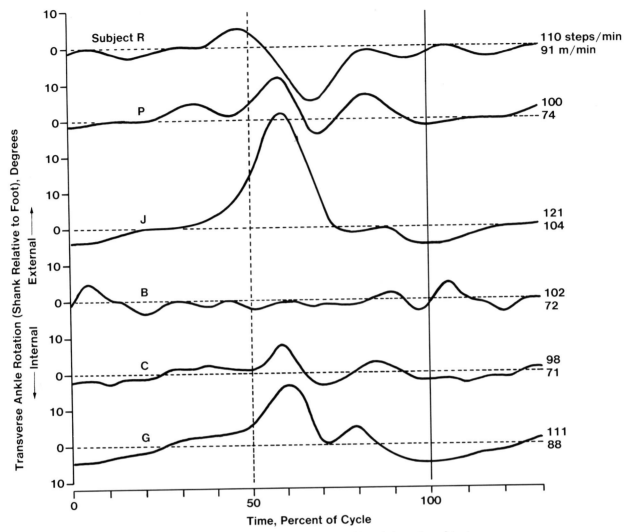

Figure 2.63. Transverse ankle rotation. Six adult male subjects.

for the three subjects of Figure 2.56, and provides some examples of the variety of patterns that have been observed.

An alternative method of measuring transverse rotation of the knee is with the use of goniometers, which can greatly reduce the distortions caused by shank inclinations in the photographic projection procedure. Lamoreux (1971) used goniometry to study the effect of changes in walking speed (Fig. 2.62). The subject displayed a pattern similar to the third of the examples of Figure 2.61. It should be noted that the changes in walking speed produced no significant change in either pattern or amplitude of rotation.

Ankle (shank–foot). The variety of patterns occurring in transverse rotation at the knee joint means, of course, that there is a similar variety of transverse rotations at the ankle joint. The pin study technique did not permit

determining ankle joint rotation, but equivalent measurements were obtained by photographing subjects walking on a glass walkway, providing a bottom view of subjects walking with an ankle clamp that carried the target for measuring shank rotation (Ryker, 1952). Inclination of the foot and shank make these measurements of little value during much of the walking cycle, but they can be considered valid while the foot is flat (7½ –45% of the walking cycle).

As with the transverse rotation of the knee, no pattern could be selected as typical, and the curves of Figure 2.63 are presented to show a variation comparable to that at the knee.

Because the subject of Lamoreux (1971) displayed a large amount of knee rotation during the central half of stance phase, the amount of ankle rotation during this period could be expected to be small, as is shown in

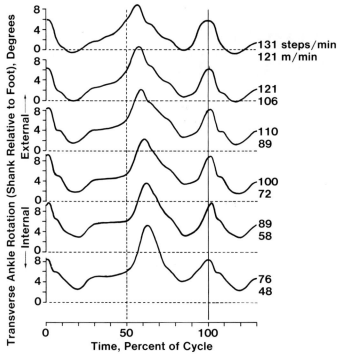

Figure 2.64. Transverse ankle rotation. One adult male subject walking at six different speeds.

Figure 2.64. Although the overall amount of rotation at the ankle joint did not change as walking speed increased, there was a tendency to increase slightly the amount of rotation during the central half of stance phase. As the heel rose in late stance phase, there was an increase in the rate of rotation and a maximal external rotation relative to the foot at toe-off.

It should be emphasized that the limited amount of data so far obtained fails to show any typical pattern or group of patterns for transverse rotations at the ankle as well as the knee. Nevertheless, measurements of thigh and foot rotations make it clear that rotations at the knee and ankle are interrelated and consequently cannot be studied independently. Because these rotations appear to be necessary for normal gait, such studies will have important implications for the treatment of joint disorders of the knee and ankle.

CHAPTER 3

Energy Expenditure

Measurement and Units

The ultimate source of energy for bodily work is the oxidation of foodstuffs. Consequently, the measurement of the oxygen consumption of the body provides a measure of the energy expenditure of the body.

For many purposes, it is convenient to translate oxygen units into heat units such as the gram-calorie (cal) or the kilogram-calorie (Kcal). It will be recalled that the gram-calorie is the amount of heat necessary to raise the temperature of 1 g of water 1° C, and the kilocalorie is the amount of heat necessary to raise the temperature of 1 kg of water 1° C.

In our laboratory, we have routinely used the method of Weir (1949) for determining energy expenditure in units of kilocalories or calories. Using essentially Weir's mathematical analysis, Passmore and Draper (1965) recommend use of the following relation between energy expenditure in Kcal/min (E) and the oxygen percentage concentration of expired air (O_e):

$$E = \frac{4.92\dot{V}}{100}(20.93 - O_e)$$

where $\dot{V}$ is the volume of expired air in liters per minute (l/min).

For most practical purposes, this can be simplified to the following conversions:

$$5 \text{ Kcal/min} \sim 1 \text{ l oxygen/min}$$
$$5 \text{ cal/min} \sim 1 \text{ ml oxygen/min}$$

and we shall use such conversion factors for certain illustrative cases in the following pages.

It would be desirable, in discussing metabolic energy expenditure, to always use the same units. However, this is not always feasible, and sometimes it is impossible because of incomplete presentation of data in the literature. It will be noted in a later section that kilocalories per hour (Kcal/h), kilocalories per minute (Kcal/min) and gram-calories per minute per kilogram body weight (cal/min/kg) are used.

Generally, we shall express rate of metabolic energy expenditure in cal/min/kg, but shall use other units when convenient or necessary.

When dealing with mechanical energy levels, work, and work rate, joules (J) and watts (W) are preferred. In a few instances, horse power (hp) is used in reference to work rate.

As an illustration of how metabolic energy expenditure may be expressed in different units, consider the following hypothetical case: a certain young man weighing 70 kg has a "lean body mass (LBM)" of 63 kg. His surface area is 1.83 m². While walking at a speed of 75 m/min, he uses oxygen at the rate of 800 ml/min ($\dot{V}_{O_2}$). The following table may then be prepared (Table 3.1):

Any one of these methods of expressing energy expenditure may be convenient, given particular circumstances.

In some cases, as in Durnin and Passmore (1967), standard gross weights for males and females may be used, e.g., 65 kg and 55 kg, respectively. In the case of the hypothetical subject mentioned previously, the metabolic rate could be expressed as 3.71 Kcal/min/65 kg, obtained from the value in column 4 by multiplying by 0.065.

As a somewhat more complex translation of oxygen values into calories, consider the following: an equation relating oxygen consumption in ml/min ($\dot{V}_{O_2}$), per kilogram body weight, to speed of walking (v) in m/min, is given as:

$$\dot{V}_{O_2}/kg = 5.9 + 0.0011\ v^2$$

Multiplying through by the conversion factor 5 yields:

$$cal/min/kg = 29.5 + 0.0055\ v^2$$

Table 3.1
Various Units in Which Metabolic Energy Expenditure May Be Expressed

(1)	(2)	(3)	(4)	(5)	(6)	(7)
$\dot{V}_{O_2}$ (ml/min)	cal/min (1) × 5.0	Kcal/h (2) × $\frac{60}{1000}$	cal/min/kg (gross wt) (2)/70	cal/min/kg (LBM) (2)/63	Kcal/m²/h (3)/1.83	cal/m (2)/75
800	4000	240	57	63	131	53

Table 3.2
Predicted Resting Values Compared with Experimental Values for Quiet Standing. See Text for Discussion

Subject	Sex	Height (m)	Weight (kg)	Predicted Resting Kcal/h Durnin and Passmore[1]	Kleiber[2]	Mayo[3]	Mean Resting Kcal/h (Predicted)[4]	Standing Kcal/h (Experimental)[5]	Ratio Standing/Resting
1	M	1.74	69	71.8	71.9	73.0	72.2	86.9	1.20
2	M	1.72	64	67.7	68.0	70.2	68.6	87.0	1.27
3	M	1.80	64	67.7	68.0	72.5	69.4	96.3	1.39
4	M	1.70	67	70.1	70.5	71.0	70.5	89.8	1.27
5	M	1.70	66	69.2	69.8	70.6	69.9	79.0	1.13
6	M	1.73	63	66.2	67.3	70.1	67.9	82.4	1.21
7	M	1.96	87	85.4[6]	85.5	87.8	86.2	126.1	1.46
8	M	1.72	68	70.9	71.0	71.9	71.3	96.2	1.35
9	M	1.89	83	82.6[6]	82.5	83.8	83.0	97.5	1.17
10	M	1.82	79	79.7	79.5	79.9	79.7	115.2	1.45
11	M	1.68	62	66.2	66.3	68.0	66.8	89.8	1.34
12	M	1.79	80	80.4	80.2	79.3	80.0	101.8	1.27
13	M	1.80	84	83.3[6]	83.2	81.3	82.6	99.6	1.21
14	M	1.79	71	73.4	73.4	75.4	74.1	92.8	1.25
15	M	1.79	79	79.7	79.5	78.9	79.4	94.2	1.19
16	M	1.87	69	71.8	71.8	76.9	73.5	92.7	1.26
17	M	1.84	75	76.8	76.5	78.8	77.4	101.1	1.31
Means		1.78	72	74.3	74.4	75.8	74.9	95.8	1.28
18	F	1.71	61	59.6	60.6	63.3	61.2	72.6	1.19
19	F	1.68	59	58.0	59.1	61.6	59.6	77.0	1.29
20	F	1.64	68	65.2	65.7	64.3	65.1	70.3	1.08
21	F	1.73	78	73.3	72.8	70.8	72.3	79.1	1.09
22	F	1.72	64	62.2	62.8	64.9	63.3	69.1	1.09
23	F	1.77	67	64.4	65.0	67.5	65.6	78.8	1.20
24	F	1.70	64	62.2	62.8	64.3	63.1	79.3	1.26
25	F	1.64	57	56.3	57.6	59.6	57.8	76.3	1.32
26	F	1.78	73	69.1	69.3	70.3	69.6	86.8	1.25
27	F	1.66	62	60.5	61.3	62.4	61.4	72.4	1.18
28	F	1.59	53	52.9	54.5	56.5	54.6[7]	49.4[7]	0.90[7]
29	F	1.62	56	55.4	56.8	58.7	57.0	79.9	1.40
30	F	1.70	59	58.0	59.1	62.1	59.7	66.4	1.11
31	F	1.65	70	66.6	66.9	65.2	66.2	78.3	1.18
Means		1.69	64	61.7	62.5	63.7	62.6	75.6	1.20

[1] Durnin and Passmore (1967), page 31. Values refer to "average" physique.
[2] Kleiber equation (1961). Coefficient 3 for males scaled down to 2.775 for females.
[3] Mayo Foundation standards (Boothby et al., 1936). Coefficient 40 for males, 37 for females.
[4] Mean of three preceding columns.
[5] Experimental data from Molen and Rozendal (1967) and present authors.
[6] Extrapolated. Other values in this column are either direct or interpolated.
[7] The values are obviously incompatible, and are unexplained. Not used in calculation of mean ratio.

The reader may find the following conversion relationships convenient to use:

To change	To	Multiply by
cal	J	4.186
Kcal	J	4186
Kcal	kg-m	427
Kcal/h	W	1.16
W	cal/min	14.33
hp	W	746

Lying, Sitting, Standing

It is sometimes important, particularly when dealing with the effects of various types of disability, to compare the energy demand of walking with that of an immobile (or relatively immobile) state, such as occurs in the lying, sitting, or quietly standing position.

Lying

It is a virtually universal custom, in textbooks of physiology, to refer to the "basal metabolic rate" as though, in the words of Durnin and Passmore (1967), "it is a fundamental biological property of the individual or species." However, we agree with these authors that it is much better to refer to a "resting" rate, measured 3–4 h after an ordinary meal. Such a measurement does not materially differ from a "basal" rate, requires no special standardization of environmental and other conditions, and, most importantly, does not assume that a "fixed minimum metabolism on which life depends" is involved.

We have tried to pinpoint the fact that resting metabolism is indistinguishable from basal metabolism by assembling the data of Table 3.2, *columns 1–4*, under predicted resting values.

Column 1 is the predicted value of the resting metabolic rate, according to Durnin and Passmore (1967), for *average* male and female subjects. These authors divide subjects into four categories—thin, average, plump, and fat, corresponding to percent fat of 5, 10, 15, and 20% for males, and 15, 20, 25, and 30% for females. (These authors also show that the differences between male and female subjects in the values of the basal and resting metabolic rates are actually eliminated when lean body mass is used instead of total body mass in the presentation of metabolic values. We shall refer to this later in connection with the cost of standing.)

Column 2 shows predicted values of metabolic rates as calculated from Kleiber's (1961) famous equation:

$$M.R. = 3 \ (W)^{3/4}$$

where *M.R.* is metabolic rate in Kcal/h and *W* is gross body weight in kg. For female subjects, the coefficient

is scaled down to 2.775 from 3, which is proportionally the same as the coefficients 37 and 40 for the values given in *column 3*.

Column 3 shows values for the basal metabolic rates as predicted by the well-known Mayo Foundation Normal Standards (Boothby et al., 1936), based on body surface area:

$$B.M.R. = 40 \ \mathrm{Kcal/m^2/h}$$

for normal young males, with the coefficient being taken as 37 for females.

It requires only a glance to see that it makes little difference in the results whether the values for metabolic rate are calculated according to Durnin and Passmore, Kleiber, or Mayo. Not only is the claim by Durnin and Passmore, that basal and resting metabolic rates are virtually indistinguishable, fully justified, but also, the Durnin and Passmore table provides a means of expressing metabolic rates in terms of lean body mass, which is a great improvement over earlier predictive tables.

Column 4 shows the average values of *columns 1–3*. These values, recalculated as cal/min/kg, will be compared later in this chapter with the values for sitting and standing.

Table 3.3 shows resting metabolic rates for 10 male subjects, measured in our laboratory, compared with values predicted by Durnin and Passmore. Except for *Subject 1*, the agreement is excellent, well within acceptable limits of prediction. It seems probable that the discrepancy in the case of *Subject 1* is due, at least in part, to age.

Sitting

Durnin and Passmore measured the energy expenditure of men and women during sitting, while engaging

Table 3.3
Experimental Values of Resting Metabolism in 10 Male Subjects, Compared with Values Predicted by Durnin and Passmore (1967)

Subject	Age	Weight (kg)	Experimental (Kcal/min)	Predicted (Kcal/min)	Ratio
1	53	70.9	0.89	1.17	1.31
2	45	77.7	1.28	1.32	1.03
3	31	87.7	1.24	1.41[1]	1.14
4	26	58.6	1.04	1.07	1.03
5	23	72.7	1.21	1.25	1.03
6	22	70.5	1.33	1.22	0.92
7	22	64.3	1.25	1.13	0.90
8	18	68.2	1.05	1.18	1.12
9	17	62.3	1.19	1.10	0.92
10	18	80.9	1.38	1.35[1]	0.98
	Means		1.19	1.22	1.04

[1] Extrapolated values. Other values in this column are direct or interpolated.

in such common activities as reading and watching television. The measurements were made at various times of day and were unrelated to food intake. We have recalculated their average results to express energy expenditure in cal/min/kg, shown in Table 3.4.

Their average values, which range from 19.5–21.4, are as is to be expected substantially higher than the average values for resting metabolism, derived from *column 4* of Table 3.2, which equal 17.2 cal/min/kg for males and 16.4 cal/min/kg for females. As will be seen below, their sitting values are practically the same as the figures for quiet standing derived from *column 5* of Table 3.2. No doubt this is a reflection of the rather "active" sitting engaged in by the subjects. If males and females are lumped together, the ratio of active sitting to resting metabolism is about 1.22.

Standing

Molen and Rozendal (1967) studied 10 males and 10 females under conditions of quiet standing in the laboratory. Their results, expressed as cal/min/kg, were virtually identical with those obtained by the present authors on 7 males and 4 females and are, therefore, lumped with ours for the 17 males and 14 females shown in Table 3.2, *column 5*.

The average value for males is 22.1 with a S.D. of 1.68 cal/min/kg, and for females, 19.9 with a S.D. of 2.60, with the ratio of means being 1.11.

The odds against this difference being due to chance are greater than 100:1. Molen and Rozendal noted the lower cost of standing in females, and pointed out that this entered into their finding that the cost of walking was slightly less in females than in males. However, the difference is so small that Molen and Rozendal lumped

men and women together in formulating the regression equation relating energy expenditure to speed.

It is of interest that the difference in the cost of standing of males compared with that of females is eliminated if lean body weight instead of gross body weight is used. The results in this case, using the values given by Durnin and Passmore (1967) for body fat content, become 24.5 cal/min/kg for males and 24.8 cal/min/kg for females.

If males and females are lumped together and values expressed as cal/min/kg, derived from Table 3.2, *columns 4 and 5*, are used, the ratio of standing to resting is 21.0/16.8, or 1.25. The low cost of standing reflects the low activity of the postural muscles during standing, as revealed by electromyography.

Durnin and Passmore (1967), Table 3.4, studied the cost of standing. Their values, recalculated as cal/min/kg, range from 20.2 in older females to 26.9 in younger males. These values, particularly in the younger age groups, are substantially higher than those described previously, and undoubtedly reflect the more active standing engaged in by their subjects.

An interesting feature of their results is the decrease in cost of standing with age. We have noticed this in some of our subjects.

Relation Between Energy Expenditure and Speed in Level Walking

In the preceding section, it was shown that a modest increase in energy expenditure, on the order of 25%, occurred when a subject assumed a quietly standing position compared with lying. As pointed out, this small increase reflects the low degree of muscle activity required for quiet standing. Now, however, we shall see that as soon as muscles are called on to move the body during walking, a great increase in energy expenditure occurs, reflecting the metabolic cost of moving the body against gravity, and of accelerating and decelerating the various body segments.

Ralston (1958) showed that a quadratic equation of the form

$$E_w = b + mv^2$$

where E_w is the energy expenditure in cal/min/kg, v is speed in m/min, and b and m are constants, predicted adequately the energy cost of walking at speeds up to about 100 m/min (Fig. 3.1, *lower, dashed curve*).

In deriving this equation, data from various investigators were used. Since that time, a number of investigators have found that an equation of the same form provides an acceptable basis for predicting energy-speed relations (Cotes and Meade, 1960; Bobbert, 1960; Molen and Rozendal, 1967; Corcoran and Brengelmann,

Table 3.4
Energy Expenditure during Sitting and Standing, Based on Data by Durnin and Passmore (1967)

Age range (years)	Sex	Mean (cal/min/kg)	S.D.	S.D./mean
		Sitting		
20–39	M	21.4	3.85	0.18
20–39	F	20.9	5.09	0.24
40–64	M	21.1	4.46	0.21
40–59	F	19.5	3.45	0.18
65+	M	19.8	3.85	0.19
60+	F	19.8	5.64	0.28
		Standing		
20–39	M	26.9		
20–39	F	24.9		
40–64	M	26.3		
40–59	F	22.2		
65+	M	21.8		
60+	F	20.2		

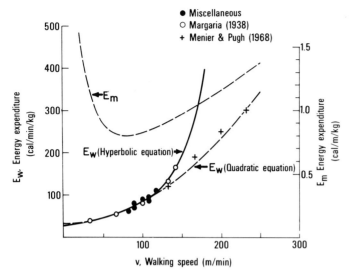

Figure 3.1. Energy expenditure during walking: top curve, E_m, cal/m/kg, calculated from equation (4); middle curve, E_w, cal/min/kg, calculated from equation (3); bottom curve, E_w, cal/min/kg, calculated from equation (1). (Adapted, with permission, from Zarrugh, M. Y., Todd, F. N., and Ralston, H. J. Optimization of energy expenditure during level walking. Eur. J. Appl. Physiol. 33:293, 1974).

1970). Combining their equations, using weighted averages of the constants according to number of subjects (86 total, 57 males, 29 females) yields a grand average equation

$$E_w = 32 + 0.0050 \ v^2 \qquad (1)$$

The previously mentioned studies included walking on treadmill, floor, firm path, and grass. There was no indication of systematic differences for the various walking surfaces. In such studies, however, close attention must be paid to the nature of the footwear. A heavy boot or slippery sole may alter the energy demand of walking.

Because the quadratic equation (1) implies that the energy cost is proportional to body weight, Wyndham et al. (1971) examined this relation in detail, and found that any error involved in such a relation could not be proved to be significant in the case of walking.

Durnin and Passmore (1967) provide a table for relating weight of subject, speed, and energy expenditure, over a range of approximately 55 to 110 m/min (2–4 mph). Table 3.5 shows the predicted values from equation (1) and average values from Durnin and Passmore.

It is clear that over the range 55–90 m/min, the predicted results in the last two columns are virtually identical. At 110 m/min the Durnin and Passmore figures underestimate the average experimental values (E_w = 95) by 11%, while equation (1) is still in good agree-

ment with experiment. At still higher speeds, up to about 145 m/min, which is about the top speed for natural walking, equation (1) also fails.

Zarrugh et al. (1974) deduced a more general, hyperbolic equation for predicting energy expenditure during walking, which takes into account step length and step rate:

$$E_w = \frac{E_0}{\left(1 - \dfrac{s^2}{s_u^2}\right)\left(1 - \dfrac{n^2}{n_u^2}\right)} \qquad (2)$$

where s is step length in meters, n is step rate in steps/min, E_0 is value of E_w when $s = n = 0$, s_u is upper limit of s as E_w approaches infinity, and n_u is upper limit of n as E_w approaches infinity.

In natural walking, where the subject adopts his own natural cadence for a particular speed, it can be shown that equation (2) reduces to

$$E_w = \frac{E_0}{(1 - v/v_u)^2} \qquad (3)$$

where v is speed and v_u = upper limit of v, equal to $n_u s_u$ (Fig. 3.1, *middle, solid curve*).

E_0 has an average value of approximately 28 cal/min/kg, and v_u an average value of about 240 m/min.

Thus, for a top natural speed of 145 m/min,

$$E_w = \frac{28}{(1 - 145/240)^2} = 179 \ \text{cal/min/kg}$$

which is in good agreement with average experimental values.

Up to speeds of about 100 m/min, equations (1) and (3) predict virtually identical values. Therefore, equation (1) may be used for most cases of natural walking.

Rather unexpectedly, equation (1) predicts energy cost within about 10% for competition walking, which is quite unlike natural walking. Menier and Pugh (1968) provide data on four male Olympic walkers studied during treadmill walking at an altitude of 1800 m. They

Table 3.5
Energy Expenditure during Level Walking, as Predicted by Equation (1) and by Durnin and Passmore (1967)

m/min	km/h	mph (approx.)	$E_w = 32 + 0.0050 \ v^2$	Durnin and Passmore (1967)
25	1.50	1.0	35	
40	2.40	1.5	40	
55	3.30	2.0	47	46
70	4.20	2.5	56	55
80	4.80	3.0	64	64
90	5.40	3.5	73	74
110	6.60	4.0	93	85

state that their findings agree with studies made at sea level by other investigators.

At a speed of 14 km/h (233 m/min) the walkers clustered closely at about 60 ml oxygen/min/kg, corresponding to 300 cal/min/kg. Equation (1) predicts:

$$E_w = 32 + 0.0050\,(233)^2 = 303$$

which is within 1% of the observed value.

At a speed of about 135 m/min, the walkers clustered about a value of approximately 25 ml oxygen/min/kg, corresponding to 125 cal/min/kg. Equation (1) predicts:

$$E_w = 32 + 0.0050\,(135)^2 = 123$$

which is within about 2% of observed value.

Age

None of the studies mentioned in this section suggest any great or systematic effect of age on the energy expenditure of natural walking, at least within an age range of about 20–59 years, when expressed as cal/min/kg.

Sex

Booyens and Keatinge (1957) found significantly lower values of E_w for women than for men at speeds of 91 and 107 m/min, and the equation of Cotes et al. (1957) predicts lower values for women than for men, as a result of the smaller step length in women. Ralston (1958) did not find a significant sex difference, and suggested a possible source of error in the study of Booyens and Keatinge.

Durnin and Passmore (1967) state that sex is not a factor. Molen and Rozendal (1967) found a small difference in favor of the female when gross energy expenditure is measured, but not when net energy expenditure (i.e., gross cost minus cost of quiet standing) is used. Inasmuch as it has been shown in an earlier section that the cost of quiet standing is slightly (but significantly) lower in the female than in the male, it might be expected that at lower speeds this would account for a slight difference between males and females. As Molen and Rozendal (1967) state, however, the difference is not important enough to justify use of different equations for males and females.

It is of interest that Corcoran and Brengelmann (1970) found a somewhat higher value for females than for males during floor-walking, which agrees with our own experience.

Significance of Constant = 28 in Equation (3)

At speed $v = 0$, equation (3) yields $E_w = 28$ cal/min/kg. This is much higher than the value for resting or quiet standing. Ralston (1958) found that the value for extremely slow walking, in five subjects, averaged 28.6. He concluded that the constant represented the cost of maintaining the body in motion at a barely perceptible speed.

It is clear, therefore, that in calculating the "net" cost of walking, as some investigators have done, subtracting the resting value, or the quietly standing value, from the gross value is neither theoretically nor practically justified. It is of added interest that use of net values for energy expenditure during walking do not permit formulation of equation (2) and its derivative equation (3), which appear, thus far, to be the only equations successfully predicting energy expenditure throughout the entire range of natural walking speeds.

Energy Expenditure Per Unit Distance Walked

A number of authors have discussed the energy cost of walking, per unit distance, per unit body weight. The curve of such energy cost, plotted as ordinate against speed as abscissa, is concave upward, and while fairly flat over quite a wide range of speeds (65–100 m/min), still exhibits a minimal value (see Fig. 3.1, top curve).

Ralston (1958) showed that the mathematical form of such a curve could be deduced from a quadratic equation of type (1) as follows:

$$E_m = \frac{E_w}{v} = \frac{32}{v} + 0.0050\,v \qquad (4)$$

where E_m is expressed as cal/m/kg.

Differentiating E_m with respect to v, and equating to zero, yields a minimal value of E_m equal to 0.80 cal/m/kg, corresponding to an optimal speed equal to 80 m/min.

Similarly, Zarrugh et al. (1974) showed that by dividing equation (3) by v,

$$E_m = \frac{E_0}{v(1 - v/v_u)^2} \qquad (5)$$

differentiating E_m with respect to v and equating to zero yields an optimal speed.

$$v_{opt} = v_u/3 = 240/3 = 80 \text{ m/min} \qquad (6)$$

as in the case of equation (4).

As shown by Ralston (1958), a person in a natural walk tends to adopt a speed close to this optimal speed. This finding was confirmed by Corcoran and Brengelmann (1970) in a study of 32 normal human subjects during floor-walking. These authors found a natural average speed of 83.4 m/min, which differs from the above optimal speed of 80 m/min by only 4%.

Because speed = n · s, where n = steps/min and s = step length (here expressed in meters), it follows that an optimal speed must be based on a choice of step rate and step length such that minimal energy expenditure per unit distance is achieved. This is an example of a fundamental feature of human motor behavior, which applies to many activities in addition to walking. It may perhaps be expressed in a form such as: "In freely chosen rate of activity, a rate is chosen that represents minimal energy expenditure per unit task." In the case of natural walk, the unit task is the traversing of 1 m of ground. A speed is adopted such that each meter is covered as cheaply, from the energy standpoint, as possible.

The principle enunciated above is a sort of biological "Conservation of Energy" law. The celebrated French physiologist E. J. Marey (1895), who was one of the great pioneers in the study of animal locomotion, anticipated the statement of this principle a century ago.

Only the use of gross energy values leads to equations (5) and (6), which establish a condition of optimality for free walking pattern and predict an experimentally verifiable optimal speed. The top curve of Figure 3.2 shows the gross energy expenditure per meter as a function of

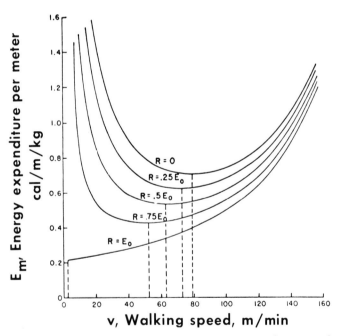

Figure 3.2. Gross energy expenditure per meter as function of walking speed v for typical subject walking naturally at different speeds. The lower curves show that as increasing amounts of energy (R) are subtracted from the gross energy expenditure per minute, the optimal speed corresponding to minimal E_m becomes smaller and smaller. (Reproduced, with permission, from Ralston, H. J. Energetics of human walking. In *Neural Control of Locomotion*, edited by R. M. Herman, S. Grillner, P. S. G. Stein, and D. G. Stuart. New York, Plenum Press, 1976.)

walking speed v for a typical subject when walking naturally at different speeds. The lower curves show that should increasing amounts of energy (R) be subtracted from the gross energy expenditure per minute, the optimal speed corresponding to minimal E_m becomes smaller and smaller. It becomes essentially zero when an amount equal to E_0 is subtracted. It is not very enlightening to find that the best way to avoid energy cost during walking is not to walk!   It is suggested that in other types of exercise the gross rather than the net energy expenditure may be the fundamental energy parameter.

Energy Expenditure Per Step

In the preceding section, it was shown that minimal energy expenditure per meter traversed per kilogram of body weight (E_m), occurred at a speed of 80 m/min. The relations will now be considered between speed, step rate, step length, energy expenditure per minute per kilogram (E_w), and energy expenditure per step per kilogram (E_n).

The relevant data from Zarrugh et al. (1974) are shown in Table 3.6, based on studies of 10 normal males and 10 normal females, ranging in age from 20–55 and 20–49 years, respectively. Standard deviations are shown in parentheses. E_w values are calculated from equation (1).

The difference in the value of s/n at the higher speeds in males and females is highly significant. For example, at v = 73.2 m/min, the odds against the difference being due to chance are better than 1000 to 1. Even at 48.8 m/min, the odds are 4 to 1. The smaller values of s and s/n in females reflect the shorter average leg lengths in women as compared with men, although this may not be the only factor involved.

The values shown in Table 3.6 do not strictly correspond to those of a natural walk, inasmuch as the treadmill imposed the speeds. However, the speed 73.2 m/min is fairly close to the natural speed (80 m/min) and, therefore, should yield values of s/n close to those of natural walk.

Molen and Rozendal (1972) studied 309 males and 224 females in natural walk along pavement and path. At an average speed of 83.4 m/min, the average value of s/n for males was 0.0072, in good agreement with the values 0.0070 and 0.0072 at speeds of 73.2 and 97.6 m/min in Table 3.6. At an average speed of 76.1 m/min, the average value of s/n for females was 0.0060, in excellent agreement with the value 0.0061 at 73.2 m/min in Table 3.6.

The near-constancy in the value of s/n in walking has deep physiological significance. Not only does the value of s/n characterize the walk of the male and female, but it also plays a fundamental role in determining the optimal speed of walking. At any given speed, imposi-

Table 3.6
Average Values of v, n, s, s/n, E_w, and E_m for 10 Male and 10 Female Subjects. Standard Deviations in Parentheses[1]

	v m/min	n steps/min (S.D.)	s m (S.D.)	s/n m/steps/min (S.D.)	E_w cal/min/kg	E_n cal/step/kg $= E_w/n$
Males	24.4	59.5 (4.33)	0.41 (0.025)	0.0069 (0.00065)	35.0	0.59
	48.8	84.4 (6.48)	0.59 (0.041)	0.0070 (0.00072)	43.9	0.52
	73.2	102.2 (5.43)	0.72 (0.056)	0.0070 (0.00066)	58.8	0.58
	97.6	116.3 (3.13)	0.84 (0.020)	0.0072 (0.00026)	79.6	0.68
Mean				0.0070 (0.0012)		
Females	24.4	60.0 (3.95)	0.41 (0.029)	0.0068 (0.00065)	35.0	0.58
	48.8	86.7 (7.26)	0.57 (0.037)	0.0066 (0.00070)	43.9	0.51
	73.2	109.0 (5.49)	0.67 (0.037)	0.0061 (0.00045)	58.8	0.54
	97.6	126.8 (8.98)	0.77 (0.031)	0.0061 (0.00050)	79.6	0.63
Mean				0.0064 (0.0012)		

[1] Source: Zarrugh et al., 1974.

tion of an unnatural step rate (or step length) for that speed results in a higher than normal value of the energy expenditure per unit distance traversed (Atzler and Herbst, 1927; Molen and Rozendal, 1972; Molen et al., 1972; Zarrugh et al., 1974).

In the following mathematical treatment, the average values of $s/n = 0.0070$ and $s/n = 0.0064$ (Table 3.6) will be used for males and females, respectively.

In a manner similar to that followed in the preceding section, equation (1) can be used to determine the step rate corresponding to minimal energy expenditure *per step*:

Since $v = s \cdot n$, and $s = 0.0070\,n$ in males, $v = 0.007\,n \cdot n = 0.007\,n^2$

Substituting in equation (1),

$$E_w = 32 + 0.0050\,v^2 = 32 + 0.0050\,(0.007n^2)^2$$

$$E_n = \frac{E_w}{n} = \frac{32}{n} + 0.005\,(0.007)^2\,n^3$$

$$= \frac{32}{n} + 2.45 \times 10^{-7}\,n^3$$

Differentiating E_n with respect to n and equating to zero, E_n (minimum) occurs at $n = 81.2$ steps/min. Interpolating from Table 3.6, this would correspond to a speed of about 46 m/min, which is *not* the speed (80 m/min) corresponding to minimal energy expenditure per meter.

Clearly, the optimal step rate for minimal energy *per step* does not represent a desirable method of walking, at least in normal subjects.

The great significance of this conclusion will be made clear in a later section (Work, Power, and Efficiency) dealing with walking of certain disabled human subjects. Here, because of inability to walk at higher speeds, energy expenditure *per step* greatly exceeds normal

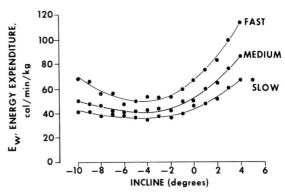

Figure 3.3. Effect of grade, at three speeds, on energy expenditure of normal young male during walking. See text for further discussion.

values. The saving feature, in such cases, is that energy expenditure *per minute* is kept low because of low step rate.

Using the value $s/n = 0.0064$ for females, E_n (optimum) occurs at $n = 85$ steps/min. Interpolating from Table 3.6, this would correspond to a speed of about 47 m/min, again representing an undesirable method of walking.

Slope-Walking

The essential metabolic features of slope-walking are graphically presented in Figure 3.3. A normal young adult male walked on the treadmill at speeds of 48.8, 73.2 and 97.6 m/min, and at grades ranging from +4 to −10° (+7 to −18%). The rapid rise in metabolic cost with increased grade is evident, as well as the more modest decrease in cost at grades in the range of 0 to −4° (0 to −7%).

The experimental points are fitted by fourth degree polynomial functions (smooth curves), all of which exhibit minima close to $-4°$. At lower grades, the metabolic cost increases, as a result of postural changes and the use of muscles in "braking" action.

A number of investigators have formulated equations relating energy expenditure to speed and grade. We have found it sufficient, for our purposes, to use representative data in tabular form, such as those provided by McDonald (1961), based on experiments by Margaria (1938) on three normal adult males (Table 3.7). The calculated values of E_w (cal/min/kg) and E_m (cal/m/kg) have been added, based on a body weight of 72 kg.

As has been noted earlier, a person during level walking tends to adopt a speed such that energy expenditure per unit distance is a minimum. In Table 3.7 it is evident that minimal values of E_m occur at slopes of $+10$ to -20%, at speeds of 80–100 m/min. It may therefore be expected that persons will adopt such speeds at those grades. Above $+10\%$, and below -20%, E_m minima do not occur within the range of speeds shown.

While the subject of Figure 3.3 exhibited minimal values of E_w at a slope of about -7% ($-4°$), the minimal value of E_w in Table 3.7 occurs at a slope of about -10% ($-5.7°$).

Stair-Climbing

Unlike the situation in level walking (and, to a limited degree, in slope-walking), no general rules relating energy expenditure to speed can be formulated for stair-climbing. This is due to a number of factors, including wide variations in height of risers and width of treads, and the great changes in body posture that occur during stair-climbing. However, it is instructive to compare normal subjects with persons having motor disability, during normal climbing of steps with low (10 cm) and high (19 cm) risers. For this purpose, normal are compared with hemiplegic subjects, both using alternating gait (Table 3.8), based on data from Hirschberg and Ralston (1965).

As might be expected, the energy expenditure *per step* is much greater, of the order of 40%, in the hemiplegic than in the normal subjects. Without doubt, if the hemiplegic patients were to attempt to maintain the same speed as the normal subjects, hazardous metabolic and cardiovascular demands might well result.

It is seen, however, that the energy expenditure *per minute* is not very different in the two types of subject, because of the fact that the hemiplegic patients adopt a low step rate. It is important to note that such physiological variables as heart rate, blood pressure, and res-

Table 3.8
Average Values of Energy Expenditure, Per Minute and Per Step, of Normal and Hemiplegic Subjects during Normal Stair-Climbing, Using Alternating Gait[1]

| Experimental Conditions | Steps/min | | Energy Expenditure | | | |
| | | | Cal/min/kg | | Cal/step/kg | |
	Normal	Hemiplegic	Normal	Hemiplegic	Normal	Hemiplegic
Rest (sitting)			18.9	15.6		
Low stairs	72	47	53.3	49.1	0.74	1.04
High stairs	70	44	70.3	61.5	1.00	1.40

[1] Source: Hirschberg and Ralston, 1965.

Table 3.7
Estimates of E_w (cal/min/kg) and E_m (cal/m/kg) at Various Speeds and Grades (Modified from McDonald, 1961, after Margaria, 1938)

| Grade | | Speed (m/min) | | | | | | | | | |
| | | 40 | | 60 | | 80 | | 100 | | 120 | |
%	Degrees	E_w	E_m	E_w	E_m	E_w	E_m	E_w	E_m	E_w	E_m
−40	−21.8	54	1.35	70	1.17	85	1.06	98	0.98	106	0.88
−35	−19.3	47	1.18	60	1.00	72	0.90	84	0.84	93	0.78
−30	−16.7	46	1.15	56	0.93	67	0.84	79	0.79	90	0.75
−25	−14.0	44	1.10	53	0.88	63	0.79	74	0.74	87	0.73
−20	−11.3	41	1.03	46	0.77	53	0.66	63	0.63	77	0.64
−15	−8.5	33	0.83	37	0.62	44	0.55	54	0.54	69	0.58
−10	−5.7	30	0.75	35	0.58	43	0.54	54	0.54	70	0.58
−5	−2.9	32	0.80	38	0.63	48	0.60	61	0.61	82	0.68
0	0	41	1.03	49	0.82	62	0.78	81	0.81	110	0.92
5	2.9	59	1.48	74	1.23	95	1.19	125	1.25	167	1.39
10	5.7	69	1.73	93	1.55	121	1.51	155	1.55	193	1.61
15	8.5	82	2.05	114	1.90	150	1.88	187	1.87		
20	11.3	98	2.45	140	2.33	185	2.31				
25	14.0	114	2.85	170	2.83						
30	16.7	133	3.33	204	3.40						
35	19.3	153	3.83								
40	21.8	174	4.35								

piratory rate are linked to the metabolic rate *per minute*, rather than to the metabolic rate *per meter* or *per step*. These physiological variables, while slightly higher in the hemiplegic than in the normal subjects, were still within acceptable limits.

Also, as might be expected, the high stairs made greater physiological demand, *per minute* and *per step*, than the low stairs, both in normal and hemiplegic subjects.

Not shown in Table 3.8, but worthy of note, is the fact that *alternating* gait required 20–30% less metabolic demand *per step* than did unilateral-leading gait, in both normal and hemiplegic subjects.

Load, Restraint, and Terrain

Load

Loading of the body increases the metabolic cost of walking, but the effects depend on the nature of the loading. Loads placed on the distal segments, especially the foot, have relatively much greater effect than loads attached to the trunk, because of the large inertial effects associated with acceleration and deceleration of the limb segments.

Figure 3.4, *bottom*, shows the effect of 2 kg on each foot on the metabolic cost of walking at +2°, 0°, and −2°. At 0°, the value of the E_w (cal/min/kg) is increased by about 30%, with similar results at +2° and −2°. This

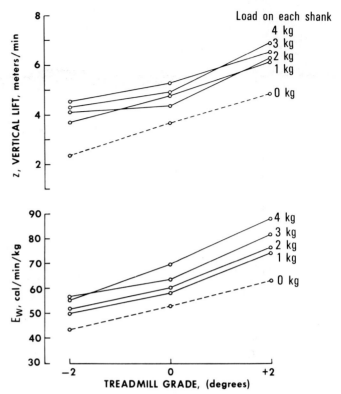

Figure 3.5. Effects of loading shank during walking at several grades. *Bottom:* Effect on energy expenditure. *Top:* Effect on vertical motion of body. See text for further discussion.

is to be contrasted with the very small effect of 5 kg attached to the trunk, where in seven subjects the mean increase in E_w was only 4%.

A comparable experiment on shank loading is shown in Figure 3.5.

Unfortunately, this type of experiment is not entirely clear-cut because, unexpectedly, the vertical motion of the body is also increased by loads on the limbs (as a result of greater step length), as shown in the upper parts of Figures 3.4 and 3.5. As a consequence of this, both inertial and gravitational effects are involved when the limbs are loaded.

The metabolic cost of trunk-loading in quiet standing is practically zero. As stated in the section, Lying, Sitting, and Standing, the E_w for quiet standing in the young male adult is about 22 cal/min/kg. In an experiment on a young male subject weighing 64 kg, the E_w of quiet standing was not measurably altered by attaching 20 kg uniformly around the trunk.

Restraint

The effects of restricting motion at ankle, knee, hip, and spine on the metabolic cost of walking were studied by immobilizing such regions with a suitable locking device (ankle) or plaster casts (knee, hip, spine) (Ralston, 1965). See Figures 3.6–3.9.

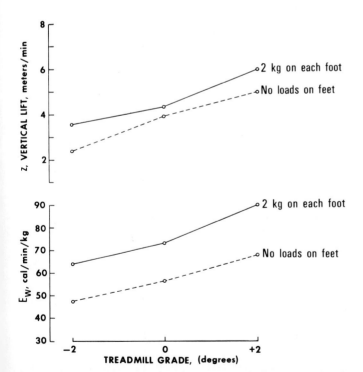

Figure 3.4. Effects of loading foot during walking at several grades. *Bottom:* Effect on energy expenditure. *Top:* Effect on vertical motion of body. See text for further discussion.

In Figure 3.6, *bottom*, the energy expenditure of three subjects walking with both ankle braces locked and unlocked is compared with normal values previously obtained (Ralston, 1958). Normal male subjects of average physique tend to adopt a walking speed of about 4.8 km/h, with a step rate of about 103/min. At this speed, the subjects with both ankles immobilized had an energy expenditure 9% above average. With one ankle immobilized, the increase was 6%.

Figure 3.7, *right*, shows the effect of knee restriction. Differences from normal values of 0°, 15°, and 30° of knee flexion were of borderline significance. At 45°, energy expenditure was significantly elevated. At 4.4

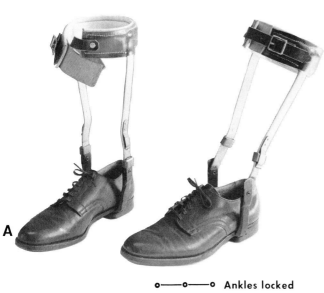

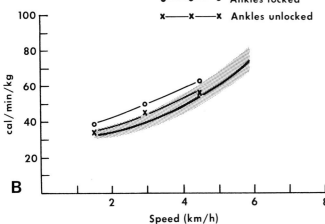

Figure 3.6. Effects of immobilization of ankle joints. *A*, Lockable braces used for immobilizing or allowing free movement at ankle joints. *B*, Average energy expenditure, as function of speed, of three subjects with and without immobilization of both ankle joints. *Heavy line*: average values for 12 normal subjects; *stippled area*: scatter of normal values. (Reproduced, with permission, from Ralston, H. J. Effects of immobilization of various body segments on the energy cost of human locomotion. Proc. 2nd I. E. A. Conf., Dortmund, 1964. [Supplement to] *Ergonomics*, p. 53, 1965.)

km/h, it was 19% higher than with a 0° knee flexion angle and 37% higher than with the knee unrestricted. Correction of leg length by use of a shoe lift did not significantly alter this result.

Figure 3.8, *right*, shows the effect of hip restriction. The values were markedly elevated with 60° of flexion. Immobilization at 30° consistently resulted in the lowest values of all the angles studied, with 0° being intermediate in results. At a walking speed of 3.4 km/h, energy expenditure with a hip flexion angle of 60° was 28% higher than at 30° and 39% higher than the normal value. Correction of leg length by use of a shoe lift did not materially alter this result.

Figure 3.9, *right*, shows the effect of trunk restriction on energy cost of walking at three different speeds. Such immobilization caused an increase in energy expenditure of about 10% over a wide range of speeds.

Restriction of arm motion in seven subjects, over a range of 2.93–5.86 km/h, had no significant effect on the energy cost of walking.

As a rough rule of thumb, the experiments described in this section may be summarized as follows: immobilization of both ankle joints, or of one knee at an optimal angle of 15°, or of one hip at an optimal angle of 30°, or of the trunk, may be expected to increase the energy cost of walking at a moderate speed by about 10%. Immobilization of the arms has negligible effect.

It may be anticipated that immobilization of two or more body segments simultaneously will have a cumulative effect.

Terrain

Passmore and Durnin (1955), in their review of energy expenditure, state: "The type of surface may have a slight effect on the energy cost of walking. However, unless the surface is markedly rough, the effect will probably not exceed 10% more than walking on a flat surface." Their Table 3 shows an increase of about 35% for a subject walking at a speed of 90 m/min on plowed field as compared with asphalt road. Strydom et al. (1966), in a study of 11 young men, found that the metabolic cost of walking at about 80 m/min with loads of about 23 kg was 80% greater on loose sand than on a hard surface.

In both cases cited, the walking speed was fairly brisk and, therefore, the results might not be relevant to the effect of loose soil at lower speeds. However, it is clear that the nature of the terrain must always be taken into account in anticipating the metabolic demand of walking.

Work, Power, and Efficiency

An adequate analysis of human walking requires knowledge of the mechanical energy levels (kinetic and

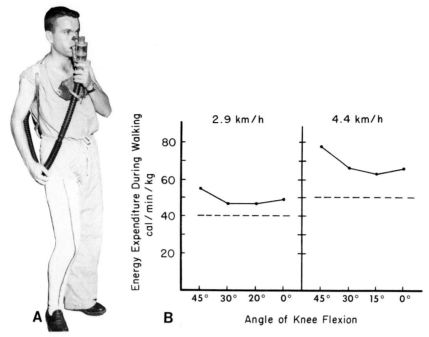

Figure 3.7. Effects of immobilization of knee. *A,* Cast used to immobilize knee of normal subject. *B,* Effect of angle of immobilization of knee on average energy expenditures of eight subjects during walking. *Broken lines:* mean values for normal walking. (Reproduced, with permission, from Ralston, H. J. *Ergonomics,* p. 53, 1965.)

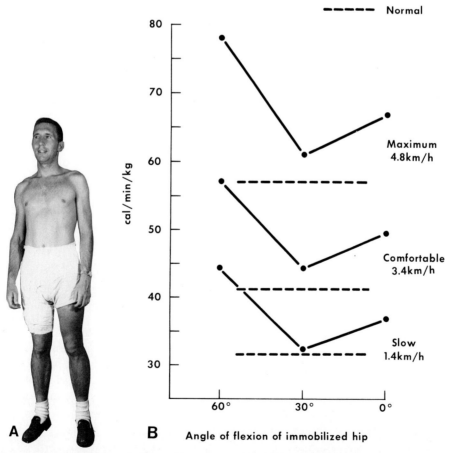

Figure 3.8. Effects of immobilization of hip. *A,* Short hip spica cast used to immobilize hip of normal subject. *B,* Effect of angle of immobilization of hip on average energy expenditures of four subjects during walking. *Broken lines:* mean values for normal walking. (Reproduced, with permission, from Ralston, H. J. *Ergonomics,* p. 53, 1965.)

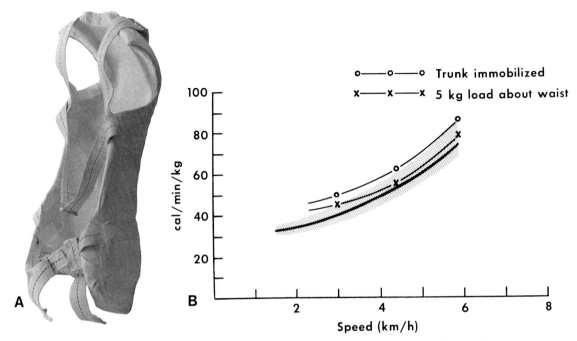

Figure 3.9. Effects of restriction of trunk motion. *A*, Body jacket used for restricting shoulder and pelvic counterrotation and spine movement. *B*, Average energy expenditure, as function of speed, of seven subjects with and without restriction of shoulder, spine, and pelvic motion. *Heavy line*: average values for 12 normal subjects; *stippled area*: scatter of normal values. (Modified, with permission, from Ralston, H. J. *Ergonomics*, p.53, 1965.)

potential) of the various segments of the body during successive moments of the walking cycle, along with measurements of energy expenditure. In this section, we briefly describe a direct method of measuring such energy levels; it is suitable for the study of certain motions of the body at moderate walking speeds, up to about 100 m/min, corresponding to cadences up to about 130 steps/min. A more complete account will be found in Ralston and Lukin (1969).

Cords are attached to the principal segments of the body: head + arms + trunk (HAT), and thigh, shank, and foot. The attachments to thigh and shank are at the center of mass of each segment, placed according to the specifications of Dempster (1955). The attachment to the foot is at the heel, and the attachment to the HAT at approximately the level of the second sacral vertebra. The cords attached to the thigh, shank, and foot run horizontally backward, and drive potentiometric transducers. Two cords are attached to the trunk, one horizontal and one vertical, which drive transducers recording motions of the HAT in both horizontal and vertical directions. The electrical signals drive a suitable recorder.

The method ignores certain motions that are of relatively small magnitude, such as rotational motions of the HAT and limb segments, and arm swing. Earlier investigators (e.g., Cavagna et al., 1963) similarly ignored such second order effects. According to Winter (1976),

who has extended the present type of study to include such second order effects, only in the case of the shank does the rotational kinetic energy have significant value, contributing about 10% of the shank energy.

Masses of the body segments are determined from volumes measured by water displacement and from values of the specific gravities provided in the literature.

From the motions and masses, potential (gravitational) and kinetic (inertial) energy levels of the body segments are calculated for intervals of 0.02 s during the walking cycle.

Figure 3.10 shows the changes in mechanical energy levels of the various body segments, as labeled, of a young woman of 58.6 kg, 169 cm, walking at a speed of 73.2 m/min.

The striking features of this record are (1) the approximate mirror-imaging of the HAT potential and HAT horizontal kinetic curves; (2) the flatness of the HAT total curve during about two-thirds of each step; (3) the disturbance of the HAT total curve during transition from stance to swing phase, which, on the basis of electromyographic evidence, coincides with the major muscle activity during the walking cycle; (4) the large change in energy level of the swinging leg, due almost entirely to velocity (kinetic energy) changes in the limb segments; and (5) the large positive work peak in the body total after heel contact.

The positive work per step, measured by the increase

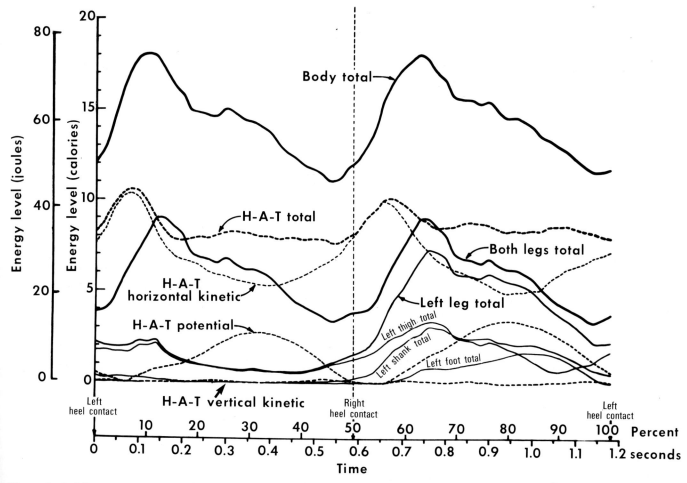

Figure 3.10. Woman, 19, 169 cm, 58.6 kg, walking speed 73.2 m/min. Energy levels of body segments and of whole body, as labeled. (Adapted, with permission, from Ralston, H. J., and Lukin, L. Energy levels of human body segments during level walking. *Ergonomics* 12:39, 1969.)

in the "body total" level, averaged 29.85 J (7.13 cal). The subject walked at an average cadence of 100 steps/min, so the positive work per minute equals 100 x 29.85, or 2985 J/min (49.7 W, 713 cal/min, 0.067 hp). Such a figure for mechanical work rate is in good agreement with the results of Cavagna and Kaneko (1977), who used a cinematographic method in their studies.

The burst of positive work in each step occurred during an average interval of 0.19 s. Hence, 29.85 J/0.19 = 157 W (2250 cal/min, 0.21 hp) was the maximal positive power output during each step.

Wilkie (1960) deduced that in single movements, of duration less than 1 s, the usable "external power output" of the body is limited to a value somewhat less than 6 hp. In brief bouts of exercise of about 6 s, he gives the value 2 hp, and for long-term work lasting all day, 0.2 hp.

Wilkie's figures are based on exercise by champion athletes, and he states that ordinary healthy individuals can produce less than 70–80% as much power. Even so,

it is evident that the power demand in the female subject walking at a natural rate of 73.2 m/min is much below her maximal capability.

It may be concluded that there is a large margin of tolerance in the power expenditure during normal levels of walking speed.

Statements regarding the "efficiency" of biological processes are notoriously confused and confusing. Spanner (1964) says, "The notion of efficiency with which a process involving energy transformation is carried out is one which comes up fairly frequently. However, the word is not always employed in precisely the same sense, and this is apt to cause some confusion." Spanner is referring to relatively straightforward chemical processes. The situation in such a complex process as human walking is vastly more difficult.

Under conditions of *level walking on the treadmill*, when virtually no "external work" is done (see discussion below of meanings of "internal work" and "external work") we shall use a definition of efficiency that is unambiguous and that we have found to be of considerable practical usefulness, especially in the comparison of work done by normal and disabled human subjects during walking. The *gross efficiency* is defined as the *total positive work per minute*, determined from the "body total" curve of Figure 3.10, divided by the *total metabolic expenditure per minute*. For the female subject of Figure 3.10, the positive work, expressed in metabolic units, was 713 cal/min, and the metabolic energy expenditure 3010 cal/min. The gross efficiency therefore is 713/3010 or 0.24. Cavagna and Kaneko (1977), who used net rather than total metabolic expenditure in calculating efficiency, obtained similar results when total is used in the calculation. This value is consistent with values of efficiency in the literature for various kinds of work, such as bicycling on a bicycle ergometer. The data of Silverman et al. (1951) for exercise on the bicycle ergometer yield values of efficiencies very close to those found by us in normal walking speeds, which commonly range from 0.20–0.25.

At first sight, a troublesome feature of using the total metabolic energy expenditure in the calculation of gross efficiency is that at very low levels of walking speed the metabolic energy cost is so much greater compared with total positive work that values of efficiency seem too low. For example, in the female subject of Figure 3.10, walking at 48.8 m/min, the total positive work, expressed in metabolic units, was 350 cal/min, and the total metabolic expenditure 2544 cal/min, yielding a gross efficiency of 350/2544, or 0.14. But there is no real difficulty here as long as the "gross efficiency" is not confused with "muscle efficiency." We are dealing in this case with a slow walk of an ungainly and rather clumsy type, so we should expect a lower gross efficiency.

It is instructive to compare normal subjects with patients with motor disability. Two below-knee amputees, wearing conventional prostheses, were studied by the means described previously. As is usual in cases of such disability, the subjects could walk comfortably only at lower speeds, up to about 50 m/min. As would be expected, the gross efficiencies were relatively low, ranging from about 0.08–0.14. However, the last figure is about the same as that for the normal female subject, described previously, when walking at 48.8 m/min. It may be concluded that one factor involved in the low value of the gross efficiency is simply the low speed, quite apart from the lack of normal muscle coordination associated with the disability.

As is usual in cases of motor disability (see section on stairclimbing, pp. 70–71, hemiplegic subjects), the energy expenditure *per step* or *per meter* was high compared with normal subjects, while the energy expenditure *per minute* was moderate, as a result of the low

speeds used. It is the moderate energy cost *per minute* that is linked to moderate changes in heart rate, blood pressure, and pulmonary ventilation.

As already mentioned, many authors have used a net energy figure in calculating efficiency. Such a net figure is obtained by subtracting a resting energy value from the energy expenditure, or by subtracting an extrapolated value from the energy expenditure. Such a procedure can lead, and frequently has led, to very misleading conclusions. It has already been noted that use of a net figure for mathematical formulation of the relation between walking speed and energy expenditure leads to nothing.

In this connection, Wilkie (1974), in speaking of human muscular exercise, says: "The usual procedure of subtracting the resting oxygen consumption from the total does not correspond to any clear hypothesis about what is being estimated. In order to determine the efficiency of the working muscles themselves one should also subtract the extra oxygen used by heart, respiratory muscles, etc. (Hill, 1965, p. 153)."

It seems desirable to end this section, dealing with the work of walking, with some comments on the use of the terms "external work" and "internal work."

Fenn (1930) refers to the elevation of the center of mass as "part of the external work" of running.

Müller (1950) refers to work against external resistance as external work. Snellen (1960) states that the external work in level walking is negligible, and describes as external work the work involved in climbing a hill. Wilkie (1960) refers to work in overcoming air resistance as external work, while work associated with raising and lowering the center of mass, and with changes in kinetic energy of the limbs, he refers to as work "dissipated internally." He evidently regards the work done in climbing a hill as external work.

Cavagna et al. (1963) refer to external work during locomotion as that associated with displacement of the center of mass of the body and to internal work as work not leading to a displacement of the center of mass. Ralston and Lukin (1969) refer to "total external positive work" as work measured by increases in the sum total of the energy levels of the body segments.

During walking, the reaction forces at the ground can do no work because the points of application of the forces are fixed (it is assumed that no slippage occurs). The ground reaction forces can cause only *acceleration* of the center of mass of the body. Conversely, the forces produced by the muscles of the body can cause no acceleration of the center of mass, but *are* responsible for the changes in energy level of the body, both kinetic and potential.

Consequently, the internal work during walking is that done by muscles, while there is no external work unless one means by this work *done by the body on the environment* (as in pushing molecules of air out of the way) or, alternatively, *by the environment on the body.*

It is obviously desirable, in describing the efficiency of human walking, to refer to work done *on the environment* (as in pushing molecules of air out of the way) as external work. Consequently, in the case of normal walking on the terrain (rather than simply level walking on the treadmill), the overall efficiency would be appropriately defined as the sum of the external work plus the internal work, divided by the metabolic expenditure. This definition was used by Winter (1979).

CHAPTER 4

Kinetics

Force and Motion

When an object at rest is pushed, it will start to move in the direction of the push, reaching a speed proportional to the strength of the push and the length of time the push is applied. As already discussed in Chapter 2, if the line of the push passes through the center of mass, the object will move without turning, so that all parts of the object will move at the same speed and in the same direction. Movement of an object without turning is called translation, or linear motion. If the line of push does not pass through the center of mass then some rotation will accompany the translation. The greater the distance between the center of mass and the line of push, the greater will be the rotational component.

If the object is on a frictionless surface, it will continue to move after the push has stopped and will maintain the same velocity and rate of rotation that it had when the push ceased. It can be slowed or brought to rest only by the application of a push in the opposite direction.

A pull on the object will have the same effect as a push, and the single term force means either a push or a pull. Like motion, force is described by two components: magnitude, which indicates the strength of the force, and direction, which requires specifying a coordinate system. The subject of forces and the associated motions is called kinetics.

Reaction Force

The three laws of motion developed by Newton are the basis on which the kinetics of locomotion will be described. Two of these—that an object will change velocity only if a force is applied and that the change in velocity is proportional to the force—have already been mentioned, but the third law is especially significant in locomotion. Called the law of action and reaction, it states that forces are always in pairs which are equal in magnitude but opposite in direction, so that if one body

pushes against another body, the second body will push back against the first with a force of equal magnitude.

Two people pushing their palms against each other can demonstrate this, because if one increases his effort the other person will do likewise, and if one person suddenly relaxes the other will be unable to maintain a force. Similarly, if a person pushes against an inert object, such as a wall, he can feel the matching reaction force from the wall against his hand, increasing and decreasing as he varies his effort. Which of the two forces is called the action and which the reaction is usually an arbitrary matter but, in human locomotion where changes in force are controlled by the body musculature, the forces exerted by the walking surface against the feet are called ground or floor reactions.

The necessity of reaction forces in locomotion can be demonstrated by a person standing on a wheeled platform. No matter what body motions he makes, he cannot set himself in horizontal motion relative to the floor. Although he may oscillate a little back and forth, at the end of his efforts he will be in his original location. If, however, he pushes against a wall in the direction *opposite* to his intended motion, the reaction force from the external surface will provide the desired displacement. The direction and magnitude of the reaction force will exactly match the direction and magnitude of the motion of the center of mass of the body (including, in this case, the wheeled platform).

For the purpose of analysis and mathematical description of a kinetic system, a procedure has been developed that substitutes for the actual pushes or pulls theoretical forces that have the same effects on the bodies involved:

Though any real force is always applied over an area, it is summarized in the procedure as a point force, which is diagramed as an arrow. The length of the arrow represents the magnitude of the force, and the direction of the arrow indicates the directional component of the force. The arrow illustrates the fact that force is a vector quantity.

It is, sometimes useful to combine two or more separate forces into a single resultant force, or, in other situations, to separate a single force into several components. The same separation into progressional, lateral, and vertical components that was used for kinematic descriptions is also used in the description of forces.

When a force has the effect of producing rotation, the measure of its rotational effect is called a moment of force, or torque. Just as translational and rotational motions of an object are separated for ease of description, the effect of a force can also be separated into two components: one with only a translational effect and another, called a pure moment (torque), with only a rotational effect.

The kinetic analysis of the motion of a body involves the relationship between displacement, velocity, and acceleration, and a brief description of the relationship between these is in order.

Figure 4.1A shows the simple displacement curve (position vs. time) of an object initially at rest which is set in translational motion and then brought to a stop. Numerical values will be assigned by assuming that the object being moved is a box with a mass of 100 kg that is mounted on a wheeled platform so that friction effects are negligible. The box is first pulled toward the person moving it and then pushed to stop it so that it comes to rest after moving 1 m in a 5-s period.

When the object is at rest, the displacement curve is horizontal, but while the object is in motion, the curve is inclined. During the third second, where the curve is nearly a straight line, the box moved a little more than one-third of a meter so that the average velocity during this time was about 0.34 m/s. To determine the velocity at each instant of time, the inclination of the displacement curve can be measured by various methods. The inclination, technically called the slope, is described as the amount of change in position per time unit, which is the same expression used for velocity. Figure 4.1B is the velocity curve for the displacement of Figure 4.1A.

The same process of determining and plotting slopes can be applied to the velocity curve to obtain the rate of change of velocity at each instant of time. The rate at which velocity is changing is called acceleration and is shown in Figure 4.1C. Note that when the velocity reaches its maximum the acceleration drops to zero, and that as the velocity decreases the acceleration becomes negative and is often called deceleration. The significance of the acceleration curve is that it correlates exactly with the force required to produce the motion.

It is a common experience that when pushes of equal force are applied to a heavy and a light object, the lighter one will move more rapidly, that is, the heavier object has the greater resistance to being moved. This resistance to being moved, called inertia, is a definitive property of bodies. The quantitative expression of inertia is called mass and in the Système International d'Unités (SI), the basic unit is the kilogram.

The force required to produce an acceleration is calculated by multiplying the acceleration by the mass. The SI unit of force is the newton (N), which is the force required to change the velocity of a 1 kg mass at the rate of 1 m/s/s (one meter per second per second). One newton is approximately the downward force a person feels pushing on his hand when supporting a 0.1 kg (100 g) object.

The relationship between force and acceleration is expressed mathematically as $F = ma$. Force (F) is in newtons when mass (m) is in kilograms and acceleration (a) in meters per second per second. In the example of the moving box with a mass of 100 kg, the force required is obtained by multiplying the acceleration by 100 to obtain the force on the scale on the right side of Figure 4.1C.

Work

When the velocity of a body is increased as a result of an applied force, work is said to have been done on it. Work in the mechanical sense has a mathematical definition which can be calculated in various ways, the usual one being that it is the product of the force applied and the distance the object moves (in the direction of the force) during that application. When force is in newtons and distance in meters, the unit of work is called a joule (J), which is the work done when a force of 1 N is continuously applied during a displacement of 1 m.

The effect of work being done on a body is to increase the energy level of that body. The amount of change in energy level is the same as the amount of work done on the body and is expressed in the same units. The energy level of a body due to its motion is called kinetic energy and is calculated by the equation kinetic energy = ½ mass × (velocity)^2 (Fig. 4.1D). Figure 4.1D shows the curve of the kinetic energy level for the box with the displacement of Figure 4.1A and can be obtained either by computation from the values of Figure 4.1C and 4.1A (summation of force applied × distance moved) or by squaring the velocity values of Figure 4.1B and multiplying by half the mass.

The rate of change in energy level can be obtained by the same process that is used to obtain velocity from displacement, or acceleration from velocity. As already noted in the discussion of work, power, and efficiency in Chapter 3, the rate of doing work is called power, which has the same units as the rate of expenditure of energy, also called power. The standard unit of power is the watt, equal to 1 J/s. Figure 4.1E shows the power required to move the box with the displacement pattern of Figure 4.1A and the force of Figure 4.1C.

Note that all the kinetic information (force, energy, work, and power) was derived from the displacement measurements of Figure 4.1A, the only modification being the inclusion of the mass of the box. Kinetic data, as with velocity and acceleration, can be measured independently, but the kinematic pattern contains all the information needed to obtain all the other measurements.

Rotational Motion

The kinematic and kinetic relationships described for translational motion also apply to rotational motion if we substitute moment of force for force, and moment of inertia for mass.

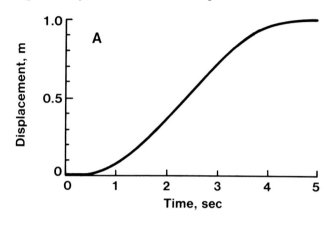

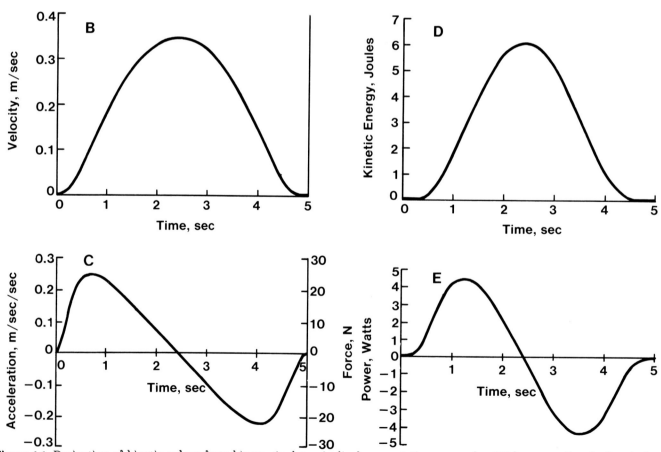

Figure 4.1. Derivation of kinetic values from kinematic data. *A*, displacement–time curve for 100-kg mass. *B*, velocity, derived from *A*. *C*, acceleration and force, derived from *B*. *D*, kinetic energy, derived from *B*. *E*, power, derived from curves in *B* and *C*. See text for further discussion.

Angular position is generally expressed in units of degrees (360°/revolution) or radians (rad: 1 rad = 57.3°). Consequently, angular velocity has units of degrees (or radians) per second, and angular acceleration has units of degrees (or radians) per second per second. A force produces angular acceleration when its line of action does not pass through the center of rotation. The greater the distance between the line of action and the rotation center, the more effective is the force in producing angular motion. As already noted, the rotational effectiveness of a force is called a moment of force (commonly shortened to moment), or torque, and is calculated by multiplying the force by the moment arm, which is the distance between the line of action of the force and the axis of rotation. Thus, the names of the units for moments contain a unit name for force and one for length; the standard SI term is the newton-meter (N-m).

The equivalent of mass in rotational kinetics is called the moment of inertia. This physical property is a measure of the distribution of mass about an axis, and is concerned with differences in motion by various parts of a rotating body. Because the motion of any one part of the body for a specified angular rotation depends on the distance of that part from the center of rotation, the moment of inertia of a body will be different about different axes. The moments of inertia of simple shapes can be calculated, but for more complex shapes, they must be experimentally determined. For analysis of the kinetics of locomotion, knowledge of inertia of body segments about the center of mass is required. The relationships between displacements, energy level, and power for rotational motion are identical to those which were described for translational motion. The only differences are the substitution of angular change, moment, and moment of inertia for, respectively, displacement, force, and mass.

If the box of the example used in Figure 4.1 was rotated in place over a 5-sec period, instead of moved across the floor, the series of curves of Figure 4.1 would serve to describe the kinetic relationships, requiring only appropriate changes in the vertical scales.

Potential Energy

So far, the discussion has described the kinetic relationships for the motion of a body with only a single force acting on it. Suppose, however, that the box was attached to a spring which stretched when the box was moved. To maintain the same displacement pattern of the box, the person would have to pull with an extra effort during the first part of the activity, but then would need to apply less of a push to bring the box to a stop. Furthermore, if the person ceased his effort when the box came to a stop, the box would be pulled by the

spring back toward its original position. In pulling the box back, the spring is doing work on the box. The spring, however, cannot generate energy by itself, and the energy being released was placed there by the extra effort made by the person when starting the motion of the box. This capacity for storing energy demonstrates what is called potential energy, to distinguish it from the energy of velocity, kinetic energy.

The elasticity of ligaments and elastic elements of muscles can be a significant factor in human locomotion. Unfortunately, the measurements needed to calculate their effects are frequently difficult to make. Some measure of success in this regard has, however, been achieved (see, for example, Cavagna et al., 1977). Further comments on this matter will be made in Chapter 5.

There is another form of potential energy, called gravitational. Its effect may be imagined as that of an invisible spring between the center of mass of a body and the earth's center, always pulling straight downward. Just as work is required to stretch a spring, so work is required to move the body upward. Similarly, the work is stored as with a stretched spring, and when the body elevation is reduced the stored potential energy can be converted to kinetic energy. The potential energy accumulated by a body in rising is calculated by the relationship already described, namely, distance × force:

$$\Delta PE = \text{rise of body} \times \text{force}$$
$$\text{joules} = \text{meters} \times \text{newtons}$$

The discussion of the process of deriving kinetic information from kinematic measurements showed the necessity of knowing three specifications of the object under observation: the mass, the location of the center of mass, and the radius of gyration. The latter is the radial distance from any given axis at which the mass of the body could be concentrated without altering the moment of inertia of the body about that axis. In studies of human body motion, these specifications have come to be known as body segment parameters.

The parameters for a segment can be determined accurately only by separating that segment from the rest of the body and performing the procedures required. This is not a practical procedure, so that the use of estimates based on studies of dismembered cadavers has been the usual practice. While theoretically, at least, some of the measurements should be possible on an intact living body, attempts to do so have failed to show a superiority over using estimates derived from the cadaver studies.

Applying cadaver measurements to living bodies of various sizes is accomplished by using ratios of the parameters to measurements which are easily obtained on living bodies. Thus, the segment masses are assumed to be proportionately the same on a living body as on the cadaver studied. Similarly, the centers of mass and radii of gyration are assumed to be proportionately related to the length of the segment. It is unlikely that these proportional relationships will be the same for all of the widely varying types of bodies found in even small groups of people. Until formulas are developed which can be more specific for the individual physiques, the use of fixed proportions must be considered to be an important source of possible error in locomotion analysis.

For their own studies on human gait, Braune and Fischer (1889) obtained measurements on a number of dismembered cadavers. The proportions selected by Fischer for his report (1906), cited by Elftman (1939), and consequently called Fischer's coefficients are the ones used for the studies reported here.

Energy Levels of the Body Segments

The energy level of a body segment at any instant is the sum of the three types of mechanical energy which have been described: translational kinetic energy, rotational kinetic energy, and the potential energy due to gravity. The velocities of each of the segment kinematic measurements of Chapter 2 can be used to calculate a corresponding energy level so that the kinetic energy total is the sum of three translational and three rotational kinetic energies. During walking, however, the energies associated with motions seen in the rear (coronal) and top (transverse) views are such a small part of the total that they have generally been considered to be negligible.

Of the various components of kinetic energy in the sagittal plane, that for forward motion is so much greater than those for vertical and rotational motion that there has been a tendency for investigators to dismiss the latter two as negligible. This dismissal appears to be justified for vertical kinetic energy, at least for the leg segments, but the rotational energy of the thigh and shank is typically some 5–10% of the total segment kinetic energy and, therefore, should perhaps not be considered insignificant (see Winter, 1976, already referred to in Chapter 3).

The description which follows utilizes the concept of Elftman (1954) which regards the lower limbs as the active component of the walking mechanism, and the head, arms, and trunk (designated the HAT) as a passive unit, the motion of which is controlled by the musculature of the lower limbs.

In Chapter 3, the energy levels of the body segments (HAT, thigh, shank, and foot) of an adult female subject during walking at moderate speed have been presented.

It is recommended that this discussion and Figure 3.10 now be reviewed by the reader. In the discussion which follows, an entirely different experimental technique, utilizing photography and force platform, is used to obtain measurements on four normal adult males (Bresler and Berry, 1951). In general, the curves of energy levels in the two types of experimental procedures are in satisfactory agreement, thus promoting confidence in the adequacy of the measurements.

HAT Energy Levels

Trunk displacements were not measured on these subjects, but they can be estimated by assuming that the motions would be approximately the same as that for the body center of mass. The body center of mass measurements were determined from force platform recordings.

The potential energy curve (Fig. 4.2), which has the same configuration as the pelvic elevation curve, is at a minimum at the middle of the double-support period (approximately 6 and 56% of cycle) and a maximum at the middle of the single-support period (approximately 31 and 81% of cycle). If the gait is symmetrical in the use of the right and left legs, both maximal and both minimal levels will be the same.

The kinetic energy curve is also simple in configuration, displaying two maximal and two minimal levels during a walking cycle. The maximal kinetic energy level occurs at the same time as the minimal potential energy level (6 and 56% of cycle), and the minimal kinetic energy level occurs at the time of maximal potential energy.

The form of the kinetic and potential energy curves suggests an interchange of energy, as in the case of the simple pendulum. However, even if the changes of

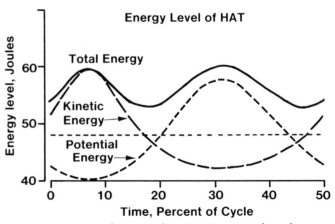

Figure 4.2. Potential energy, kinetic energy, and total energy of the HAT during one-half of one walking cycle. In computing the total energy, the minimal level on the curve of potential energy is equal to zero. Average of four normal adult males walking at an average 88.5 m/min and 109 steps/min.

potential and kinetic energies of the HAT during walking were equal in magnitude, it is evident from the differences in the shapes of the two curves that energy conversion is not complete. Thus, summing of the two curves, as shown in the figure, shows substantial fluctuations in energy level.

The shapes of the curves in Figure 4.2 conform to what can be considered well-established patterns of HAT energy levels. This confidence is also based, in part, on the kinematic observations of Chapter 2, which showed that the patterns of pelvic translation remained the same, except for amplitude, throughout the range of walking speeds. Also, the simplicity of the patterns and timing of the maximal and minimal points were consistent among the subjects studied.

The potential energy curve is essentially identical to the pelvic vertical displacement curve and consequently, its amplitude closely correlates with the step length for any individual. However, substantial differences between individuals can be expected from the data presented in Chapter 2.

In the case of the kinetic energy of the HAT, two statements may be said to be obvious: in a steady state of walking, where an average velocity is being maintained from cycle to cycle, the kinetic energy level must fluctuate about the level represented by the average velocity. Second, the velocity pattern (Chapter 2) indicates that the increase above the average level would be on the order of twice the decrease below the average level.

Measuring the actual magnitude of the fluctuations in HAT kinetic energy requires knowing the kinematics of the trunk (assuming, as has been done, that the arm motion does not appreciably change the anatomic location of the HAT center of mass). The only substantial study of this was by Waters et al. (1973), who published only a relatively brief account. This study demonstrated that while the vertical displacements are the same at different levels of the trunk, changes in horizontal velocities increased progressively from the head to the pelvis. According to the figures presented, at usual walking speeds the change in forward velocity at the pelvis is substantially greater than that at T-10 (approximately the level of the center of mass of the head, arms, and trunk). Other evidence, notably that from force platform measurements, indicates that the differences in forward velocity between pelvis and T-10 are not as great as those suggested by Waters et al. This is a subject that needs further study.

Energy Levels of the Leg

The curves of Figure 4.3 of the energy levels of the leg segments can be considered representative and similar to the measurements obtained in other studies (see Chapter 3). It should be repeated that these do not

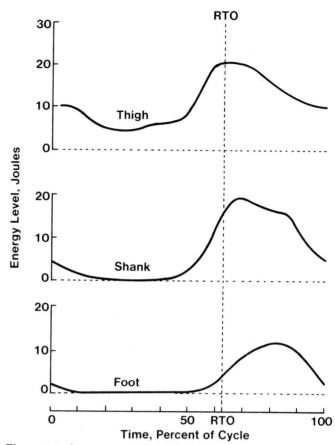

Figure 4.3. Average energy levels of thigh, shank, and foot. Four normal adult males walking at an average 88.5 m/min and 109 steps/min.

include rotational kinetic energy which, as already mentioned, at times can be about 10% of the total energy.

As expected, the leg segments reach minimal levels during stance phase and maximal levels during swing phase. It should be noted that the thigh reaches its maximal energy level at about the time of toe-off, when a sharp increase in the energy level of the shank-plus-foot begins. The increase of the shank-plus-foot after toe-off is accompanied by a decrease in the energy level of the thigh, and it appears here that energy is being transferred from the thigh to the shank-plus-foot. When the total energy of the leg is summed (Fig. 4.4), a plateau of relatively little energy change can be observed during this transfer period.

With the assumption that the energy level pattern of the left leg is a duplicate of that of the right leg, a sum of the energy level for both legs can be obtained. It might be assumed that energy lost in one leg is transferred to the other leg if the latter's energy level is increasing at that time. The mechanics of this assumed process is not known at the present time and it may ultimately prove to be, at least in part, a false assumption.

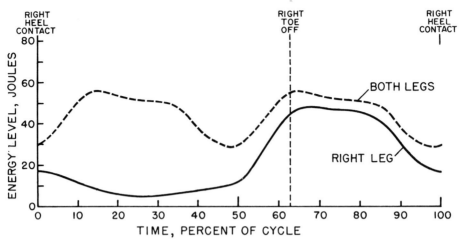

Figure 4.4. Average total energy of right leg and both legs during a walking cycle. Four normal adult males walking at an average 88.5 m/min and 109 steps/min.

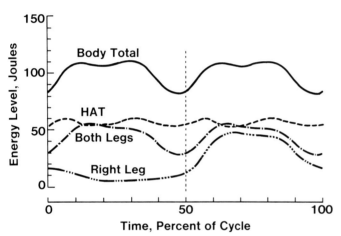

Figure 4.5. Average energy levels of whole body, HAT, both legs, and right leg. Four normal adult males walking at an average 88.5 m/min and 109 steps/min.

Energy Level of the Entire Body

By summing the energy levels of the HAT and the two legs, and ignoring arm swing, the energy level of the entire body can be calculated (Fig. 4.5). As each arm swings, there are changes in the energy of the arm. However, it has been noted in Chapter 3 that restriction of arm motion in seven normal subjects, walking at speeds of 2.93 to 5.86 km/h, had no significant effect on the energy cost of walking. It therefore seems justified to ignore arm swing, at least for moderate speeds of walking.

Power Requirements of the Body

As was shown in Figure 4.1, the rate at which the energy level is changing can be calculated to determine the power requirements of the body during walking.

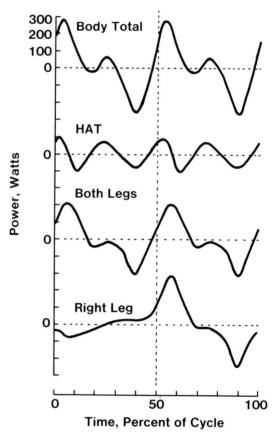

Figure 4.6. Average power requirement of whole body, HAT, both legs, and right leg. Four normal adult males walking at an average 88.5 m/min and 109 steps/min.

Figure 4.6 shows the power required during the walking cycle by the HAT, each leg, both legs, and the entire body.

As in Figure 4.1, when an increase in energy level is taking place, the power curve has positive values, which means that an energy source must do work on the unit requiring power. For the subunits of the body, i.e., HAT and legs, the sources of energy input can be either those muscles of the body capable of acting on the unit, release of potential energy by elastic elements of the body, or the transfer of energy from other units. Where there is a decrease in energy level, on the other hand, with a consequent negative power requirement, then the unit must do work on some structure capable of absorbing energy. Again, for the subunits these structures may be muscles themselves, the elastic connective tissue elements which convert kinetic energy to elastic potential energy, or other subunits to which energy can be transferred.

For the body as a whole and also for the HAT unit, the energy level is increasing half the time and decreasing half the time, changing eight times during a cycle.

The period of energy increase for the legs is only about two-thirds as long as that for energy decrease. Most of the energy increase occurs during the double-support period, while the single-support period is principally a time of decreasing energy.

Energy input to a leg occurs during the latter 60% of stance phase and into the period just after toe-off, leaving most of swing phase and the first 40% of stance phase as a period of energy loss.

At this speed (88.5 m/min) the power required by the body reaches levels of over 250 W, positive and negative, about the same as that required by each leg.

Although it is not presently possible to measure muscle forces in the intact body directly, it is possible to determine the magnitude of muscle action at each joint from the resulting kinetic effects. These measurements, combined with joint angular velocity, can then be used to calculate the muscle power. Some of this power meets the power requirements of the leg, but, as will be shown, there is a difference between the power *output* and power *requirement*. A surplus is presumably applied to other parts of the body, whereas a deficit indicates that energy from other parts of the body must be transferred to the leg. The remainder of this chapter will show these relationships, based on the study of the four adult males which was the source of the energy level data already presented.

Joint Moments

The principle on which the calculation of muscle moment is based is Newton's third law, that for every action there must be an equal and opposite reaction. Thus, if the muscles acting at a joint are producing a moment, there must be other forces acting to produce an opposing moment.

As already discussed, one of these forces, which is constant and always present, is that of gravity. In effect,

gravity acts at the center of mass of the body segment. Although gravitational force is constant, the moment produced will depend on the location of the center of mass of the segment and the center of rotation; thus, as the body configuration is constantly changing, so are the gravitational moments.

A second force opposing the muscle force arises from the inertial properties of the body segment and is consequently called inertial force. It is proportional to the acceleration of the segment but acts in the opposite direction.

The third force is the reaction force exerted by the walking surface against the foot. This surface does not generate a force of its own (except during an earthquake), and the force developed is a reaction to the forces developed by the moving body. Because the reaction force is an external force acting on the body, it can be calculated from the changes in the linear and angular momentum of the whole body.

Use of the force platform, which measures these forces directly, has become the usual procedure. As an example, Figure 4.7 illustrates the moments about the knee that result from these three forces acting on the shank–foot. At the time of the walking cycle shown (about 42%), all three forces are producing a counterclockwise (extension) moment and the muscles at the knee joint are producing a clockwise (flexion) moment.

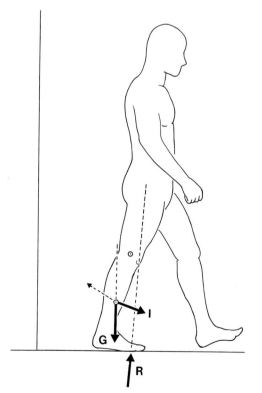

Figure 4.7. Gravitational (*G*), inertial (*I*), and reaction (*R*) forces acting to produce moments about knee.

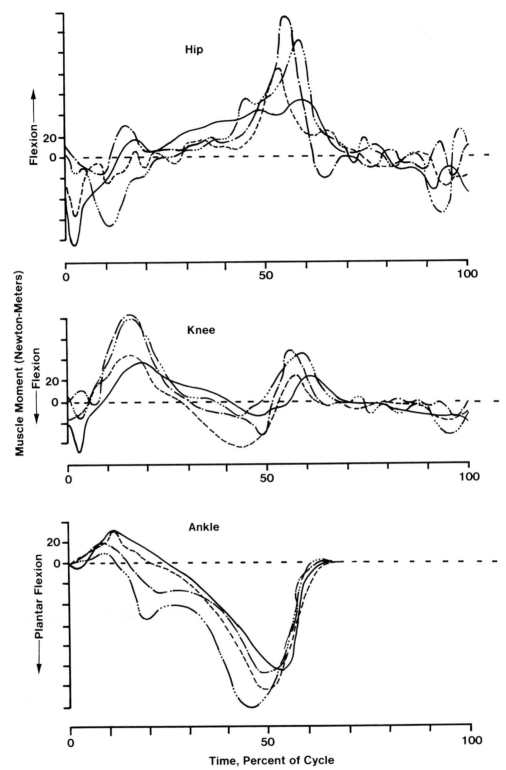

Figure 4.8. Muscle moments at hip, knee, and ankle. Four adult male subjects walking at an average 88.5 m/min and 109 steps/min.

The muscles that produce flexion of the knee are principally the hamstring group and the gastrocnemius. However, these are principally two joint muscles so that in developing a flexion moment at the knee, they must also develop extension moments at the hip in the case of the hamstrings or plantar flexion moments at the ankle in the case of the gastrocnemius.

When the moment effect of each of these forces is

known, they can be summed to calculate what the required resisting moment developed by the musculature must be. This has been done for the hip, knee, and ankle joints, and the results are shown in Figure 4.8 for four male subjects walking at a moderate speed. The pattern shown is typical and is similar to that obtained by other investigators. It should be noted that the indicated muscle activities have been corroborated by electromyographic studies (Chapter 5).

It can be assumed that just as the kinematic patterns change systematically as walking speed is changed, so would joint moment curves, but there is presently a lack of such studies.

Power Output

Figure 4.9 presents the power output at the hip, knee, and ankle joints of the right leg, computed from the moments at the joints and the angular velocities at the joints. At each joint, the peak of activity is reached during the double-support period after left heel contact.

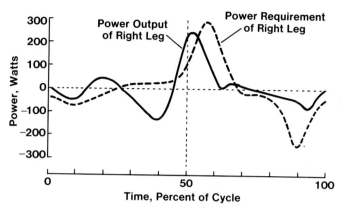

Figure 4.10. Average power output and power requirement of right leg. Four normal adult males walking at an average 88.5 m/min and 109 steps/min.

The muscles acting at the knee, however, are absorbing energy, whereas those at the other joints are producing energy. The areas under the curves are proportional to the work output at the joint; the areas above the zero line represent work done on the body, whereas the areas below the zero line represent an energy reduction.

The knee is principally an energy absorber, its output being, in this case, only about 30% of its input (energy absorbed). In contrast, the output at the hip is about double and at the ankle about three times the input. The work output at the hip, knee, and ankle was 25, 10, and 37 J, respectively. The energy absorbed at these joints was 11, 39, and 13 J, respectively. Many of the muscles involved span two joints so that energy which appears to be absorbed at one joint can, in fact, be transferred, apparently producing energy at the other joint. By summing the joint power outputs to obtain a total power output for the whole leg, the assumption is that any apparent energy absorption is being transferred to the extent that energy is being simultaneously produced elsewhere in the leg. This assumption correlates with the previous one that energy lost by one body segment is being transferred, *if* there is an energy gain by one or more other body segments.

The total power output of the leg, thus computed, is presented in Figure 4.10. Also in the figure is a *dashed line* showing the power required by the leg. The differences between the two curves indicate where energy transferral is occurring between the leg and other parts of the body. When the power output of the leg muscles exceeds the power required by the leg, then the surplus power is being applied to the rest of the body. When the power required by the leg exceeds the leg muscle output, the necessary energy must come from other parts of the body.

Three points of interest should be noted:

1. From about 25–45% of cycle the leg musculature is

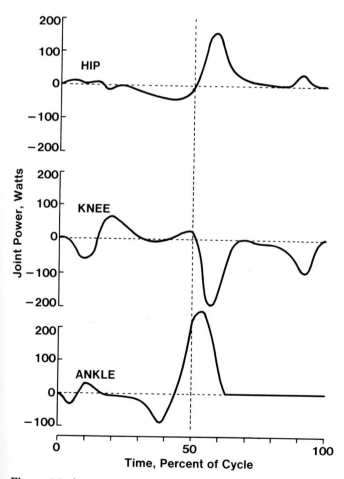

Figure 4.9. Average joint power at hip, knee, and ankle. Four normal adult males walking at an average 88.5 m/min and 109 steps/min.

absorbing a large amount of energy, although the leg itself requires a small increase.

2. The major energy output of the leg musculature (from 45% to toe-off) precedes the major need of leg energy (in preparation for leg swing) by about 6% of cycle. This indicates an energy storage by a process not yet defined.

3. Only about one-fifth of the energy lost by the leg as it ends its swing is absorbed by the leg musculature. The remainder must then be absorbed elsewhere in the body.

By assuming that the power output and requirement of the left leg are the same as those for the right leg, the total for both legs can be estimated, with the result shown in Figure 4.11. The fairly close match between the combined power requirement and output of the right and left legs during the second half of the swing phases (30–50% and 80–100% of cycle) implies that most of the energy lost by the swinging leg as it decelerates is absorbed by the musculature at the hip and ankle of the other leg. The differences between power required and produced in Figure 4.11 may be attributed to energy transferrals to and from the HAT.

Finally, the energy output of the two legs, which has been assumed to be the sole energy source for walking, can be compared with the calculated energy requirements of the whole body (Fig. 4.12). Quantitatively, the

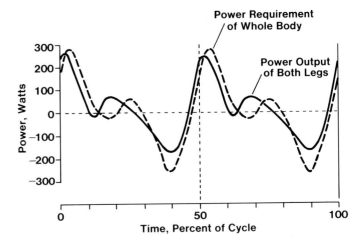

Figure 4.12. Average power requirement of whole body and power output of both legs during one walking cycle. Four normal adult males walking at an average 88.5 m/min and 109 steps/min.

two curves appear to be in reasonably close agreement, except for the failure of the leg musculature to absorb all of the energy lost at 40% and 90% of the cycle. It is possible that the surplus energy is absorbed by the trunk, which has generally been assumed to be a passive contributor to the walking process.

A second discrepancy, that the power output of the legs appears to precede the power requirement during much of the cycle, cannot be so easily resolved. The delay implies that some of the output of the legs is stored in some way and later released to accomplish the observed motions of the body. Although several mechanisms for this apparent storage might be suggested (e.g., elastic action of ligaments, transverse trunk rotations, arm swing), it is also possible that errors in moment calculation arising from erroneous estimations of joint center locations may be responsible. Furthermore, possible contributions by joint action in the coronal and transverse planes have been ignored on the assumption that they are negligible, but collectively they may prove to be significant.

The only conclusion which may be confidently stated is that there is a need for additional experimental information aimed at resolving these questions.

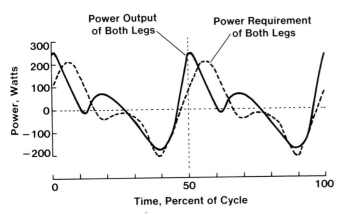

Figure 4.11. Average power output and power requirement of both legs. Four normal adult males walking at an average 88.5 m/min and 109 steps/min.

CHAPTER 5

Muscles

The human walking machine is composed of many articulated skeletal parts. During walking, the pattern of movement of each part depends on several factors. The most obvious are its physical structure and the characteristics of articulation with adjacent skeletal segments. However, within the limits imposed by these structural arrangements, the ranges of motion utilized during walking are largely dependent on certain laws of muscle action. The muscles seem to be used in a manner that is most effective in achieving the necessary angular displacements. To fully understand how this is accomplished requires a rather detailed review of the separate components involved in the production of movement of the skeletal segments by muscles. A discussion of these components falls into three general categories: the functional characteristics of isolated voluntary striated muscle, certain compensatory skeletal arrangements of the muscles within the body, and the phasic action of muscles during walking.

Functional Characteristics of Striated Muscle

Muscles are described in textbooks of anatomy as separate entities and are designated by individual names. The description of the action of each muscle is usually stated in terms of its contraction producing a specific movement about the joint over which the muscle acts. Although such a description may be true in a restricted sense, it ignores the following facts. In the complex phenomenon of human walking, a single muscle rarely acts alone; rather, it acts in conjunction with other muscles to achieve the required effect. A muscle may be activated and not produce the precise motion described in textbooks of anatomy: it may simply resist the opposite motion. Furthermore, a muscle may be elongated by other forces while attempting to contract, thus, having work done on it rather than doing work. Finally, there are inherent in striated muscle certain deficiencies that limit its ability to develop tension. To properly understand the entire phenomenon of human

walking requires that the basic behavior of striated muscle under various conditions be reviewed.

Laboratory studies on isolated muscle obviously are necessary for an adequate understanding of muscle function, but it should be kept in mind that the behavior of muscles in the intact body may be modified in accordance with various restrictions and requirements not encountered by the isolated muscle in the laboratory. For example, the changes in length of muscles in the body are limited by their attachments to the bony skeleton. The "innervation" of muscles, that is to say, the extent to which they are stimulated by the activity of a variable number of motor neurons firing in a variable, asynchronous manner, leads to a variety of types of response not usually seen in isolated muscles electrically stimulated. There is, however, some information available on the behavior of isolated human muscle in the cineplastic amputee, in whom the muscle is under completely normal neural control. Such information helps to fill in the gap between the isolated, electrically stimulated laboratory muscle and the intact muscle in the normal human subject.

Concept of Contractile as Compared with Elastic Components of Muscle

For many years, physiologists have thought of muscle as a composite structure consisting of a contractile chemical system, which is responsible for the tension generated when a muscle is thrown into action, plus elastic elements such as connective tissue, which occur both in parallel and in series with the contractile component. Recent studies (Huxley, 1974) indicate that a part of the elastic component actually resides in the contractile machinery itself, in the "cross-bridges" that occur between the actin and myosin protein filaments making up the contractile machinery. A "sliding" of filaments occurs during contraction, due to action of the cross-bridges, and this sliding accompanies the production of force. When a quiescent muscle is stretched by an external force, such as gravity or action of an antagonist muscle, the muscle is said to be "passively" stretched, or to exhibit "passive" tension. When an active muscle is stretched, the relation between stretch and tension now involves the behavior of the contractile machinery, so that the "elasticity" of the active muscle may be grossly different from that of the passive muscle. Such considerations play an important role in the understanding of muscle physiology.

Factors Influencing the Response of Muscle

The response of muscle in the body depends on several factors: (1) the number of motor neurons activating the muscle at any given moment; (2) the rates at which the various motor neurons are firing; (3) the asynchronous firing of the various motor neurons; (4) the length of the muscle at the time of activation; and (5) the effect of immediately prior stretch.

The muscle *twitch* has been a common object of study in physiology laboratories. This is the type of response that occurs when a muscle is stimulated by an electrical shock, in which the various fibers of the muscle are thrown into a brief, sudden, essentially synchronized contraction. This type of contraction does not generally occur in the body.

Tetanus is a type of contraction in which the muscle is stimulated by a rapid succession of stimuli, such as occurs during prolonged application of electrical shocks, resulting in a relatively smooth, sustained contraction, usually of much greater force than in the case of the twitch. Such a contraction is not typical of muscle activity in the intact body, although a maximal voluntary contraction may approximate a tetanus in smoothness and vigor.

Brief, tetanic-like bursts of activity of muscle commonly occur in the body, as in the muscles used in walking. In this case, a short train of impulses lasting, perhaps, only 0.1 sec may activate the muscle concerned, with the generation of tension well below that which would occur in a maximal tetanus.

Prolonged submaximal contractions, at low rates of stimulation, are common in the intact body. An example of these is the contraction in the elbow flexors when the forearm is elevated against gravity.

Types of Contraction

It is customary to speak of three types of contraction of muscle: isotonic (free), isometric, and lengthening (restraining). Isotonic contraction occurs in association with obvious shortening of muscle, such as is seen when a load held in the hand is lifted. Isometric contraction is a contraction in which the ends of the muscle are fixed. Force is generated, but the only appreciable shortening is that which occurs *within* the muscle; the contractile machinery stretches the internal series elas-

tic component, thereby producing a force that may be measured externally. Lengthening contraction is a contraction in which a muscle, while activated, is stretched by a greater external force. Such contractions are common in the body; an example is that which occurs in the tibialis anterior after heel strike during walking, thereby easing the forefoot onto the ground.

The Isometric Length–Tension Diagram

Figure 5.1 shows the relation between length of the sternal portion of the human pectoralis major and tension in a voluntary maximal contraction. The experiment was done with a cineplastic amputee, whose muscle contained a skin-lined tunnel through the distal end, which had been freed from its distal attachment. The lower curve shows the "passive" tension, i.e., the relation between length and tension in the quiescent muscle. It is evident that at an intermediate length, approximately corresponding to the length at which passive tension just begins, the generated ("developed") tension

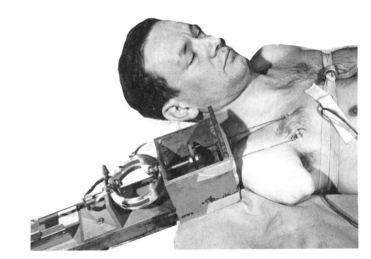

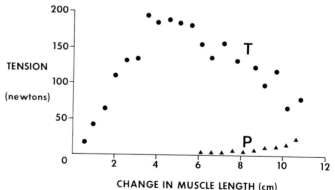

Figure 5.1. Isometric length–tension relationship as recorded from pectoralis major muscle in cineplastic amputee. *T*, total tension; *P*, passive tension. (Reproduced, with permission, from Ralston, H. J., Inman, V. T., Strait, L. A., and Shaffrath, M. D. Mechanics of human isolated voluntary muscle. *Am. J. Physiol.* 151:612, 1947.)

is at a maximum, falling off rapidly at lesser and greater lengths. On the basis of experiments done on isolated muscle fibers of the frog, it has been shown that the curve of generated tension may be adequately explained by the sliding filament mechanism of muscle contraction, mentioned previously. The "total" tension observed in an active muscle is the sum of the generated and the passive tensions. In the case of the pectoralis muscle in Figure 5.1, the passive tension is so low that the total tension is virtually identical with the generated tension.

In general, the length of muscle fibers decreases and the content of noncontractile connective tissue increases as muscles are located more distally in the limb. This is evident in isometric length–tension diagrams in cineplastic amputees. In the biceps brachii (Fig. 5.2), the total excursion is approximately three-quarters that of the pectoralis, and the increasing passive tension curve obscures the rapid decrease in developed tension be-

yond the rest length of the muscle. These effects are even more marked in the amputee whose tunnel was created through the superficial wrist flexor mass (Fig. 5.3). Here, the excursion was only 16 mm and the passive tension curve rose abruptly, modifying the total tension curve.

The tension that a muscle can generate depends on the cross-sectional area of the muscle. Table 5.1 shows the relation between maximal isometric tension and cross section in several muscles of the human cineplastic amputee (Ralston et al., 1949). Values for cross sections are taken from Weber (1851). According to Haxton (1944), maximal isometric tension in the human ankle flexors is of the order of 38 N/cm^2.

Figure 5.1 shows a record of the maximal isometric tension in the isolated pectoralis muscle of a human cineplastic amputee. The tension generated was approximately 16 N/cm^2.

Rest Length of a Muscle

In this book, the term "rest length" will refer to that length at which *passive* tension just begins to occur as an unstimulated (quiescent) muscle is stretched. The reader is warned that a variety of other terms ("optimum" length, "natural" length, "equilibrium" length, "slack" length) are used in the literature of physiology, and it is incumbent on the reader to make sure what the given author means by the term he uses. Particularly confusing is the term "natural" length, which usually

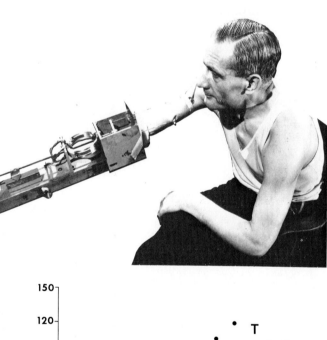

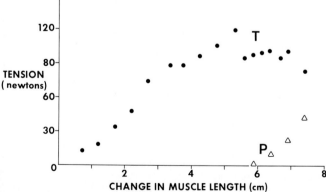

Figure 5.2. Isometric length–tension relationship as recorded from biceps brachii in cineplastic amputee. *T*, total tension; *P*, passive tension. (Reproduced, with permission, from Ralston et al. *Am. J. Physiol.* 151:612, 1947.)

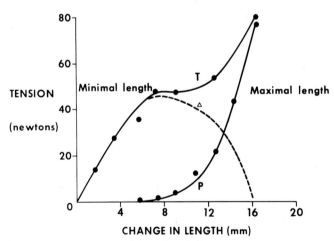

Figure 5.3. Isometric length–tension relationship in amputee whose skin tunnel was created through the superficial wrist flexor muscles in the forearm. Note that the excursion of the muscle is only 1.6 cm. The total tension curve (*T*) increases progressively with elongation of the muscle. This is due to the abrupt rise in the passive tension curve (*P*). If the passive tension curve is subtracted from the total tension curve the result is the broken curve (Δ), the contribution of the contractile elements, which rapidly decreases beyond the rest length of the muscle. (Reproduced, with permission, from Ralston et al. *Am. J. Physiol.* 151:612, 1947.)

Source: Ralston et al., 1949.

Table 5.1
Maximal generated tension in human isolated muscle

Muscle	Cross section (cm²)	Maximal tension (N)	Tension/cm² (N/cm²)
Pectoralis	12.8	205	16
Biceps brachii	9.15	214	23
Triceps brachii	15.98	205	13

means the *greatest* length that a muscle can attain in the intact body. Why this length is any more natural than any other length is not clear.

As a general rule, our rest length will not differ very much from the length at which a muscle develops greatest tension in an isometric contraction.

Use of Stretch in the Intact Body

A noncontractile structure, such as the iliotibial tract, may be used in the body to support load, without the need for metabolic energy expenditure. Stretch of the quiescent muscle may be used as a source of nonmetabolic force, but for many muscles of a relatively extensible type, such force would not be of any great usefulness. Only in the case of muscles of relatively low extensibility would a passive force of this type contribute very much to a force requirement. Stretch of an active muscle may produce large and useful forces. An example of such a force is that produced in the hamstrings during deceleration of the leg at the termination of its swing phase.

An interesting example of the effect of stretch is provided by the studies of Cavagna et al. (1968) and Cavagna (1973), who have shown that immediately after stretch a contracted muscle may contract with a greater output of mechanical energy than a muscle that contracts without immediately previous stretch, even though the muscle in both cases begins final contraction at the same length.

This effect of immediately prior stretch may play a role in the action of muscles during walking, because those muscles that initiate motion, e.g., the calf muscles, appear to be momentarily stretched just before contraction.

Excursion of Muscle

By *excursion* is meant the change in length that a muscle may undergo. In the intact body, unlike the situation with the isolated muscle, the maximal shortening (or lengthening) is obviously limited by the skeletal attachments of the muscle. Several factors are involved in change of length:

Overall change of length is greater in a parallel-fibered muscle than in a pennate type.

Other things being equal, the longer a muscle, the greater the excursion possible. It is best to express the

excursion in terms of the muscle length. Thus, if a muscle with a maximal length of 20 cm can undergo a maximal change in length of 10 cm, the excursion would be expressed as 10/20, or 0.5 cm/cm, or 0.5 muscle length.

According to Haines (1934), the maximal excursion of straight-fibered muscles in the intact human body averages 57% of the maximal extended length.

In the body, unlike the situation in maximally (electrically) stimulated isolated muscle, the same excursion may occur with widely different loads, simply by the use of a variable number and variable firing rates of motor units, and total duration of excitation.

However, in the cineplastic, normally innervated human muscle, when a maximal effort is made, the length-tension relationship becomes the important factor. As the load is increased the amount of shortening, from a given initial length, that the muscle can achieve is less. This is shown for the biceps brachii in Figure 5.4.

Speed of Shortening

As in the case of muscle excursion, speed depends on muscle fiber arrangement, muscle length, and load. It is best to express speed in terms of muscle length, if this is known. Thus, if a muscle has a maximal length of 20 cm and can shorten with a maximal speed of 140 cm/sec, its speed may be expressed as 140/20 or 7 cm/sec/cm, or 7 muscle lengths/sec. Table 5.2 shows maximal speeds of shortening for several isolated muscles in the human cineplastic amputee (Ralston et al., 1949).

As in the case of excursion in the intact body, the same speed of shortening may occur with different loads, by simply adjusting the number and firing rate of motor units. In the isolated muscle, maximally (electrically) stimulated, the speed becomes lower as load is increased.

Power

The power generated by a muscle is equal to the load lifted times the speed at which the load is being lifted. Figure 5.5 shows the relation between maximal speed of shortening and load in the isolated pectoralis muscle of the human cineplastic amputee. Maximal power occurred when a load of 82 N was being lifted at a speed of 42 cm/sec, corresponding to 34.5 W, or about 0.25 hp/kg of muscle. Value for weight of muscle is taken from Weber (1851). This figure agrees well with figures in the literature for striated muscle (see, for example, Wilkie, 1960).

Positive versus Negative Work During Walking

An example of positive work occurs in the increase in value of the "body total" in Figure 3.10 (Chapter 3)

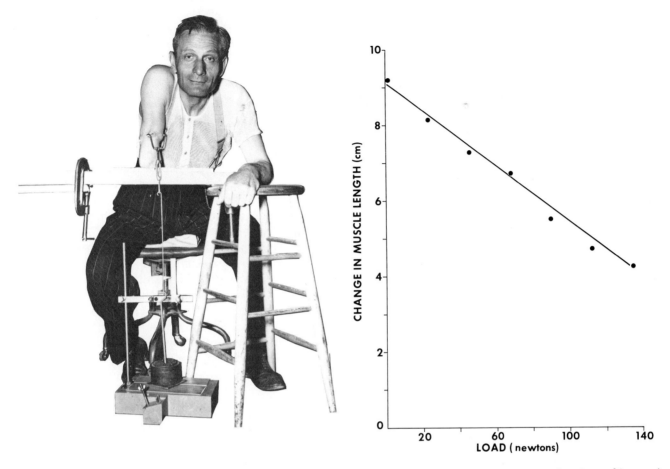

Figure 5.4. Ability of a muscle (biceps brachii) to shorten from a given initial length under successive applications of increasing loads.

and negative work in the corresponding decrease in body total during the rest of the step. A number of studies (Abbott et al., 1952; Asmussen, 1953; Margaria, 1968) have shown that the efficiency of negative work is much higher (threefold to ninefold) than positive work. Electromyographic studies show that the electrical activity of muscle is much lower during a lengthening contraction, for a given load, indicating that less motor unit activity is needed. This would account for the lower metabolic cost of negative work. It is clear that negative work plays an important part in normal level walking.

Compensatory Skeletal Mechanisms

Because of deficiencies in the ability of muscle to produce the same degree of maximal tension at varying lengths, certain compensatory mechanisms have been provided in the skeleton to offset these deficiencies. Three such mechanisms can be readily identified: muscles acting over two or more joints (multiple joint muscles), variations in the lengths in the effective lever arms in single joint muscles, and a special mechanism in the shoulder joint, consisting of rotation of the scapula on

Table 5.2
Free contractions in human muscles, starting at near rest length

Muscle	Maximal speed (cm/sec)	Maximal excursion (cm)	Minimal time for total shortening (sec)
Pectoralis	145	8.7	0.10
Biceps brachii	92.5	8.4	0.17
Triceps brachii	55	4.0	0.10

Source: Ralston et al., 1949.

the thoracic cage with elevation of the arm, which is necessary to prevent undue shortening of the deltoid.

Multiple Joint Muscles

Muscles that pass over two or more joints are in a favorable position in that they can be maintained at or near their rest length. By simultaneous and related movement of the joints over which such a muscle acts, the origin and insertion of the muscle can be kept at a relatively constant distance from one another. This is shown in the arrangement of the muscles of the hand and forearm (Fig. 5.6). A small object is grasped firmly, with the wrist extending and maintaining the length of the flexor muscles, whereas if a larger object is grasped

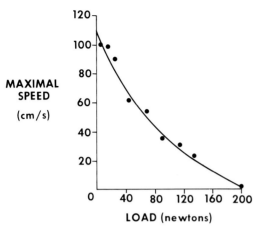

MAXIMAL SPEED (cm/s)

LOAD (newtons)

Figure 5.5. Speed of shortening versus load. The plotted values were obtained from a cineplastic amputee in whom a skin-lined tunnel was placed in the right pectoralis major muscle. Note that the speed of shortening decreased with increasing load. (Reproduced, with permission, from Ralston, H. J., Polissar, M. J., Inman, V. T., Close, J. R., and Feinstein, B. Dynamic features of human isolated voluntary muscle in isometric and free contractions. *J. Appl. Physiol.* 1:526, 1949.)

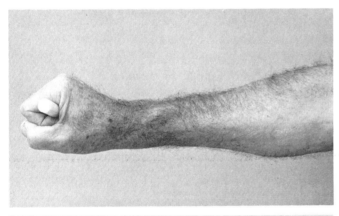

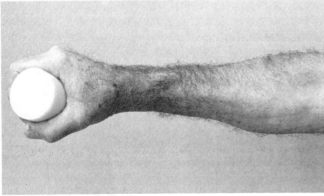

Figure 5.6. Position of wrist when objects of varying size are firmly grasped. Note that when a smaller object is grasped the wrist is extended to a greater extent than when a larger object is grasped. The position of the wrist automatically and unconsciously adjusts to maintain the flexor muscles at their rest length to develop maximal tension.

the wrist is more flexed, permitting the entire muscle mass to move toward the hand and maintain the rest length of the flexor muscles. If this mechanism did not function, the power of grasp would decrease with shortening of the muscles. The relationship between grip strength and wrist position is seen in Figure 5.7.

The hamstrings are a particularly well-known group of muscles that act over two joints, the hip and the knee. They are relatively short-fibered muscles, but related flexion of the hip and knee causes the entire muscle mass to be displaced while the individual muscles are kept close to their rest lengths. This is easily demonstrated by measuring the moments about the knee joint created by the hamstrings while the hip remains in extension. It is noted that the moment rapidly decreases as the knee is flexed (Fig. 5.8). Indeed, if one simply flexes the knee while leaning backward to produce extension of the hip joint, the degree of knee flexion is decreased and one is likely to suffer a severe cramp in the hamstring muscles. Conversely, if the knee flexion is accompanied by hip flexion the flexion moment remains relatively constant (Fig. 5.9).

An interesting situation exists in the hind leg of the frog, in which the principal muscles acting on the knee, ankle, and foot pass over two or more joints (Fig. 5.10). Lombard (1903) spent several years studying this special arrangement and puzzling over the fact that the action of such muscles produced opposite effects on the more

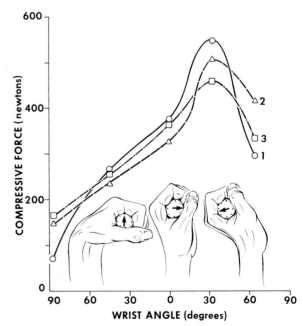

Figure 5.7. Strength of grasp with varying positions of wrist. A dynamometer measures the maximal strength of grasp. Note that with increasing flexion the strength of grasp decreases. With marked extension there is also a decrease in strength. Maximal strength of grasp is only achieved when the flexor muscles are at their rest length.

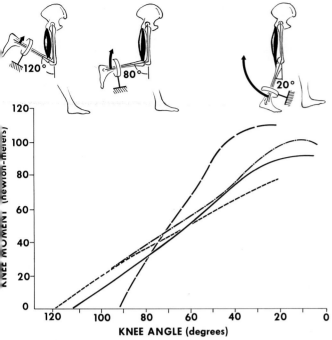

Figure 5.8. Knee moment versus angle of knee flexion as measured in four subjects. The hip is maintained in extension while the knee moment is measured during maximal effort. Note that the muscles shorten with knee flexion, with subsequent decrease in tension.

proximal joint that the muscle passes over, compared with the more distal joint. For example, the gastrocnemius caused flexion of the knee and extension of the ankle and foot, while the quadriceps produced flexion of the hip and extension of the knee. Lombard constructed a model patterned after his dissections of the hind leg of the frog in which the two joint muscles were represented by inextensible cords. He demonstrated that flexion of the hip caused simultaneous flexion of the knee, ankle, and foot, while extension of the hip produced simultaneous extension of the knee, ankle, and foot (see Fig. 5.10). This observable phenomenon was correctly explained by Lombard as due to changes in effective lever arms when all the muscles are activated; in this case, the motion that occurs will be "in the direction of the greatest leverage." Lombard left unanswered the crucial questions of why there exist, in the frog, muscles that pass over two or more joints, and why movements of simultaneous flexion and extension of the knee, ankle, and foot are possible with replacement of muscles with inelastic cords. He demonstrated that the muscles remain at approximately the same lengths during the entire motion of flexion and extension. This seems to be the critical factor and is readily explained if one considers the length–tension relationship of striated muscle. By preventing undue shortening of the muscles during the extension, the muscles can

continue to exert their maximal tension during the initiation of the leap.

Changing the Effective Lever Arm in Single Joint Muscles

In muscles whose skeletal attachments are on adjacent bones and, therefore, can act only over a single joint, a decreasing moment should be evident as the muscle shortens. This would be expected from the length–tension relationships as demonstrated in isolated muscles (see previous section). In general, this is found to be true, but in some joints, a partial compensatory mechanism exists that consists in an increasing effective lever arm as the muscle shortens and becomes weaker. This mechanism is available in the body for the movement of flexion in joints of both the upper and lower limbs, although complete compensation is never achieved (Fig. 5.11). In the extension mechanisms of the body, effective skeletal lever arms show minimal change. Therefore, plotting of measurements of maximal moments for extension will give curves that resemble the pure length–tension curves of isolated muscles.

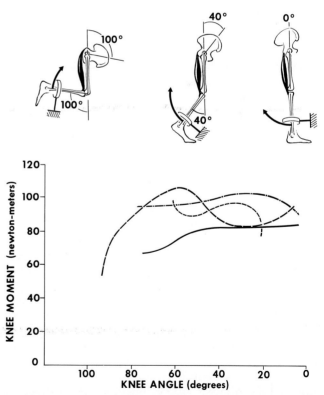

Figure 5.9. Knee moment versus angle of knee flexion in same subjects as in Figure 5.8. The hip is flexed simultaneously with knee flexion, thus maintaining a constant muscle length. Note that the moment at the knee remains relatively constant during knee flexion.

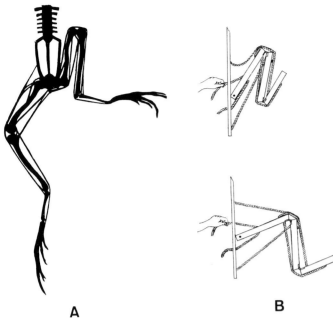

Figure 5.10. Reproductions of drawings from Lombard (1903). *A,* Diagrammatic representation of arrangement of muscles in hind limb of frog. Note that all major muscles extend over two or more joints. *B,* Model constructed with inelastic cords replacing major muscles. Note that flexion and extension of the hip produce simultaneous flexion and extension of the knee and ankle.

Abduction of the Shoulder

The importance of preventing too great an amount of shortening in muscle to maintain strength is exemplified in the elevation of the arm at the shoulder. The deltoid acts over a single joint and is the principal muscle involved. To compensate for the decreasing strength with shortening, the scapula rotates on the thorax, thus moving the origin of the deltoid away from its insertion on the humerus as the arm is raised. If the scapula is fixed to the thoracic cage, elevation of the arm is accomplished with excessive shortening of the deltoid, which becomes progressively weaker (Fig. 5.12).

Moments About the Major Joints of the Lower Limb

It is important for two reasons to study the maximal moments that can be generated about the major joints of the lower limb. First, the moments demonstrate in the intact body the effect of the length–tension relationship in muscle and the use of the available compensatory skeletal mechanisms. Second, they provide an understanding of why certain positions of the joint are assumed in daily activities: these positions are such that maximal moments are utilized.

The following data were obtained on young male adults. Although few in number, the observations are

consistent and demonstrate the variations in the moments with different positions of the joint.

Measurements of Moments about Joints

Hip Flexors

Measurements of the maximal hip moment during flexion reveal that progressive flexion is accompanied by a decrease in the moment. Figure 5.13 shows a lack of compensation for the decrease in tension with shortening of the muscles. The maximal moment is developed at approximately 40° from the position of full extension. Apparently the increasing effective lever arm provided by flexion of the hip joint is inadequate to compensate for the decreasing tension of the flexor muscles.

Hip Extensors

During extension of the hip, the maximal moment developed is at around 70° of flexion and falls off progressively (Fig. 5.14). The values presented in Figure 5.14 were obtained with the knee flexed well beyond 90°. This prevented the hamstrings from contributing to the force of hip extension. Waters et al. (1974) report that the extension forces in the hip are increased by approximately 30% with the knee held in extension. The shapes of the curves, however, were the same with or without the added contribution of the hamstring muscles.

During hyperextension, the moment becomes insignificant. Again the skeletal compensatory mechanism

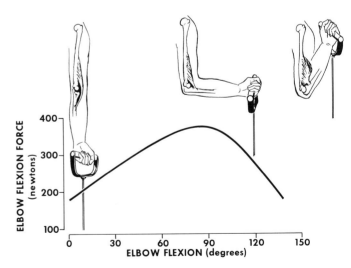

Figure 5.11. Maximal muscle forces versus degree of flexion. Note that the effective lever arm as measured from the center of the elbow joint to the insertion of the flexor muscles increases with flexion. However, the increasing lever arm fails to compensate completely for the decreasing strength of the muscle as it shortens. (Redrawn, with permission, from Williams, M., and Stutzman, L. Strength variation through the range of joint motion. *Phys. Ther. Rev.* 39:145, 1959)

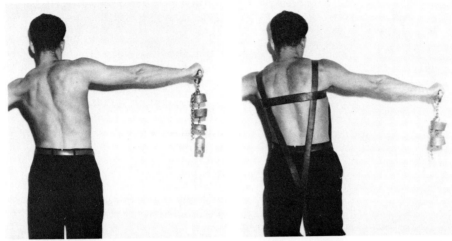

Figure 5.12. Effect of scapular fixation. The scapula normally rotates progressively on the thorax with elevation of the arm. This maintains the length of the deltoid muscle. If the scapular rotation is suppressed by straps, the strength of the deltoid is almost halved when the arm is elevated 90°. (Reproduced, with permission, from Inman, V. T., Saunders, J. B. deC. M., and Abbott, L. C. Observations on the function of the shoulder joint. *J. Bone Joint Surg.* 26:1, 1944.)

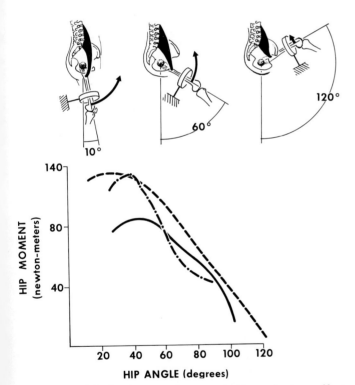

Figure 5.13. Maximal moments generated by voluntary effort with changing angle of hip flexion (three subjects). Note the rapid fall in the magnitude of the moments due to shortening of the flexor muscles.

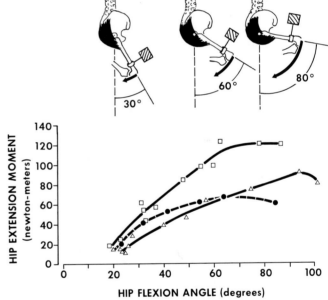

Figure 5.14. Maximal moments generated by voluntary effort with changing angle of hip extension (three subjects). Note the rapid fall in magnitude of the moments due to shortening of the extensor muscles.

of changing effective lever arms is inadequate to compensate for the decreasing tension with shortening of the extensor muscles.

A review of the data in the previous graphs of flexor and extensor moments indicates that, for effective use of the muscles, flexion should be not greater than 40–60° and extension should be not more than 0–20° of flexion. It will be pointed out later (Phasic Action of Muscles) that during walking, the hip joint does not exceed these maximal values of flexion and extension.

Hip Abductors

The investigations of maximal moments developed on abduction of the hip were carried out on above-knee amputees (Fig. 5.15). There is a progressive and almost linear decrease in the moment as the hip is abducted.

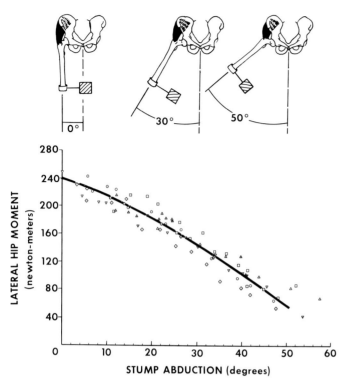

Figure 5.15. Hip moment versus hip abduction. Data plotted for maximal strength of hip abduction in three above-knee amputees. Note the rapid decrease in hip moment due to muscle shortening with progressive abduction.

There seems to be little or no skeletal compensatory mechanism for changing the effective lever arm to compensate for the decrease in tension with shortening of the abductor muscles. To use the maximal moment of the abductors to stabilize the hip joint during walking the pelvis is dropped on the non-weight-bearing side, while adduction of the femur during stance phase elongates the abductor muscles (see Chapter 1). Furthermore, the iliotibial tract is a noncontractile structure, which acts to spare the abductors (Inman, 1947).

Knee Flexion

Knee flexion is the principal action of the hamstrings, which are two joint muscles (review Figs. 5.8 and 5.9). Complete compensation for the decreasing tension occurs, as seen in the length–tension diagram, because of the interrelation of hip with knee flexion, which keeps the knee moment relatively constant.

However, should the hip remain in extension during flexion of the knee produced by contraction of the hamstrings, a rapid fall-off in the size of the moment occurs.

Knee Extensors

Essentially, the quadriceps can be regarded as a single joint muscle, and the magnitude of the extensor moment

resembles very closely the length–tension diagram of the isolated muscle (Fig. 5.16). It should be noted that with marked flexion or extension the forces fall rapidly from the maximum of around 50° of flexion.

Although there is some evidence that an attempt is made to compensate for the length–tension relationship in the quadriceps muscle by employing a patellar mechanism, this is far from optimal. It is interesting to note that the average riser in a staircase has a height of around 18–19 cm, and when a person goes upstairs the knee is flexed to approximately 60° (Fig. 5.17). Reference to the data plotted in Figure 5.16 will show that the maximal moment is developed in this region. It is a common experience that if one encounters a higher step, requiring greater knee flexion, one immediately appreciates the increased effort that is required to climb it.

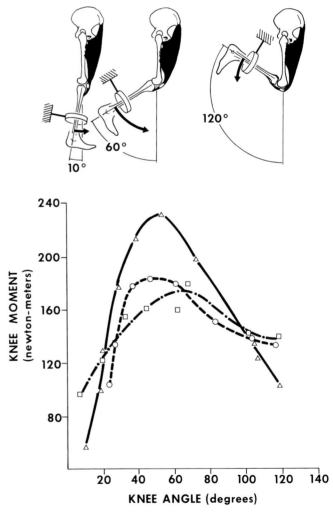

Figure 5.16. Maximal extensile moments generated by quadriceps through voluntary effort with changes in knee angle (three subjects). Note that the maximal moment is attained when the knee is flexed about 50°.

Figure 5.17. Stair-climbing. Note that the height of the riser in usual stairs is such that the knee is flexed about 60°.

A number of investigators have reported studies relating knee angle to the maximal force of extension of the knee. Generally, two methods of measurement have been employed, leg press (Hugh-Jones, 1947; Lindeburg, 1964; Berger, 1966; Linford and Rarick, 1968) or the maximal height achieved in a vertical jump (Martin and Stull, 1969). In general, the results are similar in that the maximal values of force achieved were at a knee angle of between 40° and 65° of flexion.

Ankle Plantar Flexors

Ankle plantar flexion is effected by several muscles located on the dorsal and lateral aspects of the leg. The total weight of all these muscles is equally distributed between the gastrocnemius (with the plantaris), the soleus, and the combined weight of the tibialis posterior, the peroneals, and the long toe flexors (Weber, 1851). The principal plantar flexors are obviously the muscles that constitute the triceps surae (gastrocnemius and

soleus), whose total weight is twice that of all the remaining muscles. It should be recalled that the gastrocnemius is a two joint muscle arising from the posterior surface of the femoral condyles. The soleus is a single joint muscle acting only on the ankle joint. The remaining muscles, while also acting on parts of the skeleton located distal to the ankle, may reasonably be considered single joint muscles when acting solely as ankle plantar flexors.

Figure 5.18 is a graph of a single person in whom maximal moments of ankle plantar flexion were measured with the knee extended and with the knee flexed to 90°. Note that the curves have a similar shape and a maximal value at approximately 10° of plantar flexion. The values of the moments fall rapidly with further plantar flexion or dorsiflexion of the ankle. There is little evidence of a compensatory skeletal mechanism, and the shape of the curves resembles a length–tension diagram of an isolated skeletal muscle. The effect of knee flexion on lowering the total value of the moment is clearly shown. The result of knee flexion is to shorten the gastrocnemius so that it can no longer exert its maximal tension. The soleus and the remaining muscles are unaffected. Because these muscles constitute approximately two-thirds of the muscle mass available for ankle plantar flexion, it may be assumed that the total moment is decreased relatively little.

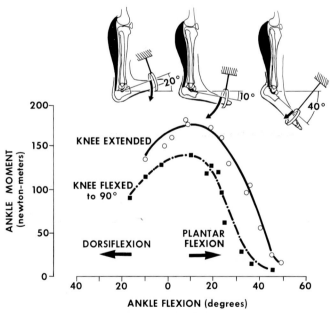

Figure 5.18. Maximal plantar flexion moments generated by voluntary effort with changes in ankle angle. Note that the maximal moment occurs when the ankle is approximately in a midposition between plantar flexion and dorsiflexion. No compensatory skeletal mechanism seems to be operating. The moment curves resemble the length–tension curves of isolated skeletal muscle.

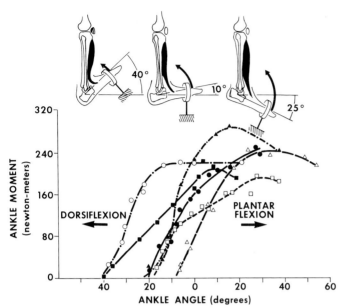

Figure 5.19. Maximal dorsiflexion moments generated by voluntary effort of the ankle dorsiflexors with changes in ankle angle (six subjects). Note that the maximal moment is achieved when the ankle is in a position of plantar flexion of approximately 25°.

Ankle Dorsiflexors

There seems to be little or no compensatory mechanism available for the ankle dorsiflexors; the curves of the moment of dorsiflexion reveal a shape that closely and directly approximates the length–tension relationships of the isolated muscles. The maximal moment is developed at around 25° of plantar flexion, and the moments decrease with increasing dorsiflexion (Fig. 5.19).

Phasic Action of Muscles

In earlier times, the action of muscles could only be studied by observation and palpation, or inferred by consideration of their points of origin and insertion. With the advent of electromyography, a powerful new tool for muscle study was made available, which uses the electrical activity of muscle as an index of contractile activity. For a general discussion of electromyography, see Basmajian (1978); Joseph (1960) has made important contributions to the knowledge of man's posture as well as movement. Also to be mentioned is the little book, "How Man Moves" (Carlsöö, 1972), which provides a lucid account of basic elements of human walking, including the electromyography of the muscles employed.

In the discussion that follows, it will be necessary to use the terms *direct* and *integrated* electromyogram (EMG). The wave form of *directly* recorded electrical potentials of muscle is ordinarily quite complex. It is

inaccurate simply to compare peak-to-peak amplitudes, and it is difficult to make any other comparisons. For this reason, planimetric, rectified–filtered, and electronically integrated methods have been used in descriptions of the electrical activity of muscle. In the present discussion, these last-mentioned methods will be designated *integrated*.

Two problems arise when the phasic activity of muscles during walking is considered. The first deals with the methods of determining the precise interval of time that a muscle is active during a single stride, and the second has to do with the manner in which the information so gathered may be clearly presented and readily related to the position and movement of the skeletal parts. These problems will be discussed in sequence.

Time Relations Between EMG and Muscle Contraction

Figure 5.20 shows the time relation between the beginning of electrical activity (direct EMG) and the onset of *knee extension*, as observed in the knee jerk of a normal human subject. There is a small lag, of the order of 30 msec, between the EMG and the actual movement of the limb. The lag between the EMG and the *contraction* of the quadriceps muscle is smaller. Many such studies show that the *onset of electrical activity* may be used to define, with sufficient accuracy, the time of *onset of the muscle contraction*.

The situation with respect to the time of *cessation of electrical activity*, in relation to the time of *cessation of contractile activity*, is not so simple. The studies of

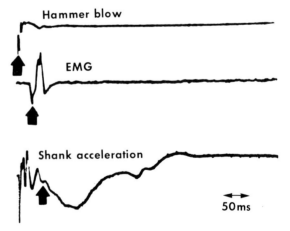

Figure 5.20. Time relationships between EMG and shank acceleration in human knee jerk. Note the small delay between the EMG and the beginning of movement and the continuation of movement after cessation of the EMG. (Adapted, with permission, from Ralston, H. J., Todd, F. N., and Inman, V. T. Comparison of electrical activity and duration of tension in the human rectus femoris muscle. *Electromyog. Clin. Neurophysiol.* 16:271, 1976.)

Cooper and Eccles (1930), Inman et al. (1952), Lestienne and Bouisset (1968), and Ahlgren and Öwall (1970), among others, have shown that muscle contraction does not "cut off" promptly upon cessation of electrical activity, because of the fact that the chemical contractile machinery of muscle takes time to fully relax, once it has been activated.

Figure 5.21 shows the lag between the end of the direct EMG and cessation of tension in the quadriceps of a normal human subject, amounting to 250 msec. Such a lag may amount to as much as 300 msec in certain types of muscle activity. Consequently, it is unsafe to identify the total *duration of electrical activity* with the total *duration of contractile activity*, at least within the limits stated previously.

Isometric Contraction of Muscle

Bayer and Flechtenmacher (1950) seem to have been the first to describe clearly the parallelism between tension of muscle and amplitude of the EMG in a muscle voluntarily contracted at a fixed length (isometric contraction). Inman et al. (1952) and Lippold (1952) made similar observations, using integrated EMGs. Figure 5.22 shows such a relationship in the isolated biceps brachii of a human cineplastic amputee and in the tibialis anterior of a normal human subject.

A Note on EMGs During Isotonic Contraction

Isometric contraction has been emphasized previously in relation to use of EMGs as an index of muscle tension. Although some authors (for example, Bigland and Lippold, 1954) have found linear relations between the integrated EMG and tension during shortening and lengthening of active muscle, under restricted conditions, it is dangerous to assume such relations if there has been considerable change in muscle length during recording of the EMG. Inman et al. (1952) showed that

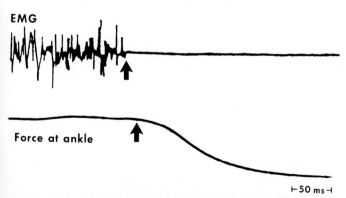

Figure 5.21. Lag between end of direct EMG (*top trace*) and cessation of tension (*bottom trace*) in normal human quadriceps. The subject pressed against a bar and then relaxed as quickly as possible. (Adapted, with permission, from Ralston et al. *Electromyog. Clin. Neurophysiol.* 16:271, 1976.)

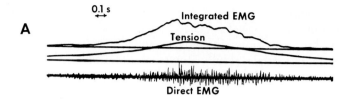

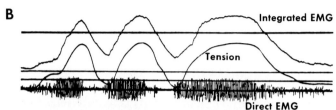

Figure 5.22. Rough parallelism between direct and integrated EMG and tension. *A*, Recordings made during graduated isometric contraction in amputee provided with cineplastic tunnel in right biceps brachii. Note the slight delay between maximal EMG and maximal tension. *B*, Isometric tension; direct and integrated EMG of tibialis anterior muscle of normal subject. The subject was asked to rapidly and repetitively dorsiflex his ankle maximally against a fixed resistance. Note the parallelism between the EMG and tension when the muscle contracts isometrically. (Reproduced, with permission, from Inman, V. T., Ralston, H. J., Saunders, J. B. deC. M., Feinstein, B., and Wright, E. W., Jr. Relation of human electromyogram to muscular tension. *Electroenceph. Clin. Neurophysiol.* 4:187, 1952.)

in the human cineplastic amputee the parallelism between the integrated EMG and muscle tension no longer obtained if muscle length changed appreciably. In fact, the EMG and tension could vary in opposite directions under such conditions. Close et al. (1960) showed a similar phenomenon in the intact human soleus. Ahlgren and Öwall (1970) found a breakdown in parallelism between the EMG and tension in muscles of mastication during isotonic contraction. In normal walking, the duration of a muscle contraction may be, for example, only 0.2 sec, and the change in length of the muscle very slight. For a firing rate of motor neurons of, for instance, 20/sec, this would only allow four action potentials per motor unit (Ralston and Libet, 1953). Each motor unit, therefore, may be considered to be in a brief partial tetanus under nearly isometric conditions. Hence, this may account for the fact that the curves of calculated moments about the major articulations and the EMGs of the muscles producing these moments are similar.

The muscles employed in walking are used both to initiate movement and to decelerate or stop movement. During a muscle's activity it may do work in the ordinary physical sense ("positive" work), or may resist motion by actively generating a resisting force against a force tending to stretch it. If a muscle is actually stretched while it is actively developing contractile tension, it is said to be engaging in a "lengthening contraction," and work is being done *upon* the muscle, rather than *by* the muscle (so-called "negative" work).

In both situations, the muscles must be activated and action potentials result. However, the EMG in itself does not reveal whether the muscle is doing positive work or is having work done on it. It simply indicates contractile activity. Whether positive or negative work is being done must be deduced from a study of the curves of angular displacements and moments. Because the interval of time that the muscle is active is so short, as indicated above, agreement between moments, angular changes, and integrated EMG is surprisingly good, regardless of whether the muscle is doing positive work or is having work done on it. This is readily seen in the curves of calculated moments, angular changes, and EMGs plotted on the same time scale.

In Figures 5.23–5.26, the angular changes and calculated moments have been combined with average inte-

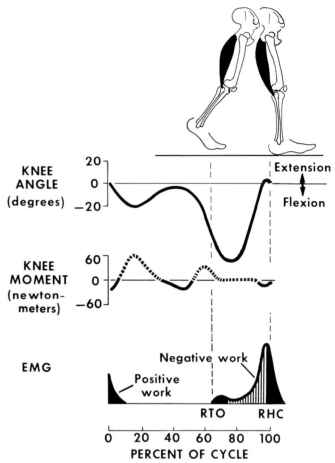

Figure 5.24. Knee motion, knee moment, and EMG of hamstring muscles plotted on same time scale. Note that the principal action of the hamstrings is to decelerate the leg at the termination of swing phase. While electrically active, the muscles are being elongated. After the foot is flat on the walking surface, they continue to show electrical activity, presumably to assist in hip extension.

grated EMG recordings for the major muscle groups acting on the knee and ankle. Reference to these figures reveals several items that require further discussion.

At a moderate speed of walking, the knee contributes a minimal amount of energy to the process of forward progression. The quadriceps acts primarily to prevent excessive knee flexion after heel strike, and the hamstrings act to decelerate the swinging leg at both the hip and knee joints. In both situations, the muscles are being elongated while electrically active. It should be noted that the quadriceps, which may initiate knee extension after maximal knee flexion of approximately 60°, is in a most favorable situation to act effectively. The muscle has been stretched before its contraction (see p. 92) and is at about its rest length, at which it can develop its maximal knee moment (see p. 91). Similarly, the hamstring muscles have been stretched before their action to assist hip extension after the foot is flat and stabilized

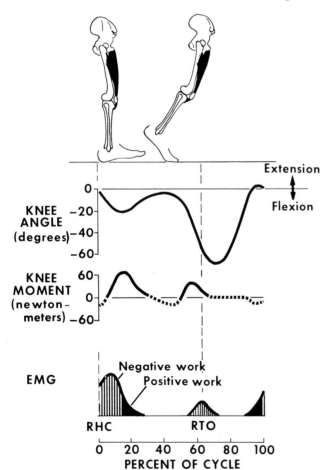

Figure 5.23. Knee motion, knee moment, and EMG of quadriceps muscle plotted on same time scale. Note that after heel strike, the knee joint flexes (see knee angle and knee moment). To prevent excessive knee flexion the quadriceps is activated but undergoes elongation. With increasing speed of walking, the quadriceps may be used to prevent excessive knee flexion and to initiate knee extension.

on the walking surface. At the ankle, the calf muscles are stretched by relative dorsiflexion of the ankle and extension of the knee, which elongates the gastrocnemius, after which these muscles are used to initiate and complete heel rise. This combination (see p. 102) and elongation beyond their rest lengths (see p. 92) places the muscles in a situation in which they can act most effectively.

Phasic Action of Muscles During Walking

Presentation of Data

In the following discussion, the EMG has been used as an index of beginning, duration, and cessation of

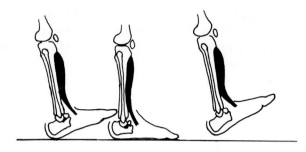

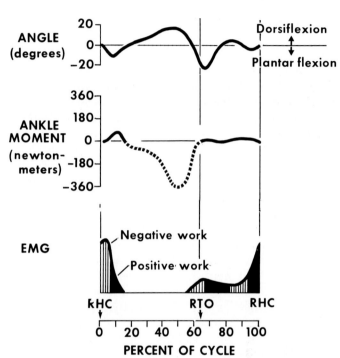

Figure 5.26. Ankle motion, ankle moment, and EMG of tibialis anterior muscle plotted on same time scale. Note that after heel strike the muscle, although electrically active, is being elongated. This prevents foot "slap." During the latter part of stance phase it is silent. At toe-off, the muscle contracts to provide toe clearance during the subsequent swing phase of the leg.

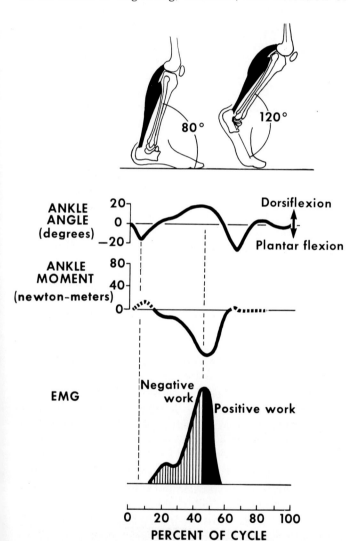

Figure 5.25. Ankle motion, ankle moment, and EMG of calf musculature plotted on same time scale. Note that the calf muscles begin to show electrical activity after the foot is flat after heel strike. However, ankle motion reveals that the foot is undergoing dorsiflexion; thus the muscles are being elongated. At the peak of the EMG, the heel begins to rise as the muscles start to plantar flex the ankle.

muscle activity (with due precautions as discussed previously), and it has been assumed that each contraction is a nearly isometric partial tetanus (or, *importantly*, a contraction involving only a small change in length).

To present, in a clear and readily understandable manner, the multiple factors that must be simultaneously considered becomes a problem. A method of pictorial presentation has been adopted, because such a presentation seems to be the only method that permits the inclusion of most of the factors. Wooden models of the pelvis and lower limbs were constructed and arranged in an expanded and sequential series depicting a single stride, although for continuity the first and last positions are identical. The various displacements of the components were arranged to approximate average values. The models were photographed to guarantee proper perspectives, and drawings were made from the photographs. Copies were made of this stride sequence, and, finally, a sketch of a single muscle group was superimposed on the drawing of each model in each sequence (Figs. 5.27–5.35).

Careful inspection of each sequence will reveal the following information. The single stride is composed of 12 different positions of the model in the series viewed from the side, and 8 different positions in the sequence viewed from the front. If an average comfortable walking speed on a straight and level surface of 5 km/h is assumed, the completion of a single stride as shown in the drawings would take slightly more than 1 sec. The interval of time between adjacent models would be about 0.09–0.14 sec. Thus, a time scale is contained in each sequence of drawings that will be employed in the further discussion of the phasic action of the muscles.

The electromyographic recordings that were employed to depict the phasic action of muscles during walking were obtained with use of both skin and inserted wire electrodes. The use of skin electrodes has definite limitations.

Because skin electrodes sample a large area of electrical activity, it is impossible to distinguish slight phasic differences that may occur in various parts of large muscles or to separate the possible differences that may occur in contiguous but anatomically distinct muscles. A more refined investigation requires the use of coaxial needle or fine wire electrodes embedded within the muscle and necessitates multiple simultaneous recordings. A comparison of the electromyographic recordings that used both skin and embedded wire electrodes in the muscles of the leg reveals these limitations.

In the larger muscles of the limb, the differences obtained when skin electrodes and embedded wire electrodes were used was so slight that it was possible to pictorially represent their phasic activity with sufficient accuracy. Differences were noted in the phasic activity of the semitendinosus, semimembranosus, and the two heads of the biceps femoris when each muscle was investigated separately with embedded wire electrodes. The differences of timing, however, were so small and their overall action was so similar that they were represented pictorially as a single muscle. The anterior tibial group of muscles demonstrates the errors that occur when skin electrodes are used. Electromyographic recordings made with skin electrodes over the anterior tibial muscles showed electrical activity during the entire stance and swing phases of walking. Embedded wire electrodes revealed a phasic difference between certain muscles. The tibialis anterior and the extensors of the toes (extensor digitorum longus, extensor hallucis

longus) showed similar phasic activity with maximal electrical activity immediately after heel strike. During the middle of stance phase, these muscles were electrically quiet but again became active after toe-off to dorsiflex the foot for toe clearance. The peroneal muscles, however, were active during midstance and demonstrated maximal activity with heel rise. Skin electrodes picked up the activity of all these muscles and thus recorded continuous electrical activity through the entire cycle of walking. The representation in Figure 5.35 depicts only the action of the tibialis anterior and extensor muscles. The peroneals are not shown but their phasic activity is the same as that of the calf muscles.

To pictorially represent the phasic action of the major muscle groups during walking, a color scheme has been employed. Within a single series, the particular model or models corresponding to the position and time of maximal electrical output (integrated EMG) of the particular muscle group, are blackened for emphasis. The individual muscle groups are colored. When the muscles are electrically quiet, they have been left uncolored. When they are electrically active, they have been colored red. The intensity of the color has been related to the curve of the integrated electrical output. When the electrical output is maximal, the color is most intense. At the half peak point of the integrated EMG curve, the color is one-half the intensity of the maximum, and when the electrical activity is just perceptible the muscles have been very lightly tinted. The intensity of the color applied to each muscle group therefore corresponds to points on the curve of the integrated electrical output (EMG).

When each sequence of drawings of the models is studied with some care, the following information may be obtained. The length of time that a muscle is active, during a single stride, can be estimated by recalling that the time interval between adjacent positions of the models is 0.09–0.14 sec. In addition, observation of the changing positions of the hip, knee, and ankle joints will make it possible to deduce whether the muscle is being elongated or is shortening at the time it is activated.

It seems appropriate at this point to call attention to certain generalities concerning the phasic action of the muscles of the lower limb that seem to be explained by Figures 5.27–5.36. Most major groups of muscles are active at or around the beginning and termination of the stance and swing phases of walking. These are periods of acceleration and deceleration of the leg and transference of body weight from one foot to the other. During midstance and midswing, most muscles (with two exceptions) are electrically quiet, although this is the period of greatest observable movement.

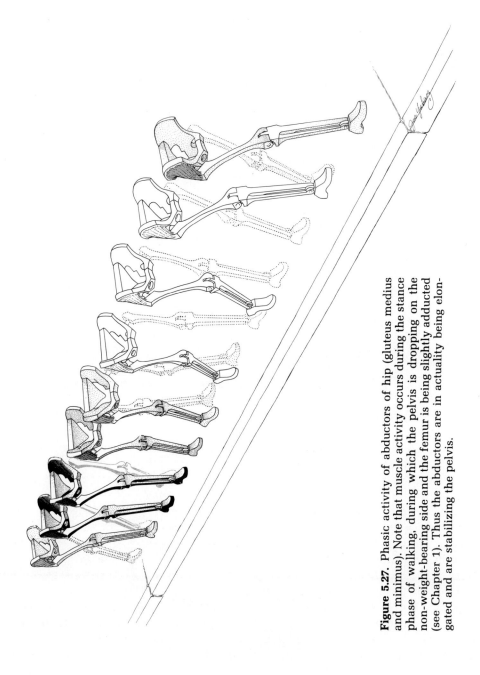

Figure 5.27. Phasic activity of abductors of hip (gluteus medius and minimus). Note that muscle activity occurs during the stance phase of walking, during which the pelvis is dropping on the non-weight-bearing side and the femur is being slightly adducted (see Chapter 1). Thus the abductors are in actuality being elongated and are stabilizing the pelvis.

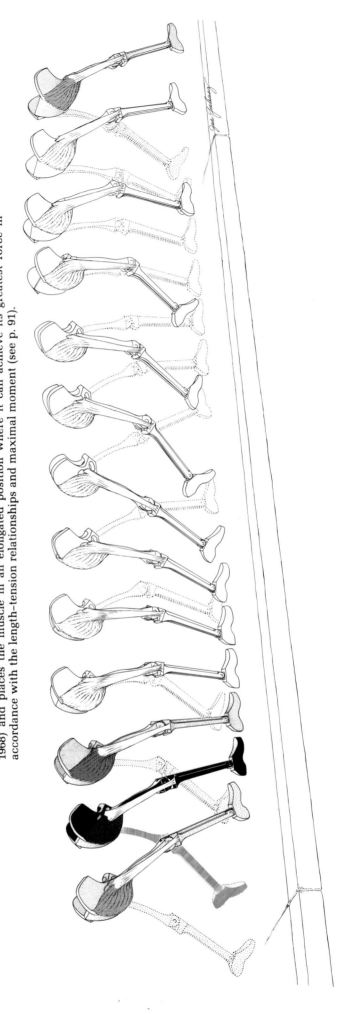

Figure 5.28. Phasic action of gluteus maximus. Note that the gluteus maximus is elongated before its maximal contraction, which occurs immediately after heel strike. This assures the development of maximal extensile force to the hip resulting from preliminary stretch (see p. 92 and Cavagna et al., 1968) and places the muscle in an elongated position where it can achieve its greatest force in accordance with the length–tension relationships and maximal moment (see p. 91).

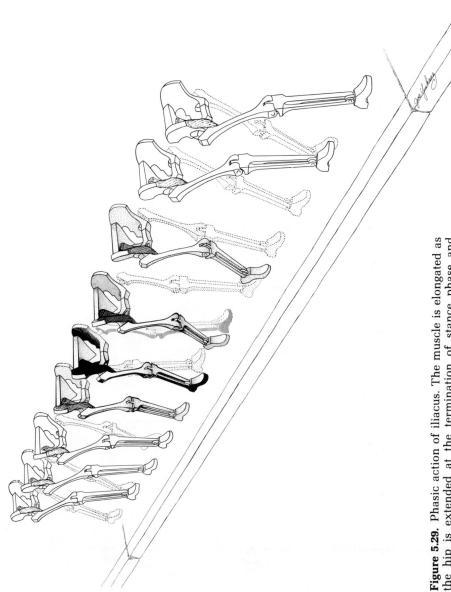

Figure 5.29. Phasic action of iliacus. The muscle is elongated as the hip is extended at the termination of stance phase and contracts at the beginning of swing phase, to initiate hip flexion.

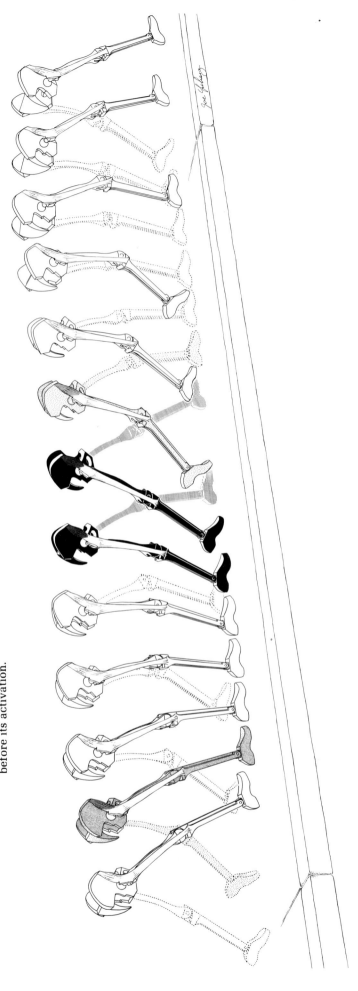

Figure 5.30. Phasic action of tensor fasciae latae. This muscle contracts twice during a single cycle. It contracts at the termination of swing phase and the beginning of stance, simultaneously with the contraction of the gluteus maximus. It is assumed that its contraction prevents the posterior displacement of the iliotibial tract, into which the greater portion of the gluteus maximus is inserted. The maximal EMG, however, is recorded at the beginning of swing phase and simultaneously with contraction of the iliopsoas, apparently to assist in hip flexion. Note that the muscle is elongated before its activation.

Figure 5.31. Phasic action of quadriceps. At moderate speeds of walking, the quadriceps is active only during the early part of stance phase. During this period the knee is undergoing flexion (see Chapter 1) and the quadriceps restricts this knee flexion. Although activated, the muscle is being elongated and therefore is having work done on it. At the moment the center of mass passes in front of the knee, its activity ceases. With higher speeds of walking, the muscle may contract to prevent abnormal knee flexion and initiate knee extension after toe-off.

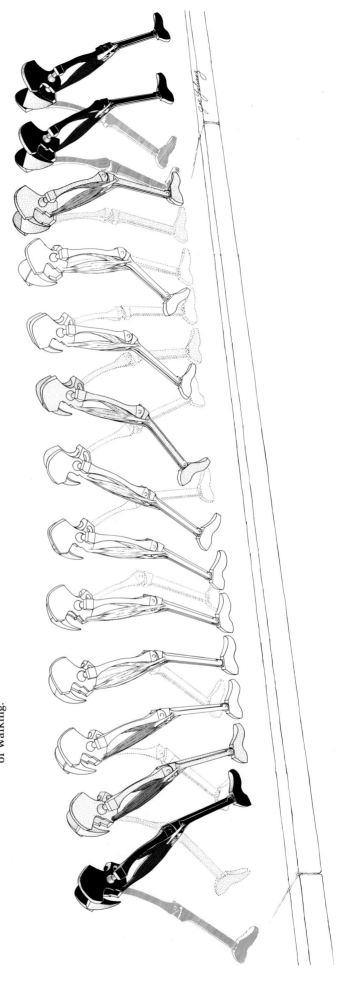

Figure 5.32. Phasic action of hamstrings. These muscles become active at the termination of swing phase. Note that they are being elongated as they act to decelerate the swinging leg. This is a very effective use of muscle (see p. 92). After they have been stretched they are in a condition to exert their maximal force (see Cavagna et al., 1968, and p. 102 for maximal moment). The hamstrings continue their activity into early stance to assist the gluteus maximus in extending the hip. The minimal activity at the time of toe-off to increase knee flexion is variable and is related to the speed of walking.

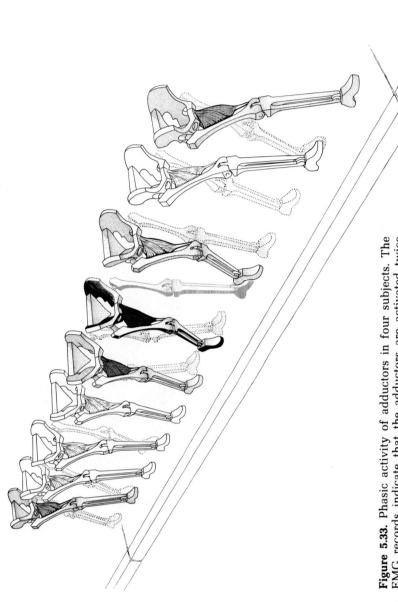

Figure 5.33. Phasic activity of adductors in four subjects. The EMG records indicate that the adductors are activated twice during each cycle—during the beginning and at the termination of swing phase. However, a review of our records reveals marked individual variations in the behavior of the adductors. For an intensive study of their activity, see Green and Morris (1970).

Figure 5.34. Phasic action of triceps surae. The action of the triceps surae is an excellent example of the manner in which muscles are utilized in walking to achieve maximal force with minimal expenditure of metabolic energy. The muscles are initially stretched (see Cavagna et al., 1968) before contraction occurs. The muscles are elongated slightly beyond their rest length, at which maximal tension can be developed (in accordance with the length–tension relationships), and the ankle is at approximately 0° of flexion, at which point the maximal moment has been shown to occur. The muscle contracts for a period only long enough to achieve heel rise (0.2 sec); the contraction is nearly isometric.

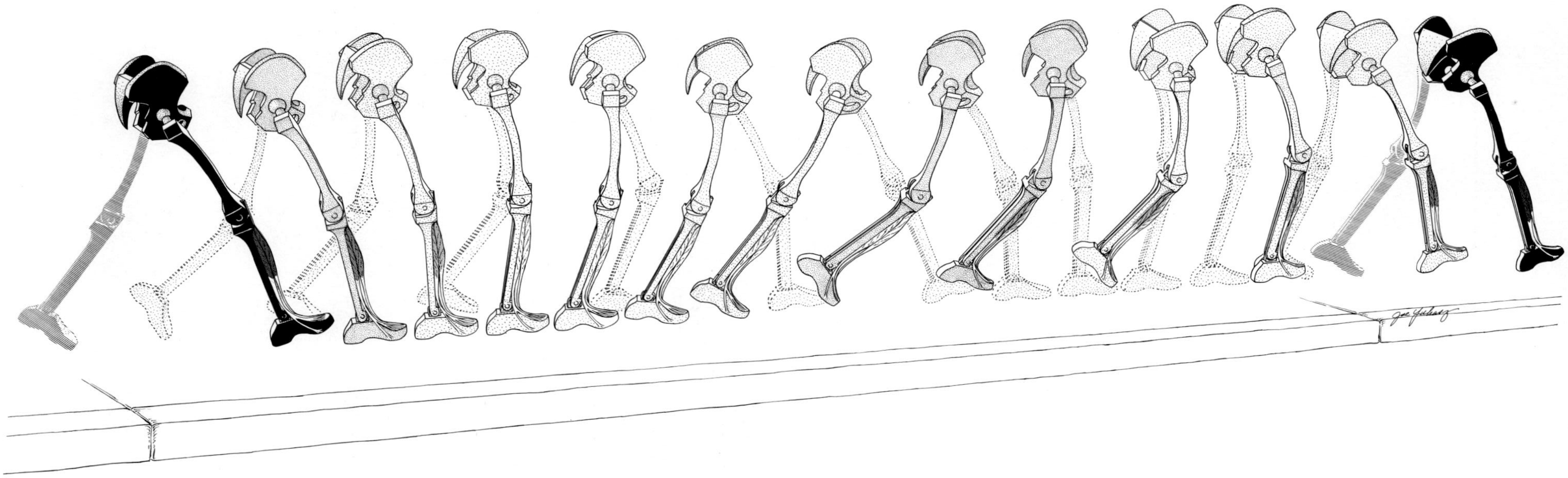

Figure 5.35. Phasic action of tibialis anterior and toe extensor muscles. These show similar phasic activity with maximal electrical activity immediately after heel strike. During the middle of stance, these muscles become electrically silent but again become active after toe-off to dorsiflex the foot. The peroneals are not shown, but their phasic activity is the same as that of the calf muscles.

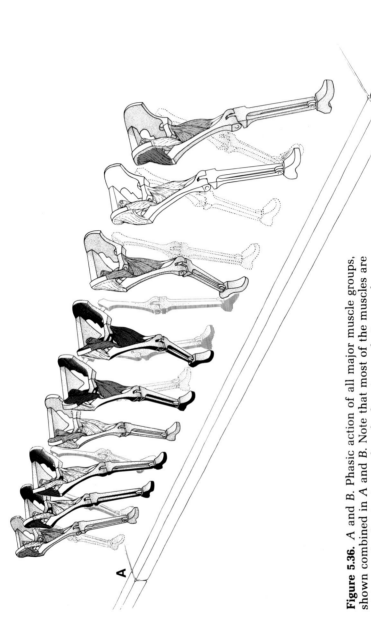

Figure 5.36. A and B. Phasic action of all major muscle groups, shown combined in A and B. Note that most of the muscles are active at the beginning and end of swing and stance phases. During midstance and midswing, there is minimal muscle activity although this is the period of maximal angular displacement. It seems that the principal action of the muscles is to accelerate and decelerate the angular motions of the legs.

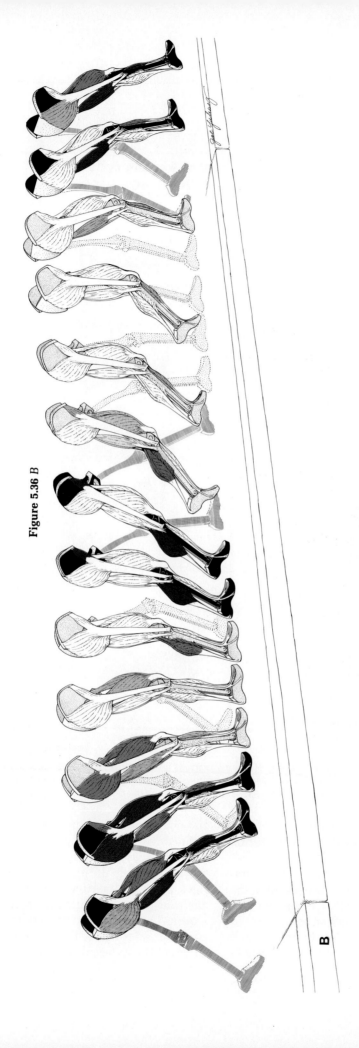

Figure 5.36 B

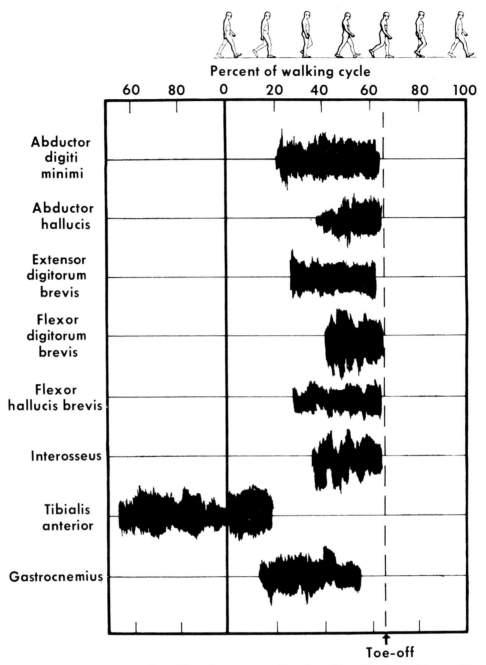

Figure 5.37. Electrical activity of intrinsic muscles of foot during normal level walking. Twelve subjects with superimposition of direct EMGs. Electrical activity of tibialis anterior and gastrocnemius shown for reference purposes. (Adapted, with permission, from Mann, R., and Inman, V. T. Phasic activity of intrinsic muscles of the foot. *J. Bone Joint Surg.* 46–A:469, 1964.)

Furthermore, inspection of the drawings reveals that muscles that are to initiate movement and thus will be called on to perform positive work, are stretched beyond their rest lengths before being activated. They are not active when in a shortened state. One would anticipate this situation on the basis of the length–tension relationship that exists in striated muscle, and on the studies of Cavagna et al. (1968) already cited. Furthermore, such stretch suggests that energy may be stored elastically in the contractile machinery as well as in noncontractile connective tissue structures. Cavagna and Kaneko (1977) discussed the importance of stretch in the positive work of muscle during walking and running, and Cavagna et al. (1977) attempted to quantitatively evaluate the role of elastic stretch in their study of "bounce" or "spring" in human and animal locomotion. On the other hand, muscles that will decelerate moving skeletal parts or resist the external force of gravity may be activated when short and be elongated during activity. This manner of using muscle tension has been shown to be very effective both from the standpoint of metabolic cost and the use of the stretch components of muscle contributed by both passive and active muscle.

As reported in Chapter 1, p. 11, and Chapter 2, p. 57, after heel strike and during early stance phase the foot pronates to a varying degree. It is during this period that the foot is flexible and can adapt itself to irregularities of the walking surface (Chapter 1, p. 11). Electromyographic recordings using embedded wire electrodes in the intrinsic muscles of the foot reveal that the muscles are electrically quiet (Mann and Inman, 1964) during the first 20% of the walking cycle (Fig. 5.37). With transmission of the body weight from heel to forefoot, all intrinsic muscles show electrical activity. This is the time when the flexible foot must be converted into a rigid structure.

CHAPTER 6

Implications and Applications

The primary objective of the information presented in the previous chapters was to elucidate as far as possible the process of human walking. In addition, a review of much of the basic material provides explanations for several common as well as clinical observations. While not strictly related to normal walking, the data are applicable to a variety of situations and it seems opportune to discuss them in some detail.

Muscle Activity

The length–tension relationship, the speed of shortening versus load, and other basic physiological characteristics of muscle behavior have been emphasized (Chapter 5). Although orthopedists perform such surgical procedures as leg lengthening, leg shortening, and tendon and muscle transplants, there is little indication in most orthopedic texts that sufficient consideration is given to these characteristics of muscle physiology. This fact is recognized in an editorial in The Journal of Bone and Joint Surgery by Samilson (1976). Hand surgeons have become acutely aware of these principles, and all recent textbooks dealing with reconstruction of the hand devote considerable space to the physiology of muscle action, particularly to the useful excursion of muscles as dictated by the length–tension relationships.

An effective manner in which to use muscles seems to be in short bursts of activity in nearly isometric contraction. This is the way muscles behave in walking at one's "comfortable" speed (see Chapter 3). Muscles tend to fatigue rather rapidly if required to maintain their contraction over an extended period. Slowly moving about, as in "shopping," is commonly found to be "very tiring."

As discussed by Joseph in his detailed monograph (1960), when a person stands at ease the weight-bearing line from the center of mass to the floor passes through the hip joint in front of the knee and ankle joints. The effect on the knee joint is to produce an extension moment that holds the knee in a locked position requiring no activity in the quadriceps muscles.

Joseph quotes Smith (1956), who reports that in full extension, in one subject, approximately 70% of knee stability was achieved by passive tension of the extra- and intra-articular connective tissue structures of the knee joint, the remaining 30% coming from muscle activity. However, Joseph points out that these figures depend a great deal on the distance between the axis of the knee joint and the line of weight. Other figures for this distance could be used to show that the passive tension is almost entirely or wholly responsible for resisting knee extension in the standing-at-ease position. Joseph reports that during standing quietly with weight borne equally on both legs, there was no electrical activity recorded from the iliopsoas, gluteus maximus, or gluteus medius.

Because the weight-bearing line passes in front of the ankle joint, there is a dorsiflexion moment on the ankle. Joseph found that there was continuous but variable activity in calf muscles, particularly in the soleus. In comparison with the triceps surae, the ankle dorsiflexors (tibialis anterior) were generally electrically quiet. Joseph concludes that the triceps surae is the principal muscle group that is active during quiet standing.

The surprising lack of muscle activity during quiet standing, as reported by Joseph in his electromyographic studies, is substantiated by studies on energy expenditure. Compared with lying, quiet standing causes an average increase in oxygen consumption of only about 25% (see Chapter 3).

A characteristic posture is commonly adopted by people when forced to stand for even short periods. The weight is often shifted to one leg, with the knee locked in extension to free the extensor and flexor muscles from activity (Fig. 6.1). The contralateral knee is flexed slightly so the pelvis can list to that side. Pelvic stability is achieved by tension on the iliotibial tract, sparing the abductor muscles (Inman, 1947). Arms folded across the chest or hands clasped behind the back or placed on the hips with arms akimbo will reduce the tension on the muscles supporting the pectoral girdle and the arms.

The body weight normally falls on the medial side of

118

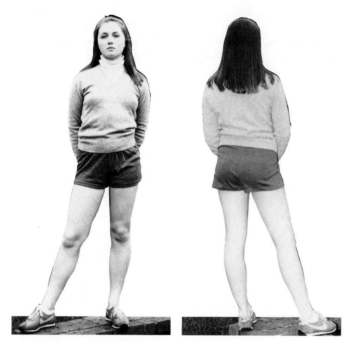

Figure 6.1. Commonly adopted posture, with weight shifted over one leg. Note the pronounced pelvic list.

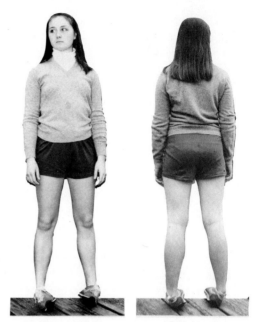

Figure 6.2. Toeing in, with external rotation of the leg, resulting in supination of foot and thus throwing weight on outer side of foot. See also Figure 1.21, Chapter 1.

the subtalar joint, causing the foot to pronate. During quiet standing, the intrinsic muscles of the foot are normally electrically quiet (see Chapter 5). Depression of the longitudinal arch is restricted by the plantar fascia and the aponeurosis. Tension in these structures may become uncomfortable after a time; to reduce the tension the arch must be elevated by muscle action (particularly of the tibialis posterior). It is common to see a person, when standing, toeing in and externally rotating the leg (Fig. 6.2). This causes the foot to supinate (see Chapter 1), thus throwing the weight on the outer side of the foot, relieving the tension on the plantar structures (see Chapter 1), and obviating the otherwise required contraction of the posterior tibial muscles.

Deviations from the normal pattern of walking often result from trauma or disease affecting the locomotor system. Such deviations are readily seen by even a casual observer, but a trained and knowledgeable clinician should be able to deduce much more than the mere existence of some abnormality of gait. A basic understanding of the biomechanics of normal walking makes it possible to explain why such deviations from the normal pattern are adopted or may be necessary. In general it can be stated, with considerable assurance, that the loss of the contribution of any single component of the neuromusculoskeletal apparatus leads to compensatory changes in the remaining functional parts. These changes are directed toward achieving a type of locomotion that minimizes energy expenditure at a given speed. A major loss always causes an increase in energy

expenditure at a given speed, and this increase becomes more marked as speed is increased (see Chapter 3).

For the purposes of this monograph, it is not pertinent to discuss in detail the various pathological conditions that may lead to abnormalities of gait. Rather, attention will be directed toward the consequences of a loss of the normal contribution of a functional component of gait, with only a passing reference to the precise etiologic factor that resulted in this loss.

The discussion is restricted to specific anatomic regions. By such an arrangement, it is possible to consider at one time a variety of conditions of differing etiology whose effects on the locomotor system may be similar. Also, it permits a discussion of the compensatory mechanisms that are employed as well as the usefulness and limitations of orthotic, prosthetic, and other assistive devices. The upper limbs are omitted because they play an unimportant role in walking at low or moderate speeds. Disabilities of the trunk, hip, knee, ankle, and foot will be discussed in that order under separate headings.

The Spine

The human trunk is probably the part of the body that most commonly requires some type of support. This can be a girdle, corset, or rigid brace. The objective of such bracing is to either unload or immobilize the spine or to achieve a combination of both.

Unloading the Spine

A decrease in the load on the entire spine caused by the weight of the trunk, head, and upper limbs can only be achieved through the use of complicated external mechanical devices. The "halo" traction system employs skull fixation with pins. Firm pelvic support is obtained by a molded cast or skeletal pins. Rigid adjustable metal rods connect the "halo" to the pelvis and transmit the weight from the skull to the pelvis. It should be remembered that the shoulders with the attached arms are essentially suspended from the skull and the cervical and upper thoracic spine by muscles. The Milwaukee brace attempts to decrease the load on the spine without the use of pins in the skull. The load is transmitted by metallic rods from occipital and mandibular pads directly to the pelvic support. These and similar devices obviously restrict the normal motions of the spine that occur during walking, and the resulting effects will be discussed in the section dealing with immobilization of the spine.

Partial support of the thoracic and lumbar spine may be achieved by increasing the intrathoracic and intra-abdominal pressures. This is a mechanism that one normally employs when lifting heavy loads. When the glottis is closed and the abdominal muscles are contracted, the intracavitary pressures are elevated and axial unloading of the spine occurs. Use of flexible compressive corsets, by increasing intra-abdominal pressure, may decrease the load on the lumbar spine by as much as 40% (Morris et al., 1961). Continuous exposure to these increases in abdominal pressure may, however, have deleterious effects on the venous return from the lower limbs. Flexible compressive corsets, on the other hand, do not necessarily restrict normal spinal movements and therefore have minor or no effects on walking.

Immobilization of the Spine

Braces, casts, and surgical fusions have been extensively used in the treatment of a multitude of disabilities of the spine. The intent is always to decrease the amount of motion between the vertebrae involved in the pathological process. During walking certain movements between spinal segments occur. Pelvic list (see Chapter 1) is permitted by lateral bending in the lumbar spine. The opposite rotations of the thorax and pelvis are permitted by transverse rotations occurring between vertebrae, particularly those composing the lower thoracic spine.

Suppression of these movements of the spine has been shown to increase the metabolic cost of walking (see Chapter 3) and has been observed to interfere with the smooth progression of the body at higher speeds of walking in both the coronal and sagittal planes. When casts or rigid braces are used to immobilize the entire trunk, the counterrotations of the thorax and the pelvis are restricted. These rotations, however, are still attempted within the restraints and cause force to be

exerted, with each step, on one side of the pelvis and simultaneously on the opposite side of the thorax. If the areas of pressure are too localized, discomfort and even tissue injury may result.

A review of the surgical literature fails to disclose any studies on abnormalities of walking when there are extensive fusions of the spine. Interest has been focused primarily on surgical techniques and the incidence of pseudarthrosis after spinal fusions. There are very few studies that have attempted to relate the frequency of pseudarthrosis to the movements between individual segments of the spine. Ponseti and Friedman (1950) published a study of 117 spinal fusions with a pseudarthrosis rate of 68%. They included a bar graph showing the relationship between individual vertebral levels and the incidence of pseudarthrosis. The highest frequencies of pseudarthrosis occurred in the regions of the thoracolumbar junction (T-9 to L-1) and the lumbosacral junction (L-4 to S-1). It is interesting to speculate that a causal relationship may exist between the frequency of pseudarthrosis and those areas of the spine that show the greatest mobility during walking, both in bending and in rotation.

The Hip Joint

The hip joint is involved in a variety of pathological processes. If etiologic factors are not considered, disabilities resulting from the inability of the hip to perform its normal role in walking may be discussed under several general categories: painful hip (antalgic gait), congenital dislocated hip, and abductor muscle weakness ("gluteus medius limp"). These conditions result in a limp that is basically similar. During the stance phase of walking, the person tends to bend his trunk so that the superincumbent body weight is over the involved hip. This tendency to displace the body over the involved hip may be partially or wholly eliminated by using a cane on the uninvolved side or by carrying packages or luggage on the side of the abnormal hip. These effects, if considered only superficially, would appear to constitute a paradox. However, with an understanding of the mechanics involved the explanation becomes apparent.

The center of mass of the body lies medial to the weight-bearing hip; therefore, when weight is borne on one leg a moment is created that tends to cause the pelvis with the superincumbent body to fall toward the side of the non-weight-bearing leg. This tendency is resisted by the action of the abductor muscles on the weight-bearing side. The combined actions of gravity and the tension of the abductor muscles are additive; the force between the head of the femur and the acetabulum is approximately 2.5 times the entire weight of the body during the stance phase of walking (Pauwels, 1935; Inman, 1947; Merchant, 1965; Rydell, 1966).

In patients with painful hips, the high forces generated by the combined forces of gravity and muscle action can be markedly reduced by eliminating or decreasing the tension developed by the abductor muscles, thus reducing the load on the femoral head. This is accomplished in two ways. The patient leans over the involved hip, which decreases the moment due to gravity by displacing the center of mass laterally to lie more nearly over the painful hip. This posture requires less force on the part of the abductor muscles to maintain the pelvis in a near-horizontal position. Second, a cane used on the side of the normal hip can exert an upward thrust to the body and replace the action of the abductors (Blount, 1956).

It has been calculated that the resultant force on the hip can be reduced by 30% with the use of a cane on the normal side (Bergmann et al., 1978). The load transmitted through the cane is relatively small—according to Murray (1969), approximately 15 kg; according to Bergmann et al., 15% of body weight; and according to Bechtol (1979), 4 to 10 kg. These values are readily understandable because the effective lever arm measured from the cane to the center of the hip joint is four to five times greater than the lever arm between the hip joint and the weight-bearing line of the body.

Normally the action of the abductor muscles forces the head of the femur into the acetabulum. With the use of a cane, the direction of the compressive force between the head of the femur and the acetabulum becomes vertical. While the total force is much less, it is concentrated on the upper surface of the femoral head and the outer rim of the acetabulum. This may be the explanation for the flattening of the upper surface of the femoral head in progressive degenerative disease of the hip (Fig. 6.3) (see also Pearson and Riddell, 1962).

When the hip is partially or completely dislocated the following factors may be active: the hip may be painful or there may be a loss of stability in the hip joint, which normally acts as a fulcrum between the moments developed by gravity and the tension of the abductor muscles. In either case, as described previously for the case of the painful hip, there is a tendency to lean over the involved hip and to use a cane on the side of the normal hip. Should the abductor muscles be weak and unable to stabilize the pelvis adequately, the gluteus medius limp results. This limp can often be improved or eliminated if the patient carries packages or luggage on the involved side. As explained previously, the added weight tends to supplement or replace the force normally exerted by the abductor muscles.

A similar limp is often seen in above-knee amputees and is more apparent the shorter the stump. The basic

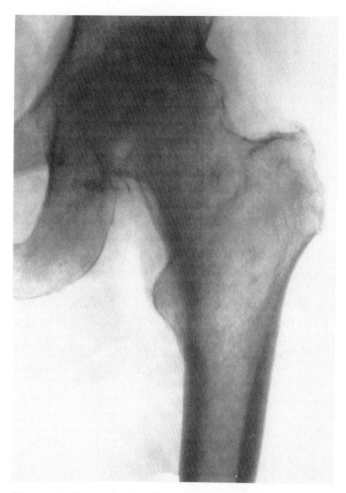

Figure 6.3. X-ray showing flattening of upper surface of femoral head in progressive degenerative disease of hip.

mechanism is similar. The compensatory moment to offset the tendency of the body to fall toward the non-weight-bearing side requires that the abductor muscles act on the pelvis. This necessitates a fixed and firm femoral attachment for these muscles. In the amputee, this is often not achieved because the alignment of the socket or a short stump permits the femoral stump to move outward, decreasing the ability of the abductor muscles to develop an adequate compensatory moment. Thus, the amputee is forced to adopt a limp similar to that of persons with weak abductor muscles.

Immobilization of the Hip

When the hip is immobilized, there is a suppression of the normal flexion and extension of the hip that occur in walking, as well as a suppression of three less apparent displacements. The normal listing of the pelvis toward the non-weight-bearing side and the slight adduction of the thigh that accompanies the lateral displacement of the trunk during stance phase are suppressed. Also, the internal rotation of the hip during the first half of stance phase is lost. Because the latter displacements are small, their loss is assumed to be of little significance. Arthrodesis of the hip in slight flexion leads to remarkably few obvious changes in walking at very low speeds (Gore et al., 1975). The required flexion and extension of the thigh are provided by flexion and extension of the lumbar spine. The suppression of the normal horizontal rotations of the pelvis and femur leads to some asymmetry of shoulder rotation and arm swing. With increasing speeds of walking the asymmetry becomes more marked and the effort exerted to move the pelvis with its rigidly attached femur becomes noticeable. Also, the step length on the arthrodesed side is limited, so that inequality of step lengths between the normal and the arthrodesed sides becomes more pronounced. It is interesting to note that the energy requirements of walking at low or moderate speeds with one hip immobilized are increased above normal in all cases. When the hip is fixed at approximately 30° of flexion (see Chapter 3) and the speed of walking is low, the energy requirements in excess of normal are minimized.

Femoral Osteotomy

Numerous osteotomies of the proximal end of the femur have been devised and performed for nonunion of fractures of the femoral neck and for the relief of pain in the osteoarthritic hip, although with the increasing popularity of total hip replacement such osteotomies are now carried out less frequently. Nevertheless, there are a variety of conditions in which femoral osteotomy is still indicated. These include congenital coxa vara, congenital pseudarthrosis, slipped proximal femoral epiphysis, and congenital dislocation of the hip, as well as other less common abnormalities. The objective of these osteotomies is to improve function and delay the onset of degenerative changes in the hip. One should remember, however, that the forces acting through the hip joint are large, and although the amount of movement of the head of the femur in the acetabulum is not great, these forces occur in all planes and are critical to the smooth function of walking. The mechanical effects of various neck–femoral shaft angles were first emphasized by Friedrich Pauwels (1935) (Fig. 6.4).

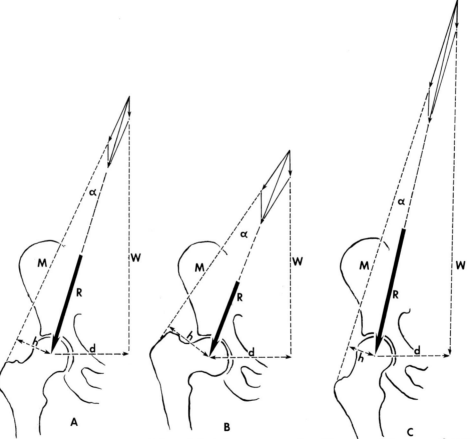

Figure 6.4. Forces acting through hip joint while weight is borne on one leg. Three conditions are shown: *A,* Hip with normal femoral shaft–neck angle. *B,* Varus hip. *C,* Valgus hip. The body weight (*W*) and the lever arm from the center of mass to the hip joint (*d*) are considered to be constant. The magnitude of the resultant force *R* depends on the length of the lever arm *h,* the angle of pull of the abductor muscles (*α*), and the force of the abductor muscles (*M*). (Redrawn, with permission, from Pauwels, F. *Biomechanics of the Normal and Diseased Hip.* Translated by Furlong, R. J., and Maquet, P. Springer-Verlag, New York, 1976.)

Total Hip Replacement

Total hip replacement is now a common orthopedic procedure and is employed to replace the older procedures of arthrodesis and osteotomy. From the standpoint of the mechanics of the hip, the problem of abductor weakness and residual limp after total hip replacement is unsolved. Surgeons are still debating the relative importance of two questions: should an adequate lever arm be maintained for the abductor muscles to develop an effective stabilizing moment on the pelvis or should muscle fiber length be retained by placing the greater trochanter distal to its normal location? Obviously both factors play a role, but from the viewpoint of pure geometry the maintenance of fiber length appears to be the more significant. This statement is based on the following considerations:

1. If it is assumed that no shortening of the neck occurs as the result of the surgical procedure, a varus displacement leads to only minimal changes in the effective lever arm. In a valgus displacement, the effective lever arm may be significantly shortened (see Fig. 6.4).

2. The length of the abductor muscles as well as the direction of their pull is definitely altered by osteotomy. The muscle is shortened in a varus osteotomy and lengthened in a valgus osteotomy. Consideration of length–tension relationships of muscle (see Chapter 5) reveals that shortening leads to weakness, and lengthening, if not excessive, results in an increase in strength. It should be noted that the effective lever arm and the ability of the muscle to develop tension are independent variables and must both be considered when the attempt is made to determine the reason for a residual limp after surgical procedures on the hip.

The role of the iliotibial band in stabilizing the pelvis during walking has not been fully investigated. Comparative anatomic studies reveal that the iliotibial tract exists only in man as a strong independent ligamentous structure extending from pelvis to knee (Kaplan, 1958). Its attachment to the lateral intermuscular septum restricts its function to separate and independent effects on the hip and knee. The forces developed by the gluteus maximus and tensor fasciae latae, which insert into the iliotibial tract, are directly applied to the femur and not transmitted to the tibia (Gardner, 1958). During stance phase, the center of mass of the body is displaced laterally a small amount (see Chapters 1 and 2). This leads to a few degrees of adduction of the leg. Simultaneously, the pelvis drops on the non-weight-bearing side (positive Trendelenburg). Both of these displacements act to produce relative adduction of the femur at the hip joint of approximately 8 to 10° (Ryker, 1952; see also Chapter 2). It has been shown (Inman, 1947) that these two displacements (lateral displacement and pel-

vic list) result not only in elongation of the fibers of the abductor muscles, improving their ability to develop tension (see Chapter 5), but cause an increasing tension in the iliotibial band estimated to contribute approximately 50% of the abducting force required to maintain pelvic stability. Unfortunately, in the numerous biomechanical analyses that have been published on hip joint function after surgical procedures, little or no attention has been directed to the possible alterations in the contribution of the iliotibial band to pelvic stability.

Bracing for the Relief of Hip Disabilities

Bracing of the lower limb is widely employed for a variety of disabilities. In arthritic processes involving the major articulations or in healing fractures, unloading of the limb may be attempted by the application of a device that transmits the superincumbent body weight through the device and bypasses the skeletal structures. Where skeletal deformities occur as a result of various pathological processes, amelioration or prevention may be attempted by an externally applied device. In cases in which muscle weakness or abnormal muscle activity hinders normal walking, improved function may be achieved through the use of a brace. The devices selected for specific disabilities may have differing effects on ambulation and therefore deserve separate discussion.

When full weight-bearing through the hip is to be avoided, as in healing fractures or in arthritic processes, the use of a long leg brace to support the body is often prescribed. An ischial (Thomas) ring has been employed, but with advances in prosthetic management the quadrilateral plastic socket similar to that used for above-knee amputees has proved to be more efficient and comfortable (see Chapter 7). To effectively transmit body weight and bypass the hip joint during the stance phase of walking, motion at the knee, ankle, and subtalar joints must be restricted. The loss of their normal contribution to the process of walking leads to radical alterations in the gait and increases in energy expenditure. The effects of knee and ankle immobilization will be discussed under separate headings.

Ischial-bearing braces have occasionally been prescribed for gluteus medius limp. The objective is to transfer the weight-bearing line to the ischial tuberosity, which is more medially placed than the hip joint. The lever arm is thus shortened, and less muscle effort is necessary to support the pelvis on the involved side in a relatively horizontal plane during the stance phase of walking.

The Knee Joint

Of the joints in the lower limb, the knee appears to the casual observer to be one of the principal contributors to the process of walking. Certainly, the knee moves through a considerably larger angle than either the hip or the ankle.

However, as discussed in Chapter 4, the knee contributes very little in the way of positive work to the process of normal walking. The knee absorbs more energy than it puts into the system (Bresler and Berry, 1951). That this is true is demonstrated in the gait of an above-knee amputee, where the major angular displacements of the knee occur without muscle action by the flexors or extensors of the knee. In fact, most prostheses have damping contrivances to prevent excessive foot rise at the beginning of swing phase and to smoothly decelerate extension at the time of heel strike.

The knee, however, does play an important role in walking. If the knee did not remain flexed during swing phase, causing a relative shortening of the leg, lateral pelvic list and toe clearance would be impossible. A knee held in extension during swing phase requires that the pelvis be elevated by exaggerated plantar flexion of the opposite ankle or circumduction of the entire leg to provide toe clearance. Normally, a plantar flexion moment at the ankle results in a ground reaction force that helps to flex both knee and hip just before toe-off, greatly facilitating the forward swing of the limb (see Chapter 4). Holding the knee in extension prevents the use of this force, and the entire leg must be swung forward as a unit through the action of the hip flexors alone. The result of all these factors is to increase the energy requirements for walking (see Fig. 6.5).

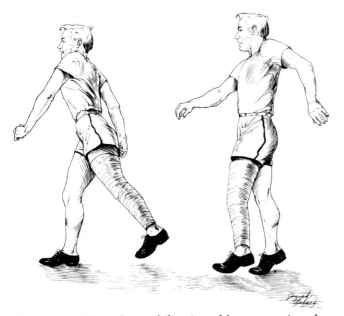

Figure 6.5. Effect of immobilization of knee on swing phase of walking. When the knee is held in extension, the pelvis must be elevated by exaggerated plantar flexion of the opposite ankle or by circumduction of the entire leg to provide toe clearance.

Immobilization of the Knee

Restriction of motion or complete immobilization of the knee may be indicated in the treatment of several medical conditions. It may be accomplished by the use of a long leg brace, a cylinder cast, or surgical arthrodesis. Besides the suppression of the normal contribution of the knee in walking, the use of braces or casts exaggerates the disability by adding weight to the lower leg. The effect of a shoe lift to compensate for the relative shortening of the leg was found to cause no appreciable change in the energy requirement for walking unless the weight of the lift was excessive. Loss of knee motion not only increased the energy expenditure at all speeds but, more significantly, limited the speed of walking to approximately one-half of the speed of a normal person with an unencumbered knee (see Chapter 3).

Osteochondromalacia Patellae

Pain due to osteochondral changes affecting the apposing surfaces of the patella and patellar groove on the femur, leads to typical complaints. At very low speeds of walking, the knee joint may show little or no tendency to flex immediately after heel strike (see Chapter 2). Because the quadriceps tendon and patellar ligament remain in line, there is little or no compressive force between patellar and femoral surfaces, and therefore pain is minimal or absent. When the speed of walking is increased to between 90 and 100 steps per minute, the knee joint flexes after heel strike. The amount of flexion is typically about 15°. The amount of patellofemoral compressive force is relatively small. This compressive force has been calculated and measured by several investigators (Reilly and Martens, 1971; Perry et al., 1975). There is excellent agreement between their published results. The forces were found to be between 0.3 and 0.5 times the body weight. At higher speeds of walking, the quadriceps may be activated after toe-off to prevent excessive knee flexion and expedite knee extension during the subsequent swing phase. At this time, the knee joint is flexed to about 65° and the patellofemoral compressive force may be considerable, with resulting increase in pain. The same mechanism is active when the patient attempts to rise from a sitting position.

Pain during walking up and down steps is a constant complaint. The increase in the angle of flexion of the knee that is necessary for stair-climbing results in an increase in the patellofemoral compressive force. This has been calculated to be approximately 3.5 times the body weight, or a seven- to tenfold increase over the compressive force that occurs during a slow or moderate walk. Walking upstairs, however, is less painful than walking downstairs. Two factors are involved. In walking up steps with normal risers of approximately 18 to 19 cm, the knee is flexed to a maximum of only about 50° (Fig. 6.6A) during total weight-bearing. The action of the quadriceps may be assisted by leaning forward; should the center of mass of the body lie in front of the axis of the knee joint, an extension moment is created that assists the quadriceps. Furthermore, a hand on the banister will help pull the body upward on the step. During walking downstairs, the knee flexes to a maximum of about 80° while bearing weight (Fig. 6.6B). One does not normally lean forward, and flexion of the knee is restrained by quadriceps action alone. The result is a large compressive force between the articular surfaces, with increased pain.

Paralysis of the Quadriceps

The development and the increasing administration of the Sabin oral vaccine has caused a dramatic decrease in the incidence of postpoliomyelitic paralysis. However, there are still people who either contracted the disease before the advent of the vaccine or some who reside in undeveloped countries where the vaccines are

unavailable or are poorly dispensed. Those patients who have a unilateral flail limb are forced to wear a long leg brace to permit ambulation without the use of crutches. The paralyzed quadriceps is particularly disabling, but if there are no contractures or deformities many people can walk slowly by leaning forward and using the hand on the same side to press on the anterior surface of the thigh at the time of heel strike, thus exerting an extensor moment on the knee. In Chapter 1, it was pointed out that at low or moderate speeds of walking, the quadriceps muscle contracts during the first half of stance; while permitting slight knee flexion, it stabilizes the knee until the ground reaction force passes in front of the knee axis. In patients with a flail limb, stability of the knee can be achieved by pantalar arthrodesis with the foot in approximately 15° of equinus. In this position, the forefoot strikes the ground first. The weight-bearing line then lies in front of the knee axis, an extensor moment on the knee is developed, and the need for the quadriceps to stabilize the knee is obviated (Matsuo and Wada, 1976). The equinus position of the foot, while providing the desired stability of the knee

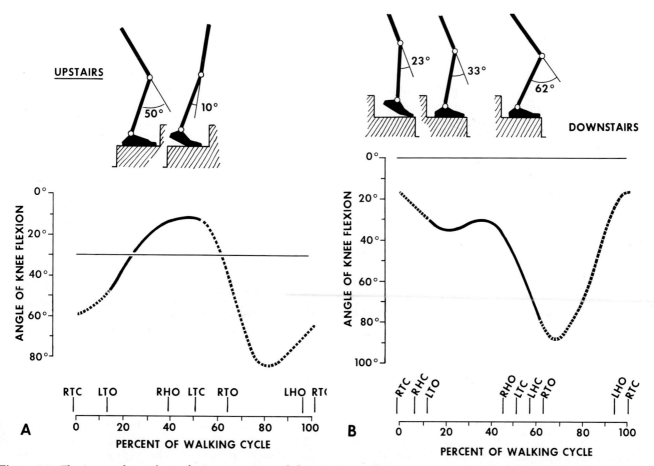

Figure 6.6. Flexion angles at knee during upstairs and downstairs walking. *A,* Upstairs walking. *B,* Downstairs walking. *Solid line* of graph shows measured angles of right knee, during weight-bearing, at foot positions indicated below graph.

during early stance, may result over an extended period in genu recurvatum. This is particularly true if the hamstring muscles are weak.

The Ankle Joint

To the casual observer, the amount of motion that occurs in the ankle joint during walking at moderate speeds appears to be small. The approximate 15° of plantar flexion that occurs immediately after heel strike is slowed by tension in the anterior tibial muscles, and the continuing forward movement of the leg over the foot tends to obscure this angular motion in the ankle joint. When the extensor muscles of the foot are weak, plantar flexion is sudden and becomes much more obvious. During most of the stance period, the leg rotates over the foot and there occurs approximately 20° of relative dorsiflexion at the ankle. This may be modified by the height of the heel; it is less apparent when high heels are worn. The greatest observable movement occurs with heel rise and is continued for a short period after toe-off. The total average motion in the ankle joint is about 30°, which is less than flexion and extension of the hip or the knee. However, this amount of movement and its proper timing are important factors in achieving a smooth displacement of the body through space (see Chapter 1).

In the past, in arthritic processes involving the ankle joint surgical arthrodesis was considered the only appropriate procedure to relieve pain and improve ambulatory function. It was believed by most surgeons that the loss of ankle motion produced little disability in walking. Difficulties were encountered in securing a solid bony union because of two factors. The surface areas between the trochlea of the talus and the mortise are small, and the bending forces on the fusion site are large. Whereas it is true that fusion of an ankle in the proper position appears to result in little visible alteration in gait at low or moderate speeds, abnormally large forces are imposed on the foot. These may eventually lead to arthritic changes in the joints of the foot.

It has been recommended (Lowman, 1950) that ambulation can be improved and the bending moments on a fused ankle greatly lessened by the use of a "rocker bottom" shoe. This is partly true. In the normal person, there is an initial downward displacement immediately after heel strike. This is caused by plantar flexion of the ankle and pronation of the foot, both of which assist in absorbing the impact of the body (see Chapter 1). A similar displacement pattern and functional result can be achieved with a soft cushion heel (Baker, 1970) (see Fig. 7.4, Chapter 7) or to a lesser extent, by a rocker bottom shoe with a proper curvature of the sole. During the remainder of stance phase, the forward displacement of the knee is relatively flat and horizontal, and

this motion can be duplicated with use of a rocker bottom shoe whose center of curvature is located at the knee joint (Fig. 6.7).

The presence of the foot always causes a bending moment on a fused ankle joint, and a rocker bottom shoe can only slightly reduce the magnitude of this moment. A rocker bottom shoe of proper curvature can modify the bending moment in two ways. It can decrease the moment somewhat, but more importantly it can extend the time of imposition of the moment on the ankle.

With paralysis of the extensor muscles, a spring-loaded short leg brace to prevent or slow down the initial plantar flexion after heel strike and to provide passive dorsiflexion of the foot for toe clearance during swing phase is a valuable device and is widely used. In a flail limb, when both flexor and extensor muscles are inactive, the addition of a stop on the brace to prevent dorsiflexion beyond 90° will improve the gait. However, the brace must be sufficiently sturdy to withstand the large bending moments imposed on it. Its weight (see Chapter 3) and the forces exerted on the anterior aspect of the leg may be definite disadvantages.

The Foot

The foot contributes more to the mechanism of walking than merely acting as a semirigid member that undergoes dorsiflexion and plantar flexion at the ankle in the sagittal plane (plane of progression). There are rotations in transverse planes of the body that involve the pelvis, thigh, and shank (see Chapters 1 and 2). Of particular interest in the following discussion is the transverse rotation of the shank and its effect on the foot. The amount of rotation of the shank varies from individual to individual and varies in each individual with step length and speed of walking. The average rotation at usual speeds of walking is approximately 19°, with a range of 3 to 29° (see Chapters 1 and 2). Unless the foot slips on the walking surface, this rotation of the shank is possible only if there is a mechanism provided in the foot to permit this rotation. Anatomically, such a mechanism is provided principally by the subtalar joint, which acts as a direction torque transmitter (see Chapter 1) and references in "The Joints of the Ankle", Inman, 1976) and to a lesser degree by the ankle joint.

The subtalar joint, while permitting rotation of the shank, offers resistance to this rotation, particularly to external rotation, which requires the foot to supinate, slightly elevating the body. The foot may slide on a slippery surface; this may be seen to occur routinely in some people at toe-off. The resistance to transverse rotations of the shank can be recorded as a torque on a force plate. The magnitude of this torque is large (7–14

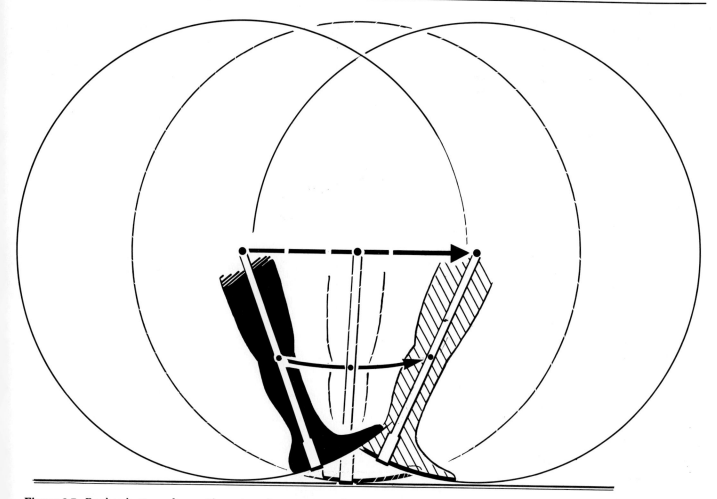

Figure 6.7. Rocker bottom shoe with center of curvature at knee joint. This curvature causes forward displacement of the knee to be relatively flat and horizontal during later stance phase.

newton-meters) (*Fundamental Studies of Human Locomotion*, 1947).

Subtalar or triple arthrodesis for various medical conditions has been employed extensively. Such procedures obviously destroy the essential mechanism in the foot that permits the horizontal rotations of the shank and place added rotatory stresses on the ankle joint. This may lead to pain and eventually to changes in the ankle. In a 10-year follow-up of 185 children who had been subjected to bilateral or unilateral triple arthrodesis, "39 percent showed evidence of osteoarthritis and a ball-and-socket appearance of the ankle" (Adelaar et al., 1976). It is interesting that ball-and-socket ankle joints, which permit horizontal rotations to occur between shank and foot, are a frequent accompaniment of tarsal coalitions. These congenital fusions of the tarsal bones eliminate subtalar motions, and apparently nature compensates with the provision of a ball-and-socket ankle.

Just before toe-off, the body weight is shared by the heads of the metatarsal bones, and the toes hyperex-

tend. This leads to a crease in the toe box of the shoe, identified as caused by the so-called metatarsophalangeal break. The angle of the metatarsophalangeal break has been measured (Moskowitz, 1967) and has been found to average 54° with the long axis at the second metatarsal. However, the variation in this angle was found to range between 40 and 70°. To distribute the body weight between all metatarsal heads at push-off, the foot must deviate laterally and supinate. This is what actually occurs and is accomplished by the external rotation of the leg (see Chapters 1 and 2).

Effect of Heel Height

It is a common observation that people wearing high heels walk differently from people walking barefoot or in flat shoes. However, there are few studies that attempt to accurately quantitate these differences. Murray et al. (1969) report findings on 30 women walking at comfortable and fast speeds while wearing shoes with low and high heels. Qualitatively, the following differences were reported. Step lengths were shorter in high heels. The total amplitude of knee motion in the sagittal plane was less in high heels; this was caused by a decrease in flexion during swing phase and greater knee flexion during stance phase. The total excursion of the ankle was less in high heels. Similar findings were reported by Gollnick et al. (1964). Pelvic rotation and pelvic tilt were not appreciably altered. Oxygen consumption was appreciably greater in women wearing high heels than in those walking barefooted or in low heels (Mathews and Wooten, 1963). This finding was to be expected with deviations from the normal walking pattern. It is noteworthy that the vertical floor reactions as recorded from a force platform revealed only minor changes (Saunders et al., 1953). Joseph (1960) quotes the studies of Basmajian and Bentzon (1954), who investigated the effects of high heels in 16 women. The main change seen was an increase in the number showing activity in all the leg muscles studied, which was thought to be due to instability introduced by the posture.

Weight of Shoes

The weight of shoes has a very definite effect on walking. Whereas loading the body in general increases the metabolic cost of walking, the effects are greater the more distally the loads are carried. Loads of 4 kg carried at approximately the center of mass of the body cause a barely appreciable increase in energy (less than 4%), whereas 4 kg divided between two feet (2 kg on each foot) increases the metabolic cost of walking by 30% (see Chapter 3). This is due to both inertial and gravitational effects. There is a tendency to take longer steps because of effort involved in acceleration and deceleration of the legs. The increase in step length results in greater vertical oscillation of the body, with consequent increase in gravitational work.

CHAPTER 7

Applications to Lower Limb Prosthetics

In the preceding chapters, human walking has been described in detail. It should be emphasized that the locomotor system is a completely integrated system, with the trunk and limbs all contributing to the smooth functioning of the whole. Amputation results in not only the physical loss of the amputated part, but a removal of its particular contribution to the entire mechanism. Therefore, it becomes necessary to compensate for the functional loss by alterations in the behavior of the remaining parts of the system.

Amputations are usually carried out through the midportions of the articulating segments and infrequently through joints. As was pointed out in Chapter 5, many muscles extend over two or more joints and influence to a varying degree the movement of both the proximal and distal joints. It should be recalled that the excursion of a muscle as well as its speed of contraction is related to the total length of the muscle. Amputation through the midportion of the thigh or shank, therefore, may affect the residual functions of the stump in several ways. The length of the bony stump is important in providing an adequate lever arm for the transmission of forces between stump and socket. The sectioning of muscles alters their ability to move the proximal articulations, particularly if they have been permitted to shorten (see Chapter 5). Because it is desirable to retain as much function as possible, it is becoming more and more accepted by surgeons that some type of myodesis (surgical fixation of the muscles) should be carried out at the time of amputation. Such a procedure consists of either suturing the extensor and flexor muscles over the end of the stump with slight tension or fixing the muscles through drill holes placed at the end of the bony stump. Thus, excessive shortening and resulting weakness of the muscles is prevented.

The ideal amputation stump should have approximately 6 mm of soft tissue over the end of the bony stump, and the deep fascia should be carefully closed so that the skin is freely movable over the deeper tissue.

The skin should be closed as one would in a plastic procedure so there is minimal scarring. The stump should have a smooth contour with no skin redundancy.

Because skeletal fixation of the prosthesis is not yet feasible, all forces between the bony stump and the socket must be transmitted through the intervening soft tissues, which are not adapted to withstand such forces. The dynamic force systems acting on the amputee during the use of his prosthesis must be understood, because they determine the socket shape, the best alignment for optimal function, and the need for incorporating certain mechanical devices into the prosthesis.

In the procedure of fitting a prosthesis to an amputee, the orthopedic technician must first fit the socket accurately and comfortably around the stump so as to form an effective connection to the prosthesis. He must choose and assemble the various components of the prosthesis as required to ensure a functional and stable device that can fulfill the needs of the individual amputee. Finally, he must align and adjust the prosthesis to the amputee to provide maximal restoration of function and minimal gait deviation, in both the stance and swing phases of a walking cycle.

To achieve maximal restoration of function for the lower limb amputee, the following general considerations are pertinent. The socket must be comfortable. The magnitudes and locations of the forces acting between stump and socket must be appreciated. Lastly, an evaluation of the effectiveness of the man–machine (body plus prosthesis) combination is indicated. The latter requires an accurate knowledge of the biomechanics of human walking as presented in the previous chapters.

In each of the previously mentioned categories, the specific problems encountered vary with the level of amputation. Amputations of the lower limb may be carried out at many levels, from partial amputation of the foot to hemipelvectomy. The discussion that follows will consider four different levels of amputation as examples of the application of knowledge about locomotion and physiology to the development and fitting of functional prostheses.

The Midthigh Amputee

An analysis of the dynamic force system acting on the amputee during the use of his prosthesis under various conditions will be presented first. Such forces can be measured where facilities exist, and the results of such studies (Radcliffe, 1954) should be carefully reviewed. However, in many cases it is sufficient to estimate the relative magnitudes of such forces on the basis of certain assumptions. Estimations of this type can help to define those areas of the stump that will be subjected to localized and/or increased magnitudes of socket–stump contact pressures under the dynamic conditions of walking or other activities. The results of these studies are useful in establishing socket contours that can provide a comfortable and long-lasting fit of the socket to the stump and, at the same time, anticipate and make provision for the functional use of the stump in the control of body movements and the manipulation of the prosthesis. The present discussion cannot hope to cover in detail all the factors that influence the fitting of above-knee prostheses. The major emphasis will be on the restoration of function to the hip musculature, the alignment of the prosthesis, and the fit of the socket.

Studies of normal human walking (Radcliffe, 1955) have shown that the average normal person walks in a manner such that points of successive heel contact occur close to the center line of progression. It is typical that such heel contact points fall within a base width of approximately 10 cm as viewed from the rear. In normal level walking, the pelvis will tend to oscillate simultaneously in horizontal and vertical directions with a range of motion of approximately 5 cm horizontally and 5 cm vertically. The control of the undulating motion of the pelvis and the supported trunk above must be provided through the hip joints and their associated musculature.

An excessively wide walking base is accompanied by inevitable gait deviations, characterized by excessive side-to-side oscillation of the pelvis and a tendency to bend the lumbar spine laterally so as to carry the trunk more directly over the prosthesis. Either of these gait defects can be caused by a socket fit or alignment that makes it difficult and often acutely uncomfortable for the amputee to attempt to walk in a more normal manner.

In the typical above-knee amputation, the abductor muscles, being inserted into the greater trochanter proximal to the level of amputation, are spared. In short stumps, loss of abductor function is common and disability results from inability to achieve adequate fixation of the proximal femur so that the abductor muscles can perform efficiently in stabilizing the pelvis. In addition, the action of the abductor muscles imposes certain requirements on the ischial-bearing socket that do not exist in other types of fitting.

The hamstring muscles play a dual role during walking. Toward the end of swing phase, they decelerate the swinging leg in anticipation of heel contact, at which time the forward velocity of the foot approaches zero. Because the hamstrings act over both the hip and knee joints, their contraction decelerates both hip flexion and knee extension. After heel contact and foot flat, their continued activity assists in the stabilization of the pelvis and, with other muscles, in initiating hip extension (see Chapter 5).

Amputation results in transection of the hamstring muscles. The loss of their function in decelerating the terminal extension of the knee is obvious, and usually requires replacement by a mechanical device in the prosthesis. The effect on the hip joint is less apparent, but it is important and requires further discussion. Should the hamstrings be permitted to retract at the time of amputation, the ensuing weakness results in the loss of their contribution to hip deceleration and initiation of hip extension. Perhaps more important is their inability to stabilize the pelvis and counteract the tendency toward increasing the lumbar lordosis. Fixation of the distal ends of the cut hamstrings to the bony stump by means of some type of myodesis has been urged by many surgeons. One difficulty, however, should be recognized. The hamstrings are relatively short-fibered muscles with a small excursion, and if their length is halved by amputation, their excursion is also halved, with resulting impairment of their ability to develop tension at a sufficiently wide range of lengths (see discussion in Chapter 5). If, when a myodesis of the hamstrings is done, they are fixed in too much tension with the hip in a neutral position, the result will be to limit hip flexion. The compromise appears to be to fix the distal ends of the hamstring muscles in mild tension with the hip in approximately 15° of flexion.

The adductors constitute a large muscle mass whose precise role in walking has not been clearly defined. They are normally active twice during a single cycle when weight is being transferred from one leg to the other (see the discussioon of the phasic action of muscles in Chapter 5). In the amputee, myodesis of the adductors appears to be important not so much, perhaps, in controlling the stump as in preventing the retraction of these muscles, which produces a deforming mass on the medial side of the stump and makes fitting of a socket more difficult.

Biomechanics of the Above-Knee Prosthesis

An essential constituent for success in fitting and aligning a prosthesis to a midthigh amputee is an appre-

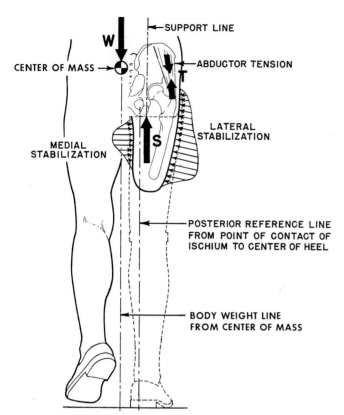

CENTER OF MASS →

SUPPORT LINE

W

ABDUCTOR TENSION

T

MEDIAL STABILIZATION

S

LATERAL STABILIZATION

POSTERIOR REFERENCE LINE FROM POINT OF CONTACT OF ISCHIUM TO CENTER OF HEEL

BODY WEIGHT LINE FROM CENTER OF MASS

Figure 7.1. Use of hip abductor musculature for lateral stabilization of pelvis. W, body weight. S, support force. T, force due to contraction of gluteus medius.

ciation of the forces acting between stump and socket. Failure to recognize and provide for these force requirements can lead to poor control as well as discomfort for the amputee.

Figure 7.1 illustrates the force patterns on the stump as viewed from the rear as an amputee walks on a properly fitted and aligned ischial–gluteal-bearing above-knee prosthesis. The amputee is shown during an instant when the full body weight is carried by the prosthesis and the amputee is making proper use of his abductor musculature for the lateral stabilization of the pelvis. He is assumed to be walking with a normal-appearing narrow-based gait.

In the ischial–gluteal-bearing type of above-knee socket, it is assumed that the contact against the ischial tuberosity is the major source of vertical support. In addition, perhaps one-third of the vertical support is provided by firm contact pressure acting upward on the gluteus maximus. Other areas of the socket, such as the anterior brim, also contribute to the vertical support in varying amounts, depending on the individual fitting. Under these assumptions a single support force, equivalent to the combined ischial–gluteal forces, would be drawn somewhat lateral to the point of contact of the ischium, as viewed from the rear. If this single equivalent support force, S, were the only force acting against

the amputee, he would be balanced on a rather unstable point of contact. The body weight, W, acting vertically downward from the center of mass, would create a moment tending to cause the pelvis to tilt toward the unsupported side. As the pelvis rotated, the amputee would react normally and attempt to prevent such motion by the natural use of his abductor musculature. Contraction of the gluteus medius would result in force T causing the distal part of the stump to move laterally within the socket until it made contact with the lateral wall. If the socket has been planned and fitted in anticipation of such stump action, the lateral motion of the stump will be blocked after a very small motion of the femur by a widely distributed and comfortable pressure against the entire lateral side of the stump, as shown in Figure 7.1. If such action has not been anticipated and the socket fit does not provide for effective lateral stabilization forces against the stump, then it is typical for the stump to abduct laterally within the socket an excessive amount. Two adverse effects result from such movement. Abduction shortens the abductor muscles and leads to a decrease in their ability to develop tension (see Chapter 5) and, more importantly, tends to concentrate the pressure between stump and socket to a small localized area at the distal cut end of the bone, often resulting in a point of painful contact. The amputee reacts by adopting a gait that does not cause painful pressure of this type. He immediately widens his walking base and leans over the prosthesis with each step. Such actions tend to bring the weight line, which acts downward from the center of mass, to a position where it is more nearly collinear with the support line. When these two lines coincide, the trunk can be balanced over the prosthesis with a minimum of abductor tension, and the need for lateral forces against the stump disappears. However, if the socket is properly fitted, the above-knee amputee with a midthigh or longer stump should be able to walk in a relatively normal manner without leaning over the weight-bearing prosthesis. The need for lateral forces against the stump can be accommodated easily and comfortably when proper fitting principles are used.

A slight weakness in the hip abductor musculature is of less consequence. The point of vertical support in the above-knee socket is medial to the normal vertical support through the hip joint. As a result the lever arm for the tilting action of the body weight is reduced and, in comparison with a normal person, the amputee is usually able to control his trunk with reduced abductor tension.

A socket for a long stump will be more effective in providing for lateral stabilization of the stump, in comparison with a short stump, because of the greater surface area and longer lever arm, measured downward from the hip joint. Both factors will tend to reduce the maximal contact pressure and result in increased comfort for the amputee. The very short stump lacks both the necessary contact area and the lever arm for effective lateral stabilization. As a result, attempts by amputees with very short stumps to walk with a narrow-based, normal sidesway gait are often frustrated by unavoidable force concentrations on the distal cut end of the femur. Therefore, in the case of the very short stump, it is sometimes advisable to construct the prosthesis up to 2 cm shorter than the normal leg in order to make it easier for the amputee to carry his center of mass more directly over the support point in the socket.

Accompanying the need for forces along the lateral side of the stump, concentrated distally, there will be a corresponding requirement for a counterforce acting against the medial side of the stump, concentrated proximally. These medial counterforces act horizontally against the abductor musculature and are not expected to contribute to the vertical support of the amputee.

Vertical support by contact of the medial socket brim against the perineum is considered undesirable, and one of the major objectives in the fitting process is to avoid vertical contact of the pubic ramus on the medial socket brim. Elimination of all painful pressure against the pubic ramus is possible when the tuberosity of the ischium is located accurately and firmly on the posterior socket brim so as to prevent the stump from sliding downward into the socket. Providing efficient mediolateral stabilization will also minimize medial shifting of the ischial tuberosity, which might result in painful skin abrasions in this important weight-bearing area.

Anteroposterior Stability

Figure 7.2 shows the pattern of anteroposterior stump–socket forces generated within the ischial–gluteal weight-bearing socket, as the hip musculature on the amputated side provides the extension and flexion moments required to control the stability of a simple,

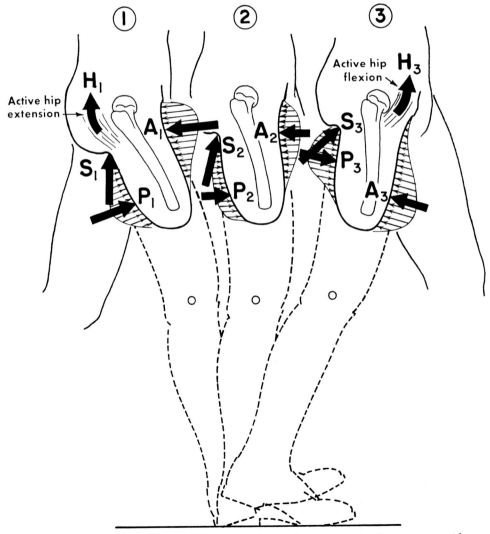

Figure 7.2. Anteroposterior stump–socket forces during stance phase of walking. *1*, heel contact. *2*, midstance. *3*, push-off (with knee flexion). *H*, hip extension–flexion muscle action. *S*, ischial–gluteal support. *P*, posterior force. *A*, anterior force.

hinge-type knee. Force patterns are shown for three instants during the stance phase of walking. These diagrams are for an alignment of components similar to that shown in Figure 7.1 and could be altered drastically by other methods of fitting, alignment, or the use of a different type of knee and/or foot mechanism.

In the case illustrated by Figure 7.2, an attempt has been made to strike a balance between alignment stability for prevention of buckling of the knee joint and what has been termed "voluntary knee control." It is possible, by alignment of the prosthetic knee joint posteriorly with respect to the hip–ankle line to achieve an amount of knee stability such that the knee will not buckle under usual conditions as long as it is in full extension at the time the heel makes contact with the ground. However, such alignment stability can be over-emphasized and although the knee will be secure at heel contact, excessive alignment stability can make knee flexion at the time of push-off a difficult maneuver. Excessive alignment stability often introduces an element of danger into situations where ability to flex the knee rapidly in a controlled manner is essential, such as on inclines and stairs. For these reasons it is good practice to use the stump and hip musculature to supplement the alignment stability and keep the control of the knee a voluntary action by the amputee. This is particularly important at the beginning and end of stance phase where a smooth transition from swing to stance and vice versa is essential to a normal-appearing gait.

Figure 7.2 shows the changes in the stump–socket force pattern to be expected as the amputee proceeds from heel contact through midstance to the push-off phase. Note that whenever the stump is actively extended within the socket, such as when maintaining the knee in a stable position, stump–socket forces are generated that act on the anterior surface of the stump proximally and along the posterior surface of the stump distally. It is essential that the anterior force act as high as possible on the stump for two reasons: first, to make use of as much of the functional length of the stump as possible in controlling knee stability, and second, to provide a positive counterpressure from the front to maintain the ischial tuberosity in the proper position on the posterior brim of the socket. The socket fit should be carried high enough that when the amputee sits or bends at the waist the anterior brim fits into the inguinal crease. If the fitting is too low, pinching of a roll of flesh in this area is to be expected. Too high an anterior socket brim will result in restriction of hip flexion by contact of the socket brim against the anterior superior spine of the pelvis.

Figure 7.2 shows that essentially the same type of force pattern exists through the midstance and roll-over phases. At the time of push-off, a change takes place.

The action of the hip muscles changes direction in order to flex the knee into swing phase. This active hip flexion should take place before the weight has been transferred completely from the prosthesis to the opposite leg, and the body weight should be used to supplement the action of the hip musculature. The body weight acts through the force exerted at the contact point of the ischial tuberosity. Such a "Tubersitz" type of amputee gait has been taught in Germany for many years and is facilitated by the use of physiological or polycentric knee constructions.

A second factor providing efficient voluntary knee control, in addition to the use of an anterior brim fitted well above the level of the ischial seat, is to align the socket in a position of initial flexion with respect to the hip–ankle line. There are many benefits to be realized from such an alignment of the socket: the extensor musculature of the hip is placed in a favorable position for controlling knee stability by active hip extension, the support on the ischial tuberosity may be partially transferred to the attachments of the hamstring tendons at the ischium, the gluteus maximus is placed in a position more favorable to sitting on the posterior brim of the socket, there is less of a tendency to push the ischium off the ischial seat at the time of push-off, and the development of lumbar lordosis is minimized, particularly when there is a flexion contracture. The only disadvantage is a cosmetic problem: long stumps obviously cannot be fitted into flexed sockets as easily as short stumps. However, because it is the short stump that usually benefits most from initial socket flexion, the cosmetic problems are generally not serious.

Figure 7.3 shows a suggested standing alignment of above-knee prostheses for short, medium, and long stumps. These diagrams are presented as guides only and considerable variation is to be expected with different amputees and with the use of different types of knee or ankle components.

Considered thus far are the means by which the amputee can make most efficient use of the remaining hip musculature to control body movements and to control the prosthetic knee during the stance and swing phases. There are, however, many functional details of socket shape and fit that make it possible for the amputee to derive these benefits comfortably. Unless these details are satisfactorily resolved, an uncomfortable socket with pain will result and none of the benefits of the alignment described above will be realized (Radcliffe, 1955).

Factors in Knee, Shank, and Foot Alignment

Once a comfortable socket has been constructed, with due consideration to the forces that are generated between stump and socket, some type of extension that contacts the walking surface must be added to the

Bisector of medial socket brim—
a convenient proximal
reference point

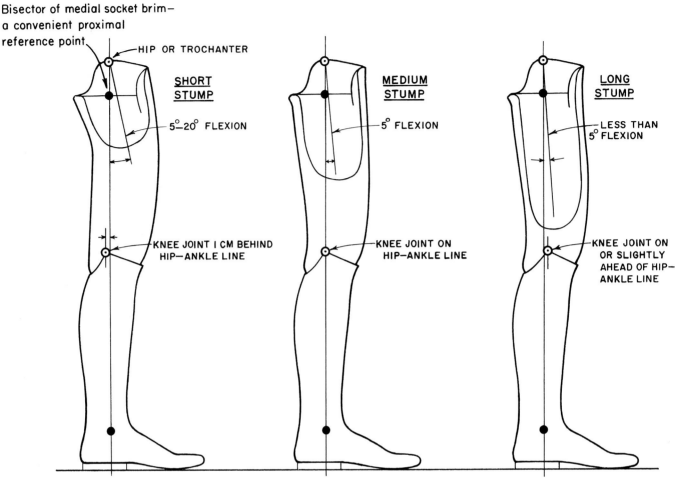

Figure 7.3.   Standing alignment variables in fitting short, medium, and long above-knee stumps.

socket in order to allow the amputee to walk. In its simplest form, this extension may be nothing more than a metal tube or wooden shaft attached to the socket and provided with a rubber crutch tip at its distal end. Such a device provides stability during the period of weight-bearing on the amputated side and offers little or no restriction of the horizontal rotations of the stump. It was widely used in many military amputation centers in World War II. It permitted early ambulation with changes in temporary sockets as the stump shrank. However, such a simple prosthesis is now rarely employed by amputees except for special purposes such as hunting on uneven terrain. With improved surgical techniques of amputation, rigid postoperative compression dressings, and the availability of plastics for the construction of sockets, amputees are being fitted early with permanent prostheses that incorporate knee joints and feet.

There are both cosmetic and functional reasons for the amputee to be provided with something more than a simple pylon. From the cosmetic standpoint, the amputee wishes the prosthesis to resemble as much as

possible the lost normal limb in both appearance and behavior. This requires the addition of a knee joint and a foot–ankle complex. From the functional standpoint, the inclusion of a knee joint permits greater ease of sitting and going up and down stairs and ramps; it also reduces the energy required in walking at higher speeds. However, the presence of a knee joint in a prosthesis also leads to complications.

In the normal lower limb, the knee flexes slightly immediately after heel contact (see Chapters 1 and 5). This initial flexion is constrained by the action of the quadriceps, and this small degree of flexion helps smoothly decelerate the falling center of mass of the body. Furthermore, the knee remains slightly flexed until the center of mass passes over the foot, at which time the knee extends. During this period of knee flexion, complete flexor collapse is prevented by tension exerted by the quadriceps. There is no quadriceps to function in the above-knee prosthesis; therefore, providing stability of the knee during stance phase becomes of paramount importance. Numerous knee mechanisms have been proposed, have been experimentally constructed, or are in use to provide the necessary stability of the knee during the stance phase of walking.

Two basic systems are being used. The first may be called "alignment stability"; it consists of aligning the knee axis in a location such that the load carried by the weight-bearing prosthesis always passes ahead of the knee axis and forces the prosthetic knee against a mechanical stop in the fully extended position. Alignment stability can be enhanced through the use of a polycentric knee mechanism, which is any device in which the instantaneous center of rotation of the knee changes its position as the knee flexion angle increases or decreases. Kinematically, all polycentric devices achieve stability by changing the location of the instantaneous center of rotation of the knee when it approaches full extension. The second basic way of increasing knee stability is through the incorporation of a device that resists the tendency of the knee to flex or collapse under load. Such devices may either lock the knee or resist the tendency for the knee to flex. These effects may be achieved by the use of friction surfaces, friction clamps, differential band brakes, or hydraulic cylinders.

The knee begins to flex before toe-off. In the non-amputee, this initial flexion is the result of several factors. Toward the end of stance phase, the line of action of the ground reaction force lies behind the knee, producing a knee flexion moment. The terminal plantar flexion of the ankle, commonly known as push-off, contributes to knee flexion, as does a characteristic descending motion of the hip just before toe-off. Another factor that encourages knee flexion toward the end of stance phase is gradual tightening of the ligamentous structures around the hip as the body moves forward over the stationary foot. In addition, active flexion of the hip causes the femur to move forward while the hinge-like effect of a free knee causes the shank to lag behind, leading to an increase in knee flexion. To prevent an abnormally high foot rise and to expedite knee extension during swing phase, the quadriceps may again act (see Chapter 5). At the termination of swing phase, the foot is normally decelerated to zero at the instant of heel contact. This angular deceleration is the function of the hamstring muscles (see Chapter 5).

Because the above-knee amputee has been deprived of the action of the quadriceps and hamstring muscles on the knee, a mechanism should be incorporated into the prosthetic knee to simulate the function of these muscles. Such a swing phase control device has three functions: (1) to limit the maximal knee flexion angle and cause the shank–foot to swing forward smoothly in a manner similar to quadriceps action in a normal knee, (2) to allow the knee to extend easily and decelerate the shank at full extension without impact in anticipation

of heel contact, and (3) to provide automatic changes in the level of resistance to allow for variations in walking speed. While various mechanisms have been used, ranging from simple elastic quadriceps assists to mechanical friction devices and rubber bumpers, greater advances have been made in the design and use of hydraulic and pneumatic damping systems incorporated in single-axis or polycentric knee joints (Wagner and Catranis, 1954; Radcliffe, 1960; Radcliffe and Ralston, 1963; Radcliffe, 1977).

In the normal person, the ankle and foot contribute several functions to the process of walking. At heel contact, plantar flexion of the ankle followed by slight pronation of the foot helps to smoothly decelerate the falling center of mass of the body. The pronation of the foot permits the continuing internal rotation of the entire leg that began during swing phase. Furthermore, pronation of the foot unlocks the midfoot and allows the forefoot to adapt itself to any unevenness in the walking surface. During the latter portion of stance phase, forceful plantar flexion of the ankle leads to relative elongation of the leg and contributes to knee flexion (see Chapter 4). Supination of the foot that occurs with heel rise is accompanied by external rotation of the leg and causes locking of the midfoot, which converts the foot into a rigid lever for push-off (see Chapter 1).

These complicated functions of the foot are not duplicated in the prosthetic foot. Passive plantar flexion and dorsiflexion of the ankle may be permitted and controlled by rubber bumpers in a single-axis joint, but rubber bumpers are subjected to high compressive forces with each step. In many designs, this results in rapid deterioration and requires frequent replacement. The SACH (Solid Ankle–Cushion Heel) foot (Fig. 7.4) has become increasingly popular because of its durability. The cushion heel absorbs the impact of the body at

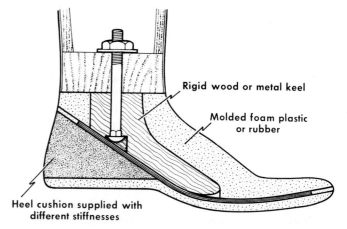

Rigid wood or metal keel

Molded foam plastic or rubber

Heel cushion supplied with different stiffnesses

Figure 7.4. SACH (Solid Ankle–Cushion Heel) prosthetic foot.

the time of heel strike and by compression gives the appearance of plantar flexion to the foot. The midfoot must be stiff to withstand the body weight after heel rise. In the SACH foot, this stiffness is provided by the incorporation within a plastic foot of a rigid member of wood or metal called a keel. The keel in the SACH foot is shaped to permit the leg to roll over the forefoot with a nearly natural appearance. The keel gives rigidity to the foot and at the end of stance phase leads to relative elongation of the leg. It provides no active plantar flexion of the ankle at push-off, such as that which occurs normally in the nonamputee. The forces required to swing the prosthesis forward must be contributed by the hip joint.

The horizontal rotations of the leg that were demonstrated to occur in the normal person during the stance phase of walking and were permitted by ankle and subtalar motion were completely ignored in the design of prostheses in the past. In fact, until a decade ago, these rotations were considered to be of little consequence. However, many skin problems occurred on the stump as a result of shearing forces between skin and socket. These were shown to be largely the result of the stump attempting to twist in an immovable socket. The degree of horizontal rotation of the leg has been shown to vary consdierably from individual to individual (13–29°) and those persons with a high degree of rotation have profited by the incorporation of rotator mechanisms into the prosthesis.

The Below-Knee Amputee

The amputee who retains a normal knee joint is fortunate. If the below-knee stump is of adequate length, the problems of knee stability and swing phase control do not occur. The major difficulty is fitting a comfortable socket for transmitting the body weight and assuring prosthetic control. The medial surface of the tibia lies directly under the skin for its entire length, and there is little musculature either laterally or posteriorly to provide subcutaneous padding. Total end-bearing on the cut bony structures is often painful. Attempts at capping the bone with bony or periosteal plugs have not proved effective in permitting end-bearing. To provide for weight transmission, two techniques are being employed, total contact between stump and socket or the molding of the socket so as to localize the forces in certain prescribed areas. A combination of these two techniques has resulted in the University of California Cuff Suspension Patellar-Tendon-Bearing (PTB) socket, which has become the most commonly prescribed socket.

In the past, a common cause of difficulty in the use of below-knee prostheses without sidebars has been the breakdown of the stump, in particular the knee joint on the amputated side. It has been due in part to overstraining of the ligamentous structures of the knee by excessive hyperextension under load. In order to protect these ligamentous structures on the amputated side, it is necessary to maintain within safe limits the forces and moments about the knee that tend to force it into hyperextension. In normal persons, a precise sense of knee position limits the hyperextension moment by maintaining the knee center close to the line of the force transmitted through the lower limb. Because in many below-knee amputees the knee action is unaffected by amputation, it is reasonable to expect such an amputee to walk with a normal knee action. When this potential is anticipated and accounted for in the fitting and alignment procedure, a below-knee amputee with average-to-long stump length can make use of the controlled flexion–extension–flexion sequence of knee action required in absorbing shock and smoothing the path of motion of the center of mass. The socket must be fitted to accommodate the dynamic forces, and the amputee must contribute voluntary control of the knee by action of the musculature.

Analysis of Stump–Socket Forces

The contact pressures between the stump and socket of a below-knee amputee are influenced by a combination of factors. In the case of the PTB prosthesis (or any other below-knee prosthesis without thigh corset and sidebars), the two major factors are the fit of the socket and the alignment of the prosthesis, i.e., the location of the foot with respect to the socket. When the thigh corset is used, there are certain modifying effects even when optimal alignment of sidebars and corset with respect to the socket is obtained. In discussing the relationship between fit and alignment, it is often helpful to discuss alignment factors first, because the method of fitting a socket to an amputee's stump is dictated largely by the manner in which he can be expected to perform while wearing his prosthesis. His performance, in turn, is influenced considerably by the structural relationship between the elements of his prosthesis, i.e., the alignment. The PTB prosthesis, without side joints or corset, is here discussed first. Thereafter, the modifying influences resulting from the addition of the side joints and corset are considered.

The following analysis is based on the assumption that a below-knee amputee with a stump of at least average length can be expected to walk in a manner similar to that of a normal person. That is, if the prosthetic foot is properly designed to minimize the effects of the loss of normal ankle function, the amputee can compensate by hip and knee action so as to achieve a gait closely approximating the normal. Accordingly, he should be expected to go through the following sequence of knee motions:

1. Control of knee flexion from the time of heel contact until the foot reaches a stable position flat on the floor

2. Control of knee flexion–extension during roll-over. The foot–shank serves as a firm base during this portion of stance phase. The position of the knee relative to the force acting on the foot can be gauged accurately by properly trained amputees. The muscle tension about the knee required to maintain a particular knee position serves as an excellent source of proprioception if the socket fit is intimate enough to reduce lost motion between stump and prosthesis to a minimum.

3. Control of knee flexion during push-off phase as an aid in accelerating the prosthesis forward in swing phase.

Mediolateral Forces, PTB Prosthesis

Figure 7.5 is a front view of a below-knee amputee in a position corresponding to the midstance phase. Two force systems are shown. Figure 7.5, *left*, shows the forces exerted on the amputee. These forces are of two types—the body weight and the forces applied through contact with the socket. Figure 7.5, *right*, shows the forces acting on the prosthesis.

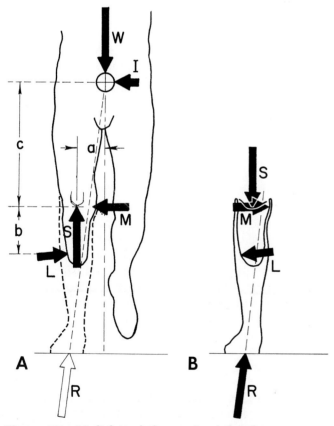

Figure 7.5. Mediolateral forces for below-knee amputee wearing PTB prosthesis. *Left*, forces on amputee. *Right*, forces on prosthesis. W, body weight. I, inertia force. M medial force. L, lateral force. S, support force. R, floor reaction.

If, as seen from the front, the prosthesis is considered as a means of supporting the body, it must be capable of providing both vertical support and mediolateral balance. It is apparent that vertical components of force are applied against the surfaces of many areas of the stump, but for purposes of simplified analysis the combined effect of all these forces is shown as the single support force S.

Considering the point of application of the support force S as a balance point, the lateral force L times the distance b equals the body weight W times the distance a, or, in equation form:

$$Lb = Wa \text{ and } L = \frac{Wa}{b} \qquad (1)$$

Unfortunately, the effect of the horizontal acceleration of the center of mass cannot be ignored in this case, and hence, in neglecting the horizontal acceleration equation (1) is incorrect.

As indicated in Figure 7.5, the horizontal acceleration of the body in a medial direction, resulting from the medial inclination of the total floor reaction R, results in a lateral inertia force that tends to oppose the acceleration. This inertia force must be included when consideration is given to balancing moments about the point of support. The correct relationship is therefore $Lb + Ic = Wa$:

$$L = \frac{Wa - Ic}{b} \qquad (2)$$

Equation (2) shows that the magnitude of the required lateral stabilizing (balancing) force L can be reduced in one of the two ways—by increasing the horizontal inertia force or by increasing the effective lever arm b. Increasing the horizontal inertia force requires that the horizontal acceleration be increased or, in other words, that the foot should be moved laterally so as to increase the medial inclination of the total floor reaction.

Effect of Foot Inset–Outset on Mediolateral Forces

The effect of changing the inset or outset of the foot is shown in Figure 7.6, where it is possible under special conditions, as shown in Figure 7.6, *right*, to eliminate the need for the lateral stabilization force L, because in this case, the weight and inertia forces are seen to be in balance:

$$Wa = Ic \qquad (3)$$

The force on the lateral aspect of the stump has shifted to the region of the head of the fibula.

Complete elimination of the lateral stabilizing force L by outset of the foot is generally undesirable, for the resulting wide-based gait is abnormal and unnecessary.

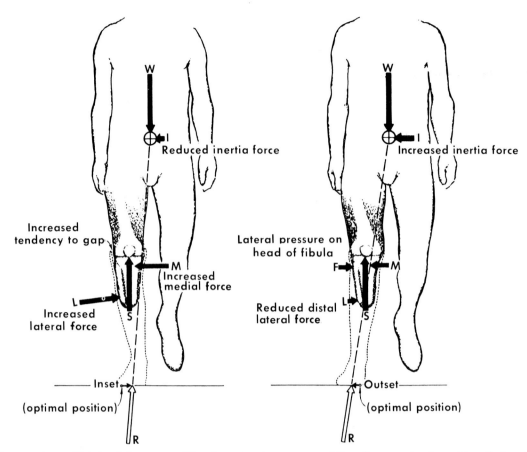

Figure 7.6.   Changes in mediolateral forces resulting from inset or outset of foot from optimal position (below-knee amputee wearing PTB prosthesis). *Left,* inset. *Right,* outset. *W,* body weight. *S,* support force. *F,* lateral force on head of fibula. *L,* lateral force. *M,* medial force. *I,* inertia force. *R,* floor reaction.

Actually, a narrow-based gait with a definite need for the lateral force *L* (and corresponding lack of force on the head of the fibula, which may be uncomfortable) is indicated for stumps 10 cm or more in length, the wide-based alignment being then reserved for very short below-knee stumps. It must be remembered, however, that planning the fit and alignment of a below-knee prosthesis to accommodate a narrow-based gait requires that the need for a definite lateral stabilizing force be recognized and accounted for in the fitting of the socket.

Effect of Thigh Corset and Sidebars on Mediolateral Forces

Figure 7.7 shows the modifying effect of the thigh corset and sidebars on the pressures between stump and socket. If the sidebars are stiff enough, it is possible to develop against the medial thigh a force *T* that acts in cooperation with the laterodistal socket contact force *L* in providing mediolateral stabilization. In fact, with judicious use of bending irons the lateral force can be greatly reduced. In the past, this has been done to compensate for uncomfortable laterodistal stump forces. With a good socket fit against the lateral aspect of average length stumps, however, the need for lateral

stabilization by the thigh corset is minimized. Use of a thigh corset is indicated only for amputees with very short stumps or those in whom other medical factors require reduction in stump-socket contact forces.

Anteroposterior Forces, PTB Prosthesis

Figure 7.8 shows a side view of a below-knee amputee and the cuff suspension prosthesis under three conditions—at heel contact, during the midstance phase, and during push-off. Just before and at the instant of heel contact, the knee is extending. The hamstrings act to prevent hyperextension of the knee resulting from the forward momentum of the prosthesis and to drive the heel to the walking surface. Further momentary stability is achieved by extension of the hip. The impact of the prosthesis on the walking surface is indicated by the vertical floor reaction *R* in Figure 7.8, *left*. This period of stance phase is very short and is followed immediately by the body weight being imposed on the prosthesis.

Analysis of the forces acting during the midstance phase shows that it is typical for the floor reaction force *R* to be acting along a line passing posterior to the knee center. Under such circumstances, a completely relaxed

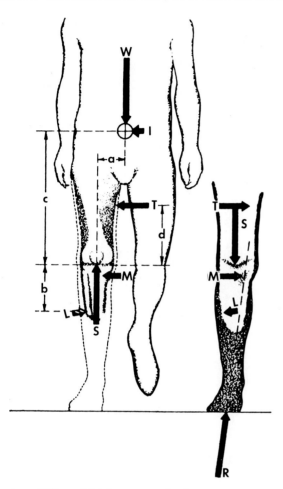

Figure 7.7. Effect of thigh corset and sidebars on mediolateral stump–socket forces. *W*, body weight. *T*, medial force provided by sidebar. *M*, medial force of socket. *L*, lateral force of socket. *S*, support force. *I*, inertia force. *R*, floor reaction.

knee would buckle, but the amputee is able to resist this tendency by active knee extension, achieved by quadriceps action and forceful extension of the hip (see Chapter 5). The resulting force pattern on the stump (disregarding end-bearing) is as shown in Figure 7.8, *middle*, where the forces are concentrated in three areas—around the patellar ligament, on the anterodistal portion of the tibia, and in the popliteal area. The socket fit must be designed to accommodate the resulting functional forces.

During the push-off phase, the floor reaction continues to pass behind the knee, and the anteroposterior forces are concentrated in the same three areas, as shown in Figure 7.8, *right*.

Effect of Thigh Corset and Sidebars on Anteroposterior Forces

If a below-knee amputee is fitted with a thigh corset and back check so that he relies on the mechanical action of the back check to resist knee extension, the force pattern is altered considerably. Figure 7.9 shows

the effect. The floor reaction *R* must now be assumed to pass anterior to the knee, because otherwise the knee would not be extended against the back check. If the knee joint is considered as a moment center, the effect of the force *R* is resisted by the back check moment *Mo* and the two forces *A* and *P* exerted by the stump within the socket. Under the proper conditions, it is possible for the mechanical back check to provide the total resistance to the floor reaction, the stump being suspended freely in the socket. This would indicate that, by proper adjustment of thigh corset, sidebars, and back check, it is possible to modify the pattern of anteroposterior stump–socket contact forces. This arrangement, however, results in high forces on the patellar ligament, which can be eliminated if the knee is allowed to flex, as illustrated in Figure 7.8, instead of being forced into full extension.

Thus it may be seen that, while the normal skeletal and neuromuscular structure of the lower limb is so organized as to accommodate the complex and precisely phased performance needed for erect bipedal locomotion, the below-knee amputee, even though provided with a well-fitting prosthesis of the PTB type, is unavoidably destined to experience in walking a continually changing set of stump–socket forces in both the anteroposterior and the mediolateral directions. Successful fitting of the below-knee amputee means, therefore, the resolution of stump–socket forces in such a way as to provide both comfortable support and adequate stabilization throughout the walking cycle. Whenever addition of thigh corset and sidebars is required, there occurs a change in the pattern of motion, and hence a change in stump–socket forces to be anticipated, and accordingly suitable modifications are required. Allowance for such factors calls in every case for the sound judgment of the prosthetist if fully satisfactory results are to be obtained.

The Hip Disarticulation Amputee

Disarticulation at the hip and hemipelvectomy are radical procedures generally made on the basis of medical indications. The functional loss is obviously the greatest of all lower limb amputations. Considerable research over a period of years has resulted in the development of a prosthesis that makes it possible for the amputee to walk with a fairly normal-appearing gait without using a cane. The functional features of the original design were developed in Canada and reported by McLaurin (1954). Some further modifications and refinements have since been made (Radcliffe, 1957).

Briefly, a continuous, laminated plastic socket–waistband is fitted so as to provide three reaction points (points of suspension), as shown in Figure 7.10. The weight-bearing area of the socket is constructed of rigid plastic laminate, while the waistband is made flexible

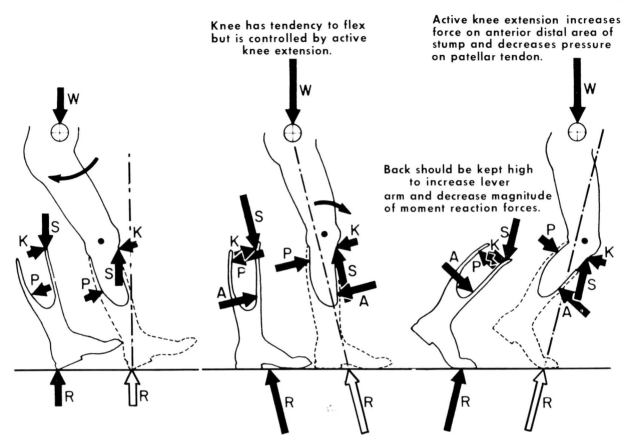

Knee has tendency to flex but is controlled by active knee extension.

Active knee extension increases force on anterior distal area of stump and decreases pressure on patellar tendon.

Back should be kept high to increase lever arm and decrease magnitude of moment reaction forces.

Figure 7.8. Anteroposterior forces in below-knee amputee wearing PTB prosthesis. *Left*, at heel contact. *Middle*, during midstance phase. *Right*, during push-off. W, body weight. S, support force. K, force on patellar ligament. P, posterior force. A, anterior force. R, floor reaction.

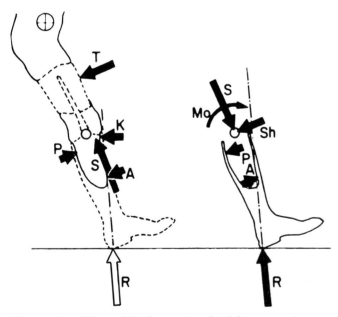

Figure 7.9. Effect of thigh corset and sidebars on anteroposterior stump–socket forces. *Left*, forces on stump. *Right*, forces on socket. T, force of thigh corset. K, force on patellar ligament. P, posterior force. A, anterior force. Mo, back check moment. S, support force. Sh, shear force absorbed by mechanical side joint. R, floor reaction.

to permit easy donning of the prosthesis. A full width hip joint similar to a prosthetic knee joint allows a strong connection between socket and thigh, and is effective in resisting lateral bending at the connection between socket and thigh piece.

In level walking, the hip joint allows approximately 15° of motion between socket and thigh. The amount of motion is limited by a hip flexion control strap (shown as "elastic band" in Fig. 7.10). This arrangement allows the leg to assume a natural inclination at heel contact without backward tilting of the pelvis.

A unique arrangement of joint locations results in improved security against buckling of the knee in any normal walking situation, the hip joint being located below and forward of the normal axis of the hip (see Fig. 7.10). With the hip joint so located, the effective length of the leg is the same in both standing and sitting. A reference line extended through the hip and knee joints passes a minimum of 2.5 cm behind the heel, so that as long as the prosthesis bears weight, the load transmitted between the foot and the hip joint always passes ahead of the knee joint, thus ensuring knee security. When required, flexion of the knee is initiated by contact of the elastic hip bumper (attached to the

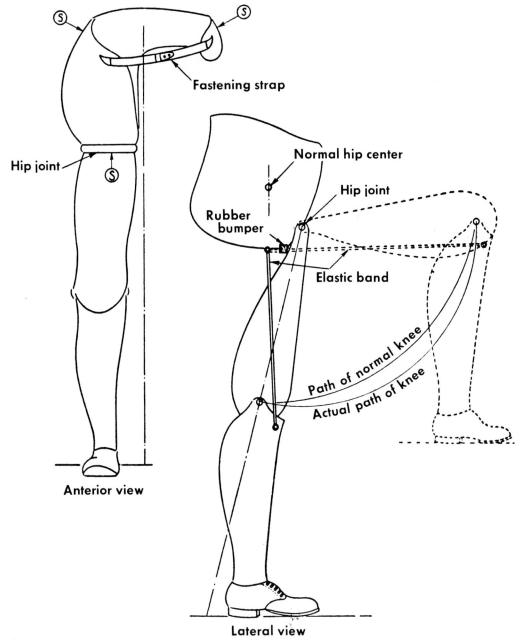

Figure 7.10. Anterior and lateral views of Canadian hip disarticulation prosthesis, showing location of three points of suspension and location of joints. S, point of suspension.

bottom of the socket) with a stop on the upper posterior portion of the thigh. As long as the hip bumper is not in contact, the knee joint is always completely stable.

Functional Sequence in Use of the Prosthesis

As the legs swings forward preparatory to heel contact, the hip flexion control strap limits the free hip joint motion to approximately 15° but still permits 90° of flexion for sitting. This hip joint motion, in combination with a slight pelvic motion, allows the leg to assume a natural backward inclination as the heel makes contact. The amputee moves forward over the prosthesis, and the heel is planted on the floor without hesitation. The foot should not swing up and then snap back into contact with the floor. The weight-bearing prosthesis is extremely stable because of the alignment of the hip, knee, and ankle joints, and the objective is to attain knee security by having an appreciable amount of force transmitted through the prosthesis at the instant of heel contact. Where additional security is desired, the amputee leans forward slightly at the time of heel contact. Doing so results in an increased tension in the hip flexion control strap, which helps to hold the knee in full extension.

As the amputee rolls over the extended prosthesis during the midportion of stance phase, knee security is increased as the weight-bearing line moves forward toward the ball of the foot. Hip joint motion causes the hip flexion control strap to relax, and the amputee rides forward with the socket balanced on the free hip joint. Pelvic stability is maintained by the momentum of the trunk.

At the end of stance phase, the prosthesis must be propelled forward into swing phase. A normal person achieves knee flexion at the time of push-off by combined hip and ankle action. The amputee using the Canadian hip disarticulation prosthesis initiates flexion by a method somewhat similar to that used by an above-knee amputee wearing a suction socket. As the prosthesis inclines forward with the weight borne through the ball of the foot, the angle of hip flexion is reduced until contact is made between the elastic bumper system at the rear of the hip joint. As the socket continues to progress forward in a straight line (without pelvic rotation), continued forward inclination of the thigh causes an increase in the compression in the bumper system. The moment thus developed about the hip joint

eventually disturbs the knee stability and causes the knee to flex forward into swing phase. By proper adjustment of the stiffness and point of contact of the hip bumper system, a very natural knee flexion at the time of push-off can be achieved. The amputee should never lift the pelvis and swing the leg forward by internal pelvic rotation. Rather, the recommended action is exactly the opposite. The amputee "sits hard" on the prosthesis in order to start the knee flexing. When more rapid knee flexion is desired, a slight backward rotation of the socket to increase the compression of the hip bumper will propel the prosthesis forward forcibly. If weight is transferred to the natural leg simultaneously, there should be no feeling of insecurity at this time.

Forces Between the Socket and the Stump

Figure 7.11 shows, as viewed from the front, the rather simple force system acting when an amputee is walking on a Canadian hip disarticulation prosthesis, the situation depicted being the period of midstance on the prosthesis, when mediolateral dynamic effects are negligible. The diagram on the *left* shows the system of externally applied forces acting on the prosthesis alone.

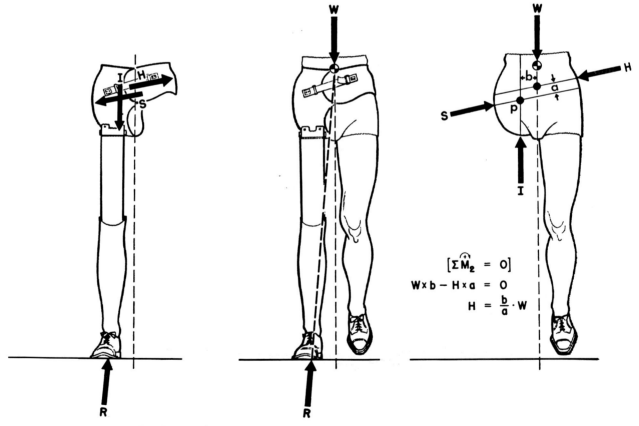

$$[\Sigma M_2 = 0]$$
$$W \times b - H \times a = 0$$
$$H = \frac{b}{a} \cdot W$$

Figure 7.11. Anterior view of hip disarticulation amputee, showing force system in effect at midstance. *Left*, externally applied forces acting on prosthesis. *Middle*, forces acting on amputee and prosthesis together. *Right*, forces acting on amputee. W, body weight. S, resultant force of socket on side of prosthesis. H, resultant force of socket on normal side. I, resultant force of vertical support. R, floor reaction.

That in the *middle* shows the forces acting on the combination of the amputee and the prosthesis. That on the *right* shows the force system acting on the amputee.

Figure 7.11, *middle*, involves the simplest force system and is therefore discussed first. Two forces are involved—the supporting floor reaction R and the downward force of the body weight W. The vertical component of the floor reaction is equal in magnitude to the downward force and hence just balances the body weight. The body can, therefore, be assumed to be in force equilibrium in the vertical direction. But the floor reaction, being inclined generally inward, has an inward component along the floor, which means that the entire body is being accelerated toward the sound side. This acceleration would result in a change in direction of motion of the trunk, that is, in a movement toward the amputee's normal side. Such mediolateral oscillating motion of the body as a whole is characteristic of normal subjects as well as of amputees. To maintain mediolateral motion within normal limits in the amputee, the inclination of the floor reaction to the plane of progression must be minimized, and the hip disarticulation prosthesis is, therefore, aligned to give a narrow walking base. Experience has shown that the walking base should be less than 10 cm from heel center to heel center.

Consideration of forces acting on the stump, which result in part from the requirement of a narrow walking base, is more complicated. As can be seen in Figure 7.11, *right*, four forces act on the combined stump and trunk of the hip disarticulation amputee—the downward force of the body weight acting through the center of mass, the distributed vertical support forces acting upward on the ischial–gluteal region, and distributed socket forces between stump and socket–waistband acting on both normal and amputated sides. A single force vector is used when necessary to approximate the effects of the actual pressure distribution.

Figure 7.11, *left*, shows the forces acting on the prosthesis considered as an isolated free body.

If the body weight W and ischial–gluteal support force I were the only two forces acting on the trunk, the body would have a tendency to rotate about the point of support and to drop toward the unsupported normal side. This tendency is counteracted by the moment of the couple formed by the two mediolateral forces H and S. For moment equilibrium, taking the summation of moments about point 2 equal to zero, $W \times b = H \times a$. Or,

$$H = \frac{b}{a} W$$

Thus, the magnitude of the reaction against the normal hip, or the tension in the waistband, or both, can be reduced by increasing the distance a. Moving the concentration of lateral forces, S, on the stump to a lower level by alteration of fit is practical only within certain limits. Too low a position would result in shear forces along the bottom of the stump and in considerable motion between stump and socket. It is also apparent that, owing to the limitations on increasing dimension a, the lateral forces H and S are of the same order of magnitude as the vertical forces W and I, because dimensions a and B would be approximately equal.

Figure 7.12 shows the pattern of forces acting on the amputee and/or his prosthesis as viewed from the side during level walking. Figure 7.12, *left*, indicates the force system acting on the prosthesis at heel contact. Figure 7.12, *middle*, shows the forces exerted by the socket on the stump–trunk, plus the action of the body weight, during the three major divisions of the stance phase in level walking—heel contact, midstance, and push-off. Figure 7.12, *right*, is a diagram of the isolated prosthesis at push-off. The use of such diagrams allows a clear distinction between forces acting on the amputee and forces acting on the prosthesis.

At the time of heel contact on the prosthesis, the normal leg is completing push-off. The force acting on the normal foot is then transmitted through the normal leg to the pelvis. This thrust of the normal leg is shown by the dotted arrow in Figure 7.12, *middle*, acting on the normal side of the pelvis. Shown in addition to the force from the normal leg are the force of body weight and the distal, posterodistal, and anteroproximal stump–socket forces. The floor reaction force causes the system of stump–socket forces shown acting on the socket in Figures 7.12, *left* and *right*. The isolated prosthesis must be in equilibrium under the action of stump contact forces plus the floor reaction. The same system of stump contact forces reacts in such a way as to appear as forces applied in the opposite sense in the diagrams of Figure 7.12, *middle*. Because of the offset lever arm between body weight and the line of vertical support through the ischium, a counteracting stabilizing force is required in the anteroproximal region. The thrust of the normal leg at heel contact tends to increase the unbalanced moment about the distal point of support and, hence, to increase the need for an anteroproximal counterforce in the inguinal region.

In the midstance phase, the normal leg is off the floor, and the four forces shown in the *middle* diagram of Figure 7.12 are acting. The anteroproximal pressure on the stump is reduced as compared with that existing in the heel contact phase. This circumstance indicates that errors in fitting would be more noticeable at the time of heel contact than in the succeeding midstance phase. If the dynamic effects of acceleration are ignored, two forces act on the combined amputee and prosthesis

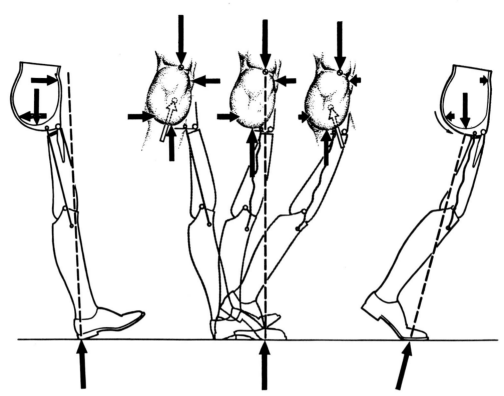

Figure 7.12. Forces acting on hip disarticulation amputee and prosthesis viewed from side. *Left*, forces acting on prosthesis at heel contact. *Middle*, forces exerted by socket on stump and trunk, plus effect of body weight, during three major divisions of stance phase—heel contact, midstance, and push-off. *Right*, forces acting on prosthesis at push-off.

during the midstance phase—the body weight and the upward floor reaction force on the sole of the foot. This situation prevails until the normal foot again makes contact with the floor ahead of the prosthesis.

At about the same time that the normal foot strikes the floor, the hip bumper system in the prosthesis makes contact and tends to flex the knee. During this push-off phase, there is again a thrust on the pelvis from the normal leg, this time from the front, as shown in Figure 7.12, *middle*. The thrust of the normal leg counteracts the offset body weight and further reduces the need for anteroproximal support from the socket. This feature gives the amputee a greater degree of control of the prosthetic knee, because the stump–socket forces are reduced and the effects of the hip bumper force acting on the bottom of the socket are, therefore, more readily distinguishable. With a properly adjusted hip bumper system, the amputee is able to exercise a more than adequate control and timing of knee flexion even though some of the body weight is still being carried by the prosthesis at this time.

Owing to the ever-changing nature of the stump–socket force system as viewed from the side, it is necessary to fit the distal portion of the socket snugly in the posterior region in order to prevent motion between stump and socket in the more highly stressed areas of vertical support under the ischial tuberosity.

Surgical Implications

Figure 7.13 shows oblique front and back views of a typical hip disarticulation stump. Cross-hatching on the surface of the stump indicates those areas where biomechanical analysis shows a functional need for supporting or stabilizing contact pressure between stump and socket. Clearly indicated are those areas where surgical incisions should be avoided, in particular the ischial–gluteal, inguinal, and laterodistal areas. The incision and resulting scar should be located along the anterodistal portion of the stump, as shown in Figure 7.13, *left*. This area is not required to tolerate localized pressure and is generally relieved during the fitting process in order to avoid pressure-sensitive areas over bony prominences in the pubic region.

Implications for Fitting

Biomechanical force analysis shows certain regions over the stump where particular attention must be paid to socket fit. They include the ischial–gluteal, inguinal, and waistband contact areas.

In the ischial–gluteal area, functional pressures must be developed on a bony prominence and a neighboring area of atrophied gluteal masculature. This requirement calls for careful location and fitting of the bony prominence of the tuberosity. In order to develop pressure on the soft tissues, considerable modification of the cast is

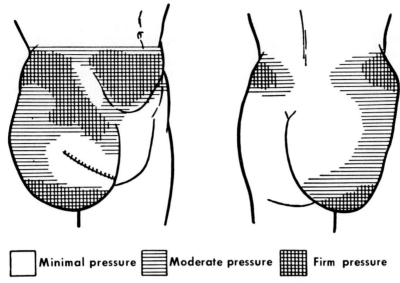

☐ **Minimal pressure**   ☰ **Moderate pressure**   ▦ **Firm pressure**

Figure 7.13.   Oblique front and back views of hip disarticulation stump, showing areas of relative pressure.

required. This displaces the soft tissues upward in the socket, and the necessary functional contact pressure is achieved. The pressure in the gluteal area is an absolute necessity in order to stabilize the distal end of the stump on the bottom of the socket. Otherwise, chafing due to shearing motions between stump and socket will result.

The inginual region must provide a major contribution to the anteroposterior stabilization of the trunk. An inaccurate fit in this region will result in concentration of pressure at a lower level in the generally sensitive pubic areas. The soft tissues of the inguinal and abdominal areas must be displaced inward if the proper functional stump–socket pressure is to be achieved. This is most easily accomplished by wrapping the cast in this region while the patient is supine.

The mediolateral force that must be transmitted by the waistband extending around the normal hip approaches the body weight in magnitude. The waistband must be fitted very carefully to avoid local concentration of pressure on bony prominences.

Training Implications

Training a hip disarticulation amputee to walk on a properly fitted, aligned, and adjusted Canadian prosthesis is not a difficult or time-consuming process. If the therapist is thoroughly acquainted with the functional principles of the prosthesis and with the methods of fitting and adjustment, a well-coordinated amputee should walk unaided, without a cane, after less than 10 hours of training. Proper adjustment of the hip bumper, hip flexion control strap, and ankle–foot characteristics is absolutely essential for efficient use of the prosthesis. For this reason, therapist and prosthetist should work together during the initial training sessions.

Particular points to be stressed by the therapist in

working with the amputee are:

1. Develop confidence in the stability of the knee at heel contact. Emphasize the necessity for a confident placing of the prosthetic heel and for simultaneous weight-bearing. Show that knee stability will increase in direct proportion to the amount of force transmitted by the prosthesis.

2. Show the action of the three-point mediolateral support of the trunk. Do not allow the amputee to bend his trunk over the prosthesis. If painful pressure develops over a bony prominence, have the prosthetist provide relief or padding.

3. Place considerable emphasis on the timing and use of the pelvis to propel the prosthetic knee forward. Remember that the amputee "sits" to flex the knee while the prosthesis continues to bear a portion of the body weight. The amputee should not lift the prosthesis off the floor and then propel it forward by internal rotation of the pelvis.

The Syme Amputee

The Syme amputee has lost the foot and ankle while retaining essentially the full length of the shank. The obvious problem is to restore foot and ankle function (or to supply the equivalent of foot–ankle function), to extend the stump so as to accommodate the loss of the tarsus and the calcaneus, to furnish adequate support for the body during standing and during the stance phase of walking, to provide suitable suspension for the prosthesis during swing phase, and to do all these things in such a way that the final result is acceptable to the wearer under both static and dynamic conditions.

As with prostheses for other levels of amputation in the lower limb, determination of the requirements of the Syme prosthesis takes its departure from a review of the normal pattern of walking and proceeds toward assessment of the means through which such a pattern may best be reproduced by application of inanimate devices.

At the time of heel contact involving shock absorption, the normal ankle plantar flexes while the knee flexes. Because ankle function has been lost, some way of compensating for it must be found. Because of the inherent space limitations in conventional Syme prosthesis, use of articulated ankle joints and elastic compression members has been for the most part unsuccessful. In order to keep stresses in elastic bumpers within reasonable limits, the bumpers must contain a certain minimal volume of material. Otherwise, the energy absorption requirements per unit volume are excessive, and overheating and fatigue occur rapidly. The alternatives are to increase the volume of shock-absorbing material so as to reduce the unit stresses, or to transfer shock absorption to some other area, or both.

The volume of shock-absorbing material can be increased by eliminating the articulated ankle joint and using in the heel the greatest possible volume of suitable sponge rubber cushion as in the SACH foot (*Evaluation* 1957). In general, function may be improved over that supplied by an articulated joint, but because of the space limitation, the Syme amputee cannot be given the same degree of shock absorption as can be supplied to the above-knee or below-knee amputee wearing a SACH foot.

To compensate for the lack of adequate function in the artificial foot, the knee joint on the side of the amputation must assume a greater proportion of shock absorption by increasing the amount of knee flexion under load just after heel contact. If the knee does not assume this function, the amputee must tolerate a definite impact force from prosthesis to stump and must accept the deviation from normal gait that might be expected to accompany such a circumstance.

As stance phase proceeds through the so-called roll-over portion, the knee of the nonamputee continues to flex under load with active plantar flexion, prolonging the function of shock absorption for the initial support of the body weight. Because of the lack of active plantar flexion in Syme amputees, maximal knee flexion during this phase is in general less than it is in normal persons.

In normal walking, the body continues to roll over the foot, which is in full contact with the floor, and the knee begins a period of active extension. In the typical Syme amputee, the foot–ankle is passively rotating, requiring no energy from the knee and thus reducing the energy requirement of the knee as compared with that of the normal person.

During the last part of normal roll-over, before push-off, the knee is forced into full extension and maintained there by the external forces acting upward on the ball of the foot. The prosthetic foot must be designed so as that the forward point of support corresponds to the ball of the foot, an arrangement that maintains the knee along a path corresponding to that of the normal. The knee should move forward smoothly, and no sensation of vaulting over the forepart of the foot should be experienced. In the amputee wearing a Syme prosthesis with a properly aligned SACH foot, knee action at the end of roll-over should be almost the same as it is in a normal person.

The push-off portion of stance phase begins when the heel is lifted from the floor. In the normal, this is accomplished by knee flexion and active ankle plantar flexion. In the Syme amputee, the ankle substitute cannot produce active plantar flexion and other means must be found to maintain a smooth path of the center of mass of the body. A comparatively simple keel contour, with a cylindrical or spherical surface at the end of the keel, has been found practical for most adults. Under these circumstances, the hip and knee joints serve as the active elements in the kinematic chain controlling the pathway of the center of mass.

Toward the end of push-off, the prosthesis must maintain the pathway of the knee by proper keel contour rather than by active plantar flexion of the ankle. The need to initiate knee flexion before the end of stance phase remains, however, and the socket must therefore be designed to permit maximal control of knee motion by the stump in preparation for swing phase.

In the patient with Syme's amputation, the knee and hip joints are usually undisturbed and swing phase should appear relatively normal. If, however, the foot–ankle does not permit a smooth transition from stance to swing, there is a noticeable effect throughout swing phase. Poor function in the prosthetic foot and pain in the weight-bearing areas of the stump are the two most common sources of unstable or erratic action during transition from stance to swing phase.

The forces that must be transmitted to the stump at the two critical times during stance phase, heel contact with shock absorption and push-off, are illustrated in Figure 7.14. Resultant forces only are shown; the socket must be shaped so that there is comfortable transmission of the contact pressures.

At heel contact, Figure 7.14, *top*, the body weight is supported at the distal end of the stump, and because of the eccentric position of the heel reaction F, a force P is developed at the back of the stump. By estimating the dimensions a and b, and using body weight plus an impact factor as high as 20% of body weight, an approximation of the magnitude of forces P and D can be obtained.

In a similar manner, the forces at push-off as shown

in Figure 7.14, *bottom*, may be estimated, determining the approximate force to be distributed along the front of the stump, force A. This force will normally be several times the posterior force P at heel contact, requiring that the prosthesis be strong enough to resist the large bending moment in the ankle region.

Because of the bulbous form of the typical Syme stump, any prosthesis devised for it will be bulky in appearance. To provide the least bulky socket requires that the thickness of the wall be kept to a minimum commensurate with structural demands. Plastic laminates, with high strength–weight ratios, that can be molded easily over a plaster model seem ideally suited for the construction of sockets for the Syme prosthesis.

Because a snug fit throughout the length of the stump is necessary if proper function is to be expected with comfort, a cutout must be provided in the narrow section of the socket to permit entry of the bulbous end of the stump. Two locations have been used, posterior or medial, but in either case care must be taken to ade-

quately strengthen the region of the cutout: for maximal tension stress at the posterior cutout and to prevent buckling of the thin wall under compressive stress when the cutout is located medially.

To satisfy the requirements of a comfortable transmission of functional stump–socket contact forces, the socket must provide the following features:

1. Comfortable support of the body weight on the distal end of the stump, on the proximal part of the socket brim, or both.

2. Firm support against the anteroproximal surface of the stump at the time of push-off. Careful fitting against the wedgelike medial and lateral surfaces of the tibia can satisfy this requirement.

3. Similar support against the posterior surface of the leg at the time of heel contact. Excessive motion between socket and stump should be prevented as the reaction point shifts from the posterior to the anterior surface of the leg.

4. Provision for shifting of the center of pressure

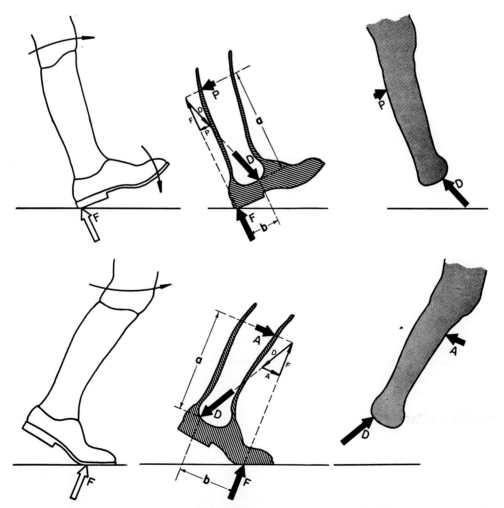

Figure 7.14.   Stump–socket forces in Syme amputee during stance phase. *Top*, shock absorption at heel contact. *Bottom*, push-off. *F*, floor reaction. *D*, reaction force on stump. *P*, posterior force. *A*, anterior force.

against the distal end of the stump as indicated in the force analysis, Figure 7.14. If a cuplike receptacle is provided for the stump end, it must extend around and up the sides of the bulbous stump far enough to prevent motion between stump and socket.

5. Adequate stabilization against the torques about the long axis of the leg. Stabilization against the medial and lateral flares of the tibia and a flattening of the posterior contour can be effective in providing necessary torque resistance. Torques acting on the distal end of the stump will result in skin abrasion and other associated difficulties in more proximal areas unless needed stabilization is provided.

REFERENCES

Abbott, B. C., Bigland, B., and Ritchie, J. M. The physiological cost of negative work. *J. Physiol. (Lond.) 117*:380, 1952.

Adelaar, R. S., Dannelly, E. A., Meunier, P. A., Stelling, F. H., and Colvard, D. F. A long-term study of triple arthrodesis in children. Proc. American Academy of Orthopaedic Surgeons. *J. Bone Joint Surg. 58-A*:724, 1976.

Ahlgren, J., and Öwall, B. Muscular activity and chewing force: A polygraphic study of human mandibular movements. *Arch. Oral Biol. 15*:271, 1970.

Asbelle, C. C., and Canty, T. J. Final Technical Report, Research Project NM 74 01 70.27. *A Functional Ankle (Cable) for Artificial Legs: A Report of Completed Investigations with Respect to the Design, Testing, Manufacture, Use and Evaluation of a Functional Ankle Unit for Artificial Legs.* Amputee Service, Navy Prosthetic Research Laboratory, U.S. Naval Hospital, Oakland, California, 1957.

Asmussen, E. Experiments on positive and negative work. In *Symposium on Fatigue*, edited by W. F. Floyd and A. T. Welford. H. K. Lewis & Co., London, 1953. p. 77.

Atzler, E., and Herbst, R. Arbeitsphysiologische Studien. Part 3. *Pflügers Arch. 215*:291, 1927.

Baker, P. L. SACH heel improves results of ankle fusion. *J. Bone Joint Surg. 52-A*:1485, 1970.

Basmajian, J. V. *Muscles Alive*, ed. 4. Williams & Wilkins, Baltimore, 1978.

Basmajian, J. V., and Bentzon, J. W. Cited by Joseph (1960), p. 50.

Bayer, H., and Flechtenmacher, C. Ermüden und Aktionsstromspannung bei der isometrischen Muskelkontraktion des Menschen. *Arbeitsphysiol. 14*:261, 1950.

Bechtol, C. O. Personal communication, 1979.

Berger, R. A. Leg extension force at three different angles. *Res. Quart. Am. Assoc. Health Phys. Educ. 37*:560, 1966.

Bergmann, G., Kölbel, R., Rauschenbach, N., and Rohlmann, A. Crutch walking and hip mechanics. Proc. British Orthopaedic Research Society meeting, Nov. 1977. In *J. Bone Joint Surg. 60-B*:281, 1978.

Bigland, B., and Lippold, O. C. J. The relation between force, velocity and integrated electrical activity in human muscles. *J. Physiol. (Lond.) 123*:214, 1954.

Blount, W. P. Don't throw away the cane. Presidential Address, Annual Meeting, Academy of Orthopaedic Surgeons, 1956. In *J. Bone Joint Surg. 38-A*:695, 1956.

Bobbert, A. C. Energy expenditure in level and grade walking. *J. Appl. Physiol. 15*:1015, 1960.

Bojsen-Møller, F., and Lamoreux, L. Significance of free dorsiflexion of the toes in walking. *Acta Orthop. Scand. 50*:471, 1979.

Boothby, W. M., Berkson, J., and Dunn, H. L. Studies of the energy of metabolism of normal individuals: A standard for basal metabolism, with a nomogram for clinical application. *Am. J. Physiol. 116*:468, 1936.

Booyens, J., and Keatinge, W. R. The expenditure of energy by men and women walking. *J. Physiol. (Lond.) 138*:165, 1957.

Braune, W., and Fischer, O. Über den Schwerpunkt des menschlichen Körpers, mit Rücksicht auf die Ausrüstung des deutschen Infanteristen. *Abh. Math.-phys, Cl. K. Sächs. Ges. Wissensch. 15*:559, 1889.

Bresler, B., and Berry, F. R. *Energy and Power in the Leg During Normal Level Walking.* Prosthetic Devices Research Project, Institute of Engineering Research, University of California, Berkeley. Series 11, issue 15. The Project, Berkeley, 1951.

Carlsöö, Sven. How Man Moves. William Heinemann Ltd., London, 1972. (Distributed by Crane, Russak and Co., Inc., New York).

Cavagna, G. A. Human locomotion. In *Comparative Physiology*, edited by L. Bolis, K. Schmidt-Nielsen, and S. H. P. Maddrell. North-Holland Publishing Co., Amsterdam-London, American Elsevier Publishing Co., New York, 1973.

Cavagna, G. A., Dusman, B., and Margaria, R. Positive work done by a previously stretched muscle. *J. Appl. Physiol. 24*:21, 1968.

Cavagna, G. A., Heglund, N. C., and Taylor, C. R. Mechanical work in terrestrial locomotion: Two basic mechanisms for minimizing energy expenditure. *Am. J. Physiol. 233*:R243, 1977, or *Am. J. Physiol. Regulatory Integrative Comp. Physiol. 2*:R243, 1977.

Cavagna, G. A., and Kaneko, M. Mechanical work and efficiency in level walking and running. *J. Physiol. (Lond.) 268*:467, 1977.

Cavagna, G. A., Saibene, F. P., and Margaria, R. External work in walking. *J. Appl. Physiol. 18*:1, 1963.

Chodera, J. D., and Levell, R. W. Footprint patterns during walking. In *Perspectives in Biomedical Engineering*, edited by R. M. Kenedi. [No publisher given], 1973.

Close, J. R., and Inman, V. T. *The Action of the Subtalar Joint.* Prosthetic Devices Research Project, Institute of Engineering Research, University of California, Berkeley. Series 11, issue 24. The Project, Berkeley, 1953.

Close, J. R., Nickel, E. D., and Todd, F. N. Motor-unit action-potential counts: Their significance in isometric and isotonic contractions. *J. Bone Joint Surg. 42-A*:1207, 1960.

Contini, R., Drillis, R. J., Gage, H., and Yatkauskas, A. *Functional Evaluation and Acceptability of the Henschke-Mauch "Hydraulik" Swing and Stance Control System.* Department of Medicine and Surgery, Veterans Administration, Washington, D.C., 1964. Report No. 1037-1.

Cooper, S., and Eccles, J. C. The isometric responses of mammalian muscles. *J. Physiol. (Lond.) 69*:377, 1930.

Corcoran, P. J., and Brengelmann, G. L. Oxygen uptake in normal and handicapped subjects, in relation to speed of walking beside velocity-controlled cart. *Arch. Phys. Med. Rehabil. 51*:78, 1970.

Cotes, J. E., and Meade, F. The energy expenditure and mechanical energy demand in walking. *Ergonomics 3*:97, 1960.

Cotes, J. E., Meade, F., and Wise, M. E. Standardization of test exercise. *Fed. Proc. 16*:25, 1957.

Dean, G. A. An analysis of the energy expenditure in level and grade walking. *Ergonomics 8*:31, 1965.

Dempster, W. T. *Space Requirements of the Seated Operator: Geometrical, Kinematic, and Mechanical Aspects of the Body with Special Reference to the Limbs.* U.S. Wright Air Development

Center. Technical Report 55-159, Wright-Patterson Air Force Base, Ohio, 1955.

Drillis, R. Objective recording and biomechanics of pathological gait. *Ann. N.Y. Acad. Sci.* 17:86, 1958.

Drillis, R. J. The influence of aging on the kinematics of gait. In *The Geriatric Amputee.* Report on Conference sponsored by Committee on Prosthetics Research and Development of the Division of Engineering and Industrial Research, Washington, D.C., April 13–14, 1961. Publication 919. National Academy of Sciences—National Research Council, Washington, D.C., 1961.

Durnin, J. V. G. A., and Passmore, R. *Energy, Work and Leisure.* Heinemann Educational Books, London, 1967.

Elftman, H. Forces and energy changes in the leg during walking. *Am. J. Physiol. 125:339, 1939.*

Elftman, H. The functional structure of the lower limb. In *Human Limbs and Their Substitutes,* edited by P. E. Klopsteg, P. D. Wilson, et al. McGraw-Hill Book Company, New York, 1954. Reprinted 1968.

Elftman, H. The transverse tarsal joint and its control. *Clin Orthop. 16:41, 1960.*

Evaluation of the Production Model Solid Ankle Cushion Heel (SACH) Foot. Prosthetic Devices Study, Research Division, College of Engineering, New York University. Report No. 115.23. The Study, New York, 1957.

Fenn, W. O. Work against gravity and work due to velocity changes in running: Movements of the center of gravity within the body and foot pressure on the ground. *Am. J. Physiol. 93:433, 1930.*

Finley, F. R., and Cody, K. A. Locomotive characteristics of urban pedestrians. *Arch. Phys. Med. Rehabil. 51:423, 1970.*

Finley, F. R., Wirta, R. W., Craik, R., Bampton, S., Bolton, A. R., and Bryant, H. Fundamental study of human locomotion. In Rehabilitation Services Administration, Rehabilitation Research and Training Center #8, Progress Report 11. May 1, 1974–April 30, 1975. Temple University in conjunction with Moss Rehabilitation Hospital, Philadelphia, Pennsylvania.

Fischer, O. *Theoretische Grundlagen für eine Mechanik der lebenden Körper mit speziellen Anwendungen auf den Menschen, sowie auf einige Bewegungs-vorgänge an Menschen.* B. G. Teubner, Leipzig and Berlin, 1906.

Fundamental Studies of Human Locomotion and Other Information Relating to Design of Artificial Limbs. Subcontractor's Report to the Committee on Artificial Limbs, National Research Council. Prosthetic Devices Research Project, College of Engineering, University of California, Berkeley. Serial No. CAL 5. 2 vols. The Project, Berkeley, 1947.

Gardner, E. Discussion of Kaplan (1958). *J. Bone Joint Surg. 40-A:831, 1958.*

Gollnick, P. G., Tipton, C. M., and Karpovich, P. V. Electrogoniometric study of walking in high heels. *Res. Quart. Am. Assoc. Health Phys. Educ. 35:370, 1964.*

Gore, D. R., Murray, M. P., Sepic, S. B., and Gardner, G. M. Walking patterns of men with unilateral surgical hip fusion. *J. Bone Joint Surg. 57-A:759, 1975.*

Gregersen, G. G., and Lucas, D. B. An *in vivo* study of the axial rotation of the human thoracolumbar spine. *J. Bone Joint Surg. 49-A:247, 1967.*

Grieve, D. W., and Gear, R. J. The relationships between length of stride, step frequency, time of swing, and speed of walking for children and adults. *Ergonomics 5:379, 1966.*

Haines, R. W. On muscles of full and of short action. *J. Anat. 69:20, 1934.*

Haxton, H. A. Absolute muscle force in the ankle flexors of man. *J. Physiol. (Lond.) 103:267, 1944.*

Hicks, J. H. The mechanics of the foot. II. The plantar aponeurosis and the arch. *J. Anat. 88:25, 1954.*

Hirschberg, G. G., and Ralston, H. J. Energy cost of stair-climbing in normal and hemiplegic subjects. *Am. J. Phys. Med. 44:165, 1965.*

Hugh-Jones, P. Effect of limb position in seated subjects on their ability to utilize maximum contractile force of limb muscles. *J. Physiol. (Lond). 105:332, 1947.*

Huson, A. *Een ontleedkundig-functioneel onderzoek van de voetwortel: An Anatomical and Functional Study of the Tarsal Joints.* Luctor et Emergo, Leiden, 1961.

Huxley, A. F. Review lecture: Muscle contraction. *J. Physiol. (Lond.) 243:1, 1974.*

Inman, V. T. Functional aspects of the abductor muscles of the hip. *J. Bone Joint Surg. 29:607, 1947.*

Inman, V. T. *The Joints of the Ankle.* The Williams & Wilkins Company, Baltimore, 1976.

Inman, V. T.: UC-BL Dual-Axis Ankle-Control System and UC-BL Shoe Insert: Biomechanical considerations. *Bull. Prosthet. Res. BPR 10-11:130, 1969.*

Inman, V. T., Ralston, H. J., Saunders, J. B. deC. M., Feinstein, B., and Wright, E. W., Jr. Relation of human electromyogram to muscular tension. *Electroencephalogr. Clin. Neurophysiol. 4:187, 1952.*

Isman, R. E., and Inman, V. T. Anthropometric studies of the human foot and ankle. *Bull. Prosthet. Res. BPR 10-11:97, 1969.*

Joseph, J. *Man's Posture: Electromyographic Studies.* Charles C. Thomas, Springfield, Illinois, 1960.

Kaplan, E. B. The iliotibial tract: Clinical and morphological significance. *J. Bone Joint Surg. 40-A:817, 1958.*

Karpovich, P. V., and Wilklow, L. B. A goniometric study of the human foot in standing and walking. *U.S. Armed Forces Med. J. 10: 885, 1959.*

Kleiber, M. *The Fire of Life.* John Wiley & Sons, Inc., New York, 1961.

Lamoreux, L. W. Kinematic measurements in the study of human walking. *Bull. Prosthet. Res. BPR 10-15:3, 1971.*

Lamoreux, L. W. Personal communication, 1976.

Lestienne, F., and Bouisset, S. Pattern Temporel de la mise en jeu d'un agoniste et d'un antagoniste en fonction de la tension de l'agoniste. *Rev. Neurol. (Paris) 118:550, 1968.*

Lettre, C., and Contini, R. *Accelerographic Analysis of Pathological Gait.* N.Y. University School of Engineering and Science, Technical Report No. 1368.01. The University, New York, 1967.

Levens, A. S., Inman, V. T., and Blosser, J. A. Transverse rotation of the segments of the lower extremity in locomotion. *J. Bone Joint Surg. 30-A:859, 1948.*

Lindeburg, F. A. Leg angle and muscular efficiency in the inverted leg press. *Res. Quart. Am. Assoc. Health Phys. Educ. 35:179, 1964.*

Linford, A. G., and Rarick, G. L. The effect of knee angle on the measurement of leg strength of college males. *Res. Quart. Am. Assoc. Health Phys. Educ. 39:582, 1968.*

Lippold, O. C. J. The relation between integrated action potentials in a human muscle and its isometric tension. *J. Physiol. (Lond.) 117: 492, 1952.*

Lombard, W. P. The tendon action and leverage of two-joint muscles of the hind leg of the frog, with special reference to the spring movement. In *Contributions to Medical Research, Dedicated to Victor Clarence Vaughan.* George Wahr, Ann Arbor, 1903, pp. 280–301.

Lowman, C. L. Therapeutic use of the rocker sole. *West. J. Surg. Obstet. Gynecol. 58:243, 1950.*

McDonald, I. Statistical studies of recorded energy expenditure of man. Part II. Expenditure on walking related to weight, sex, age, height, speed and gradient. *Nutr. Abstr. Rev. 31:739, 1961.*

McLaurin, C. A. *Hip Disarticulation Prosthesis.* Report No. 15, Prosthetic Services Centre, Department of Veterans Affairs, Toronto, Canada, 1954.

Marey, E. J. Movement. Translated by E. Pritchard. Appleton, Century, Crofts, New York, 1895.

Margaria, R. Positive and negative work performances and their efficiencies in human locomotion. *Int. Z. angew. Physiol. 25:*339, 1968.

Margaria, R. Sulla fisiologia e specialmente sul consumo energetico della marcia e della corsa a varie velocità ed inclinazioni del terreno. Vol. 7. Atti Reale Accad. Naz. Lincei. Giovanni Bardi, Rome, 1938.

Martin, T. P., and Stull, G. A. Effects of various knee angle and foot spacing combinations on performance in the vertical jump. *Res. Quart. Am. Assoc. Health Phys. Educ. 40:*324, 1969.

Mathews, D. K., and Wooten, E. P. Analysis of oxygen consumption of women while walking in different styles of shoes. *Arch Phys. Med. Rehabil. 44:*569, 1963.

Matsuo, T., and Wada, H. Stabilizing operation for paralyzed lower limb due to poliomyelitis. *J. Jap. Orthop. Assoc. 50:*275, 1976.

Menier, D. R., and Pugh, L. G. C. E. The relation of oxygen intake and velocity of walking and running, in competition walkers. *J. Physiol. 197:*717, 1968.

Merchant, A. C. Hip abductor muscle force: An experimental study of the influence of hip position, with particular reference to rotation. *J. Bone Joint Surg. 47-A:*462, 1965.

Molen, N. H. *Problems on the Evaluation of Gait.* Thesis. Ph.D., Health Sciences. Vrije Universiteit, Amsterdam, 1973.

Molen, N. H., and Rozendal, R. H. Energy expenditure in normal test subjects walking on a motor-driven treadmill. *Proc. Kon. Ned. Akad. Wet., Ser. C 75:*192, 1967.

Molen, N. H., and Rozendal, R. H. Fundamental characteristics of human gait in relation to sex and location. *Proc. Kon. Ned. Akad. Wet., Ser. C 75:*215, 1972.

Molen, N. H., and Rozendal, R. H. Some factors of human gait. *Proc. Kon. Ned. Akad. Wet., Ser. C 69:*522, 1966.

Molen, N. H., Rozendal, R. H., and Boon, W. Graphic representation of the relationship between oxygen-consumption and characteristics of normal gait of the human male. *Proc. Kon. Ned. Akad. Wet., Ser. C 75:*305, 1972.

Morris, J. M., Lucas, D. B., and Bresler, B. Role of the trunk in stability of the spine. *J. Bone Joint Surg. 43-A:*327, 1961.

Morton, D. J. *The Human Foot: Its Evolution, Physiology and Functional Disorders.* Hafner Publishing Company, New York, 1935. Reprinted 1964.

Moskowitz, P. S. *Anthropometric Studies of the Human Metatarsus As Seen on X-Ray. I. Normal Feet.* Student thesis [Unpublished], 1967.

Müller, E. A. Der Wirkungsgrad des Gehens. *Arbeitsphysiologie 14:*236, 1950.

Murray, M. P. Gait as a total pattern of movement, including a bibliography on gait. *Am. J. Phys. Med. 46:*290, 1967.

Murray, M. P., and Clarkson, B. H. Vertical pathways of the foot during level walking. *J. Am. Phys. Ther. Assoc. 46:*585, 1966.

Murray, M. P., Drought, A. B., and Kory, R. C. Walking patterns of normal men. *J. Bone Joint Surg. 46-A:*335, 1964.

Murray, M. P., Kory, R. C., Clarkson, B. H., and Sepic, S. B. Comparison of free and fast walking patterns of normal men. *Am. J. Phys. Med. 45:*8, 1966.

Murray, M. P., Kory, R. C., and Sepic, S. B. Walking patterns of normal women. *Arch. Phys. Med. Rehabil. 51:*637, 1970.

Murray, M. P., Seireg, A. H., and Scholz, R. C. A survey of the time, magnitude and orientation of forces applied to walking sticks by disabled men. *Am. J. Phys. Med. 48:*1, 1969.

Passmore, R., and Draper, M. H. Energy metabolism. In *Newer Methods of Nutritional Biochemistry,* edited by A. A. Albanese. Academic Press, New York, 1965.

Passmore, R., and Durnin, J. V. G. A. Human energy expenditure. *Physiol. Rev. 35:*801, 1955.

Pauwels, F. *Der Schenkelhalsbruch: Ein mechanisches Problem.* Ferdinand Enke, Stuttgart, 1935.

Pearson, J. R., and Riddell, D. M. Idiopathic osteo-arthritis of the hip. *Ann. Rheum. Dis. 21:*31, 1962.

Perry, J., Antonelli, D., and Ford, W. Analysis of knee-joint forces during flexed-knee stance. *J. Bone Joint Surg. 57-A:*961, 1975.

Ponseti, I. V., and Friedman, B. Changes in the scoliotic spine after fusion. *J. Bone Joint Surg. 32-A:*751, 1950.

Popova, T. Quoted in *Issledovaniia po biodinamike locomotsii,* Chapter 3, vol. 1: Biodinamika khod'by normal'nogo vzroslogo muzhchiny, edited by N. A. Bernshtein. Idat. Vsesoiuz. Instit. Eksper. Med., Moscow, 1935.

Radcliffe, C. W. Alignment of the above-knee artificial leg. In *Human Limbs and Their Substitutes,* edited by P. E. Klopsteg, P. D. Wilson, et al. McGraw-Hill Book Company, New York, 1954. Reprinted 1968.

Radcliffe, C. W. Biomechanical design of a lower-extremity prosthesis. An ASME Publication, Paper No. 60-WA-305. American Society of Mechanical Engineers, New York, 1960.

Radcliffe, C. W. Functional considerations in the fitting of above-knee prostheses. *Artif. Limbs 2:*35, 1955.

Radcliffe, C. W. The biomechanics of the Canadian-type hip-disarticulation prosthesis. *Artif. Limbs 4:*29, 1957.

Radcliffe, C. W. The Knud Jansen Lecture: Above-knee prosthetics. *Prosthetics and Orthotics International 1:*146, 1977.

Radcliffe, C. W., and Ralston, H. J. *Performance Characteristics of Fluid-Controlled Prosthetic Knee Mechanisms.* Biomechanics Laboratory, University of California, San Francisco and Berkeley. [Technical Report] 49. The Laboratory, San Francisco, 1963.

Ralston, H. J. Effects of immobilization of various body segments on the energy cost of human locomotion. Proc. 2nd. I.E.A. Conf., Dortmund, 1964. [Supplement to] *Ergonomics,* p. 53, 1965.

Ralston, H. J. Energetics of human walking. In *Neural Control of Locomotion,* edited by R. M. Herman, S. Grillner, P. S. G. Stein, and D. G. Stuart. Plenum Press, New York, 1976.

Ralston, H. J. Energy-speed relation and optimal speed during level walking. *Int. Z. angew. Physiol. 17:*277, 1958.

Ralston, H. J., and Libet, B. Effect of stretch on action potential of voluntary muscle. *Am. J. Physiol. 173:*449, 1953.

Ralston, H. J., and Lukin, L. Energy levels of human body segments during level walking. *Ergonomics 12:*39, 1969.

Ralston, H. J., Polissar, M. J., Inman, V. T., Close, J. R., and Feinstein, B. Dynamic features of human isolated voluntary muscle in isometric and free contractions. *J. Appl. Physiol. 1:*526, 1949.

Ralston, H. J., Todd, F., and Inman, V. T. Comparison of electrical activity and duration of tension in the human rectus femoris muscle. *Electromyog. Clin. Neurophysiol. 16:*271, 1976.

Reilly, D. T., and Martens, M. Experimental analysis of the quadriceps muscle force and patello-femoral joint reaction force for various activities. *Acta Orthop. Scand. 43:*126, 1972.

Rydell, N. W. Forces acting on the femoral head-prosthesis: A study on strain gauge supplied prostheses in living persons. *Acta Orthop. Scand. 37,* Suppl. 88, 1966.

Ryker, N. J., Jr. *Glass Walkway Studies of Normal Subjects During Normal Level Walking.* Prosthetic Devices Research Project, Institute of Engineering Research, University of California, Berkeley. Series 11, issue 20. The Project, Berkeley, 1952.

Samilson, R. L. Tendon transfers in cerebral palsy. [Editorial] *J. Bone Joint Surg. 58-B:*153, 1976.

Saunders, J. B. deC. M., Inman, V. T., and Eberhart, H. D. The major determinants in normal and pathological gait. *J. Bone Joint Surg. 35-A:*543, 1953.

Scott, E. Personal communication, 1969.

Silverman, L., Lee, G., Plotkin, T., Sawyers, L. A., and Yancey, A. R. Air flow measurements on human subjects with and without respiratory resistance at several work rates. *Arch. Industr. Hyg. Occ. Med.* 3:461, 1951.

Smith, J. W. Cited by Joseph (1960), p. 75.

Snellen, J. W. External work in level and grade walking on a motor-driven treadmill. *J. Appl. Physiol.* 15:759, 1960.

Spanner, D. C. *Introduction to Thermodynamics.* Academic Press, New York, 1964.

Strydom, N. B., Bredell, G. A. G., Benade, A. J. S., Morrison, J. F., Viljoen, J. H., and van Graan, C. H. The metabolic cost of marching at 3 m.p.h. over firm and sandy surfaces. *Int. Z. angew. Physiol.* 23:166, 1966.

Wagner, E. M., and Catranis, J. G. New developments in lower-extremity prostheses. In *Human Limbs and Their Substitutes*, edited by P. E. Klopsteg, P. D. Wilson *et al.* McGraw-Hill Book Company, New York, 1954. Reprinted 1968.

Waters, R. L., Morris, J., and Perry, J. Translational motion of the head and trunk during normal walking. *J. Biomech.* 6:167, 1973.

Waters, R. L., Perry, J., McDaniels, J. M., and House, K. The relative strength of the hamstrings during hip extension. *J. Bone Joint Surg.* 56-A:1592, 1974.

Weber, E. F. Ueber die Längenverhältnisse der Fleischfasern der Muskeln im Allgemeinen. *Ber. Verh. K. Sächs. Ges. Wissensch., Math.-phys. Cl.*, p. 63, 1851.

Weir, J. B. de V. New methods for calculating metabolic rate with special reference to protein metabolism. *J. Physiol. (Lond.)* 109:1, 1949.

Wilkie, D. R. Man as a source of mechanical power. *Ergonomics* 3:1, 1960.

Wilkie, D. R. The efficiency of muscular contraction. *J. Mechanochem. Cell Motility* 2:257, 1974.

Winter, D. A. Analysis of instantaneous energy of normal gait. *J. Biomech.* 9:253, 1976.

Winter, D. A. A new definition of mechanical work done in human movement. *J. Appl. Physiol. Respirat. Environ. Exercise Physiol.* 46:79, 1979.

Wright, D. G., Desai, S. M., and Henderson, W. H. Action of the Subtalar and ankle-joint complex during the stance phase of walking. *J. Bone Joint Surg.* 46–A:361, 1964.

Wyndham, C. H., van der Walt, W. H., van Rensburg, A. J., Rogers, G. G., and Strydom, N. B. The influence of body weight on energy expenditure during walking on a road and on a treadmill. *Int. Z. angew. Physiol.* 29:285, 1971.

Zarrugh, M. Y. Personal communication, 1975.

Zarrugh, M. Y., Todd, F. N., and Ralston, H. J. Optimization of energy expenditure during level walking. *Eur. J. Appl. Physiol.* 33:293, 1974.

Index